principles of SCIENCE

Book One

Author

Charles H. Heimler is a Professor of Science Education at California State University, Northridge, CA. He received his B.S. degree from Cornell University and his M.A. and Ed.D. degrees from Columbia University and New York University. He has 30 years of teaching experience at the junior high, high school, and university levels. Dr. Heimler is a member of the American Association for the Advancement of Science, National Science Teachers Association, and the National Association of Biology Teachers. He is currently a consultant in science education to several California school districts. Dr. Heimler is author of the Merrill *Focus on Life Science* program and co-author of the *Focus on Physical Science* program.

Consultant

Charles D. Neal is Professor Emeritus of Education at Southern Illinois University, Carbondale, IL. Dr. Neal has taught at the junior high school level and has lectured extensively on the teaching of science in the elementary and junior high school. He received his B.S. degree from Indiana University, his M.A. degree from the University of Illinois, and his M.S. and Ed.D. degrees from Indiana University. He is a member of various professional organizations and is the author of numerous science books for children.

Content Consultants

Earth Science: Dr. Jeanne Bishop, Parkside Junior High School, Westlake, OH
Life Science: Lucy Daniel, Rutherfordton-Spindale High School, Rutherfordton, NC
Physical Science: Dr. Richard H. Moyer, University of Michigan–Dearborn

Reading Skills Consultant

Dr. David L. Shepherd, Hofstra University

Charles E. Merrill Publishing Co.
A Bell & Howell Company
Columbus, Ohio
Toronto, London, Sydney

A Merrill Science Program

Principles of Science, Book One Program

Principles of Science, Book One and Teacher's Annotated Edition

Principles of Science, Book One, Evaluation Program, Spirit Duplicating Masters

Principles of Science, Book One, Evaluation Program, Reproducible Masters

Principles of Science, Book One, Activity-Centered Program, Teacher's Guide

Principles of Science, Book One, Laboratory and Review Guide and Teacher's Annotated Edition

Principles of Science, Book Two Program

(This program contains components similar to those in the Principles of Science, Book One Program.)

Reviewers

Donald Baumann, Science Teacher: Franklin Junior High, Nutley, NJ

David Graham, Science Teacher: Squaw Peak School, Phoenix, AZ

Jerry Hayes, Science Coordinator: Chicago Board of Education, Chicago, IL

John P. Newton, Principal/Science Teacher: Immokalee Day School, Fort Meyers Beach, FL

Betty Rivinius, Science Teacher: Merrill Junior High, Denver, CO

Greg Rottengen, Science Teacher: Brooklawn Junior High, Parsippany, NJ

Donna Seligman, Science Dept. Chairperson: Riley Middle School, West Bloomfield, MI

Cover Photograph: The photograph symbolizes the interaction of matter and energy in our environment. Plants use energy from the sun to make food and to grow. A spider builds a web to trap insects for food. The insects provide energy for the spider to live and to build other webs. In these interactions, energy is being used. In other interactions, energy is released. Energy is released as water in the atmosphere changes form and collects as dew on the spider's web. The interaction of matter and energy in our world represents the theme of **Principles of Science, Book One.** Photograph by *Lynn M. Stone/Animals, Animals.*

Series Editor: Ellen Lappa; *Project Editor:* Francis R. Alessi, Jr.;
Editors: Eric Smith, Patricia Cunningham; *Book Design:* Joan Shaull;
Project Artist: Patricia Cohan; *Artist:* Kathy Light-Robison;
Illustrators: Don Robison, Jim Shough; *Photo Editor:* Sue Marquart;
Production Editor: Janice Wagner

ISBN 0-675-07732-X
Published by
Charles E. Merrill Publishing Company
A Bell & Howell Company
Columbus, Ohio 43216

Preface

Principles of Science, Book One is a modern general science program. The interrelationships among the life, earth, and physical sciences are emphasized. Basic science principles of matter and energy and their interaction in understanding natural phenomena are stressed. Interesting everyday examples using science concepts and their practical applications are presented throughout the text to stimulate student interest and motivation. Science activities are included where appropriate to teach the methods of scientific inquiry through direct student involvement. Science is presented as an ever expanding body of knowledge that is useful in everyday life and in science related–careers.

Principles of Science, Book One is organized to provide the maximum flexibility and adaptation to middle, junior high, or high school programs. Emphasis is given to the organization of the material for improved teachability and maximum student learning. The six units provide comprehensive coverage of important topics in the life, earth, and physical sciences. The first unit introduces the basic principles of metric measurement, matter, and energy. The following units discuss mechanics, earth science, animals and plants, ecology and heredity, and conservation. Science content has been carefully selected to provide a unified, basic general science program that furnishes a proper background for the students' future study of science. Concrete examples of abstract concepts are provided. Relevant topics such as solar energy, plate tectonics, oceanography, and the ecological energy pyramid are included.

Chapters are subdivided into numbered sections that form logical teaching blocks. The chapter organization provides students with a basic outline for the chapter. Reading level is carefully controlled by monitoring sentence length and the introduction of new terms. Margin notes, most in the form of questions, are printed in the margins of each chapter. These notes serve as guides for learning and reviewing important concepts, thereby increasing student comprehension.

Each chapter contains attractive, scientifically accurate diagrams, photographs, and tables which are related to the text material, both in content and placement. Important new terms are emphasized by boldfaced type and are defined where they first appear. Many new terms are spelled phonetically to assist the student in learning the correct pronunciation. Science activities which provide for student participation are included in all chapters. These activities are especially designed to increase student motivation and strengthen skills in problem-solving methods. *Making Sure* questions at the end of some sections provide for immediate review and reinforcement.

Chapter-end material contains study aids designed to enhance student achievement. The *Main Ideas* section summarizes the content of the chapter. Important new terms introduced in the chapter are listed in *Vocabulary. Study Questions* section provides for a thorough review of the chapter. The student is given both recall and applications questions. *Investigations* contain ideas for enrichment projects and special assignments. Selected reading references are listed under *Interesting Reading*.

Magazinelike pages entitled *Perspectives* in many chapters contain articles and photographs describing interesting careers and current developments in research and technology. Skills pages are designed to assist students in developing reading skills important to the study of general science. *Side Roads* are special feature pages which present interesting additional information related to the unit.

The primary goal of **Principles of Science, Book One** is to develop the student's understanding of the environment. The textbook will be valuable in preparing students for future studies in science and in developing knowledge necessary for making decisions regarding the choice of science-related careers.

To the Student

Science is interesting and exciting. Why? Science explains the world in which you live. For example, science explains why airplanes fly and how birds find their way when they travel long distances. In addition, people use science to make discoveries that have practical value. One of these discoveries is the use of light to carry telephone messages through a glass wire. Another is the lengthening of human life through the use of heart pacemakers and other mechanical devices.

In your future, there will be an endless number of new scientific discoveries. These discoveries will affect your career and how you live your daily life. Television, computers, and space shuttles are part of today's world. Who can imagine what new, yet to be discovered, developments lie ahead? In the future, scientists may discover how to predict earthquakes and how to produce an endless supply of energy. Someday you may live and work in a space station placed in orbit around the earth. Scientists will continue to make discoveries that will change the world in which you live.

A science class provides a great opportunity. It offers you the chance to learn about your environment and to become part of the future that is science. You may find you like science so much that you may plan to become a scientist. Also, there are many interesting careers related to science such as nursing, engineering, and electronics.

This textbook contains many study aids to help you achieve your goals. For example, pictures and diagrams are included to increase your understanding. Margin questions are designed to help you get more out of your reading. Questions at the end of many sections as well as the chapter review questions will help you sum up what you learned. Many interesting hands-on activities allow you to experience some of the methods scientists use.

As with any opportunity, much depends on you. Your success in the study of science will be related to the time and effort you give. Learning science is not any more difficult than other subjects. However, it does take time and practice, just like sports or anything else worth doing. Success in the study of science will be richly rewarding. It will give you knowledge and skills you will use throughout your life.

Textbook Inventory

A student's textbook is his/her primary learning tool. Therefore, an inventory is an excellent way to introduce a new textbook. An inventory introduces the general structure of the book. It also points out the various features of the textbook as well as highlight the different kinds of study aids.

Use your textbook to answer the following questions.

A. Parts of Your Book

1. Where would you find the number of the first page of Chapter 14, "Life and the Cell?"
2. Where would you find page numbers which discuss the topic of motion?
3. Where in the text would you quickly find the definition of declination?
4. What is the purpose of the Making Sure questions found in each chapter?
5. What is the purpose for the listing of the main ideas at the end of each chapter?

B. Graphic Aids

6. Look at Table 2–5, page 33, and list the elements found in sand.
7. Turn to Figure 8–9, page 156, and give the approximate latitude of Philadelphia.
8. Turn to page 484 and use the graph to determine how much more land is used for houses than for farming.
9. Look at Figure 1–6 on page 10. Why is the diagram placed next to the activity?

C. Following Directions

10. Turn to the activity, "Finding Density of Wood," page 28. Explain why you need to measure the length, width, and height of each block of wood.
11. Turn to the activity, "Using Pulleys," page 90. What is the purpose of the activity?
12. Turn to the activity, "Osmosis in Carrot Cells," page 297. How far into the carrot should the glass tube extend?

D. Understanding Symbols

13. Look at Table 1–2 on page 12. What is the symbol for a cubic meter?
14. Turn to Table 2–3 on page 29. What element does the symbol Au represent?
15. Using the information on page 94, write the equation $W_i = F \times d$ in sentence form.

E. Understanding Vocabulary

16. Read Section 1:2. Describe what an entomologist does.

17. What is a hypothesis as defined in Section 1:3?

18. In Section 1:4, what is meant by the statement, "The control is part of the experiment which is held constant?"

19. Which paragraph in Section 21:4 gives the definition of natural selection?

F. Noting Main Ideas

20. In Section 1:1, "What Is Science?" what do you think would be the main idea?

21. After reading Section 8:2, determine how we know the earth moves.

22. Read Section 22:1. What seems to be the goal of conservation?

23. After reading Section 8:4, determine how places on the earth are located.

G. Noting Details

24. Read Section 21:6 and note which kind of mutations cause organisms to be better adapted to their environment.

25. Read Section 20:1 and find out how an organism gets its inheritance.

26. After reading Section 14:7, note how the amoeba gets its food.

H. Interpreting What You Read

27. After reading Section 14:4, explain why scientists classify living organisms on Earth.

28. Read Section 22:5. Why should we be concerned about our water resources?

29. After reading Sections 2:6 and 2:8, explain the difference between a compound and a mixture.

Table of Contents

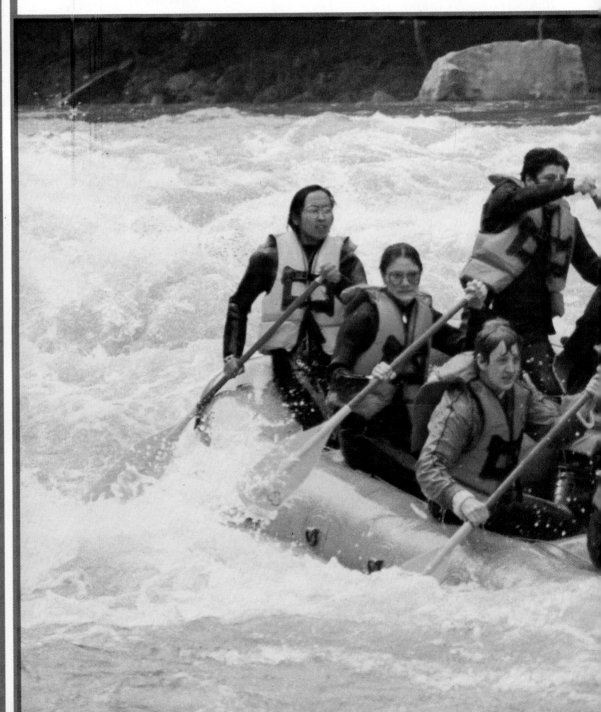

Matter and energy are all around you. Your clothes, food, and even your body are matter. There are different kinds of matter. How is matter classified? Of what is matter made? How are matter and energy related? How is the energy of the water affecting the people in the raft? How does energy affect you?

At an outdoor education center, students collect data to learn more about the ocean. There are still many unanswered questions about the ocean. Using the methods of science, a student like yourself or a scientist may find solutions to these questions. What is the scientific method? Why is measurement important in science?

Steve Lissau

Science and Measurement

1:1 What Is Science?

Why is tap water more safe to drink than pond water? Why do some birds fly south for the winter? How can solar energy be collected and used? You may already know the answer to the first question. Scientists are searching for answers to the second and third questions.

Answers to these questions can be useful in many ways. New methods for cleaning water can be used to increase our water supply. Knowing why birds migrate may help to protect them. Sunlight may someday become a source of energy for home, work, and travel. In this chapter you will learn how scientists search for answers.

Science can be thought of as having two parts. These two parts are the product and process of science. The product of science consists of the facts and ideas that have been discovered by scientists. For example, plants grow and reproduce. Nine planets move around the sun. These facts represent the product of science.

The process of science is the way in which scientists go about discovering facts and finding answers. It is the methods scientists use to study things and to solve problems. Measuring and doing experiments are two kinds of methods used by scientists.

GOAL: You will gain an understanding of scientific methods and the use of SI units.

What are the two parts of science?

Martin Rotker/Taurus

FIGURE 1–1. The process of science is the way in which scientists discover facts and search for answers.

Scientists use both the product and process of science. They read books and journals to obtain facts and ideas discovered by other scientists. Scientists make careful observations of events and changes in the environment. They may also do experiments to test their ideas. New facts that result from this research become part of the product of science. Due to the process of science, the product is always changing.

activity READING ABOUT SCIENCE

Go to a library and locate the periodical literature section. Make a list of the titles of five magazines that deal with science. Choose one magazine and write a brief report that tells what it is about.

MAKING SURE

1. Why is reading an important activity in science?

1:2 Careers in Science

Have you ever thought about your future job or career? There are many jobs in science and related fields. Being a scientist is one kind of career. Scientists usually specialize in one field of science. For example, a geologist (jee AHL uh just) studies rocks and changes in the earth such as earthquakes. An entomologist (ent uh MAHL uh just) is a scientist

Name two kinds of scientists.

who studies insects. Some scientists may teach science and do research at colleges and universities. Many scientists work in various kinds of research laboratories. Not all scientists are found in laboratories, however. Some scientists do their work in outdoor areas.

Many jobs require a background in science. For example, science is used in nursing, agriculture, and electronics. Nursing students take science courses concerning the human body. They also learn about different medicines and how they affect a person's health. Agricultural students study science related to soils, climate, plants, and animals. A person who plans a career in electronics studies science courses related to electricity.

FIGURE 1–2. X-ray technicians work in hospitals, clinics, and doctors' offices (a). Entomology students work outdoors locating and identifying many types of insects (b).

a

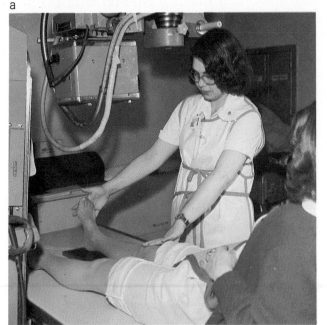

Lester V. Bergman & Assoc.

b

Peter Arnold, Inc.

Table 1–1.
Careers Related to Science

Agronomist	Dentist	Forester
Astronomer	Doctor	Science teacher
Botanist	Electrician	Veternarian
Chemist	Engineer	X-ray technician

Name five jobs related to science.

FIGURE 1–3. The microscope is a tool used by scientists to observe nature.

Larry Hamill

1:3   Using Science Skills

Scientists learn to observe nature with great skill. They record their observations by keeping notes, taking photographs, and making tape recordings. Another important science skill is organizing information so it can be understood. Scientists make graphs, charts, and tables in which information is organized and classified.

In your science class you will learn many skills used by scientists. Some of the skills have practical value and can be applied in everyday life. For example, you will learn the methods scientists use to solve problems. Then you can use these methods to solve your own problems.

What methods do scientists use to solve problems? Here are the steps in scientific problem solving.

(1) *Make a clear statement of the problem.* Try to understand the problem for which you seek an answer.

(2) *Collect information that relates to the problem.* Find as much information as you need from books and other written records.

What steps are used in scientific problem solving?

(3) *Form a hypothesis.* Form your own hypothesis (hi PAHTH uh sus), or "best prediction based on information." A **hypothesis** is a possible solution for a problem. A hypothesis is formed after studying the facts and ideas relating to the problem.

(4) *Test the hypothesis.* Design and perform some experiments to see if your hypothesis is acceptable. An experiment is a way of testing a hypothesis. You can test many of your ideas by trying them.

(5) *Accept or reject the hypothesis.* To accept or reject your hypothesis, study the results obtained in experiments. In some cases, you may change your hypothesis as a result of testing. This new hypothesis must then be tested by an experiment.

(6) *Report the results.* You must inform others of your work so they can test your results.

These steps might not be followed in the order listed here. The work of successful scientists shows that the process is not always a step-by-step process. Scientists are creative people and they approach their work in many ways. Skill, luck, trial and error, and intelligent guessing are all involved in their success.

FIGURE 1–4. Computers are important for collecting data and are frequently used by scientists to test their hypotheses.

MAKING SURE

2. How could scientific methods be used to solve each problem?
  (a) Repairing a car engine that is not working properly.
  (b) Choosing a new typewriter for your personal use.

1:4 Experiments

An **experiment** is used to seek an answer to a question or to test a hypothesis. In an experiment, you perform tests on an object or group of objects and then observe what happens. Often you are able to see something happen, or hear it, or smell it, or taste it, or touch it. The observations made in an experiment should be carefully recorded. You must have accurate information to accept or reject your hypothesis.

FIGURE 1–5. Experiments must be carefully controlled and observations must be accurately recorded.

Throughout your course in science, you will do many experiments. In this book, experiments and other activities are under the heading ACTIVITY. Keep a record of the activities in your notebook. The following activity is an example of the type of activity found in this book. Read the activity carefully. When performing the activity, be sure safety procedures are observed at all times.

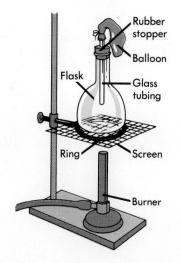

FIGURE 1–6.

activity HEATING AIR

(1) Insert a 10-cm piece of glass tubing into a one-hole rubber stopper. **CAUTION:** Moisten the end of the glass tubing with a lubricant such as glycerol. Hold the tubing with a rag or towel as you slide it into the stopper. (2) Fit the stopper into the mouth of a flask. (3) Place a rubber balloon over the end of the tubing and tie it tightly with a piece of string. (4) Then warm the flask for a short time with a laboratory burner. What happened to the balloon? Explain your observations. What would happen if the flask did not contain any air?

Each activity should be organized into five parts: Title, Objective, Procedure, Observations, and Conclusion. The previous activity would be organized as follows:

(1) Title—Heating Air

(2) Objective—Purpose of the activity. The question you wish to answer: What happens to air when it is heated?

(3) Procedure—Your explanation of how you did the activity.

(4) Observations—Your answer to the question, "What happened to the balloon?"

(5) Conclusion—Your answer to the question, "What happens to air when it is heated?" Base your answer on the observation you made.

How can an experiment be organized into five parts?

An important part of many experiments is a control. The **control** is a part of the experiment which is held constant. It is a standard of comparison for the results. The control for the preceding activity would be a flask and balloon left to stand without heating.

What is the control in an experiment?

If a scientist believes a certain drug will cure a disease, an experiment is done to test this belief. In the experiment, a control may be used. The scientist selects two groups of animals that have the disease. One group, called the experimental group, is given the new drug. The other group, called the control group, does not get the drug. Both groups have exactly the same living conditions, except for the drug. The groups have the same diet, housing, and activities. Only one aspect is different—the condition being tested.

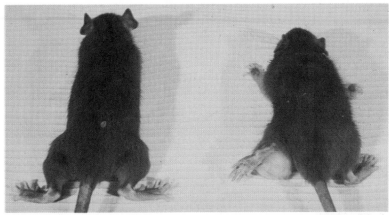

Courtesy of H.M. Olson, Ohio State University

FIGURE 1–7. One of these rats is from an experimental group in a cancer experiment. The other is from a control group.

1:5 Metric Measurement

Over 90 percent of the world's people use the metric system of measurement. Scientists in all countries use metric units. The metric system of measurement is a decimal system, just like the United States' money system. Metric units are based on ten and multiples of ten. For this reason, it is easy to change from one unit to another. The modern form of the metric system is called the **International System of Units** or **SI.** Table 1–2 lists some metric units. Note the abbreviation for each unit.

What are SI units?

Table 1–2.
Frequently Used Metric Units

Length		Mass	
1 millimeter (mm)	= 1/1000 meter (m)	1 milligram (mg)	= 1/1000 gram
1 centimeter (cm)	= 1/100 meter	1 gram (g)	= 1/1000 kilogram (kg)
1 decimeter (dm)	= 1/10 meter	**Time**	
1 dekameter (dam)	= 10 meters	1 millisecond (ms)	= 1/1000 second(s)
1 hectometer (hm)	= 100 meters	**Volume**	
1 kilometer (km)	= 1000 meters	1 liter (L)	= 1000 milliliters (mL)
		1 cubic meter (m³)	= 1 000 000 cubic centimeters (cm³)

A **meter** (m) is the base unit of length in SI. A meter is about the same as the width of most doors in your home. Other units of length which are smaller than a meter include the millimeter (mm) and the centimeter (cm). A metric ruler is marked in centimeters and millimeters. The smallest divisions are the millimeters. A kilometer (km) is a unit of length which is larger than a meter. A kilometer is about the length of five city blocks.

What units are used to measure length?

FIGURE 1–8. On a meter stick, the smallest divisions are millimeters; the largest are decimeters.

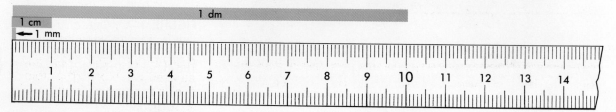

Most SI units contain a prefix which gives a clue to the size of the unit. The prefix *milli-* means one-thousandth (1/1000). *Centi-* means one-hundredth (1/100). *Kilo-* means one thousand (1000). These prefixes indicate how to change from one unit to another. Changing from one unit to another is easy because you multiply or divide by multiples of ten. For example, to change millimeters to meters you divide by 1000. To change kilometers to meters you multiply by 1000.

State the meaning of *milli-*, *centi-*, and *kilo-*.

Example

Change 5000 mm to centimeters.

Solution

Step 1: Determine the number of millimeters in a centimeter.

$$10 \text{ mm} = 1 \text{ cm}$$

Step 2: You are changing from a smaller unit to a larger unit. Divide by 10 to find the answer.

$$\frac{5000 \text{ mm}}{10 \text{ mm/cm}} = 500 \text{ cm}$$

$$5000 \text{ mm} = 500 \text{ cm}$$

Another method for changing units is through the use of a scale (Figure 1–9). The scale tells you whether to multiply or divide. It also indicates the number with which you are to multiply or divide. For example, to change 8000 m to kilometers you must move to the left three places from meter to kilometer on the scale. The number of places moved indicates the power of ten with which you will divide or multiply ($10 \times 10 \times 10 = 1000$). Since you are moving to the left, you divide. Thus,

$$\frac{8000 \text{ m}}{1000 \text{ m/km}} = 8 \text{ km}$$

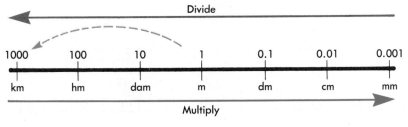

FIGURE 1–9. This scale may be used when changing from one metric unit of length to another.

Example
   Use Figure 1–9 to change 24.5 m to centimeters.
Solution
Step 1:   Determine the direction and the number of
            places you move from m to cm on the scale.
            Since you are moving two places to the
            right, you multiply by 100 (10 × 10).
Step 2:   Multiply to find the answer.
$$24.5 \text{ m} \times 100 \text{ cm/m} = 2450 \text{ cm}$$
$$24.5 \text{ m} = 2450 \text{ cm}$$

MAKING SURE
   3. How many centimeters are in 1 m?
   4. Change 3 m to centimeters.

1:6   Area and Volume

   Area is the number of square units required to
cover a surface. Finding area is one kind of
measurement in science. For example, the size of a
forest is determined by the area of land on which
the trees grow.
   Two ways of expressing area are square
centimeters (cm²) and square millimeters (mm²). A
square centimeter is a square that is 1 cm long on
each side. The area of the leaf in Figure 1–11 can be
given in square centimeters. The area of a blood
vessel may be expressed more simply in square
millimeters. A square millimeter is a square that is 1
mm long on each side.

What units are used to
express area?

FIGURE 1–10.   There are 100
square millimeters in 1 square
centimeter.

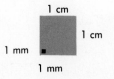

FIGURE 1–11.   The area of an
irregular shape can be
estimated by counting the
number of square centimeters
covered by the shape.

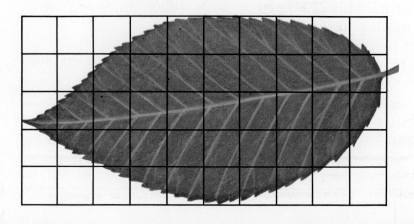

The volume of an object is the space occupied or filled by the object. One important use of volume is measuring the amount of gas or liquid used in an experiment. The units for volume are derived from units for length. One unit for volume is the **cubic meter** (m^3). A wooden tub 1 m in length on each side would hold a cubic meter of water. A much smaller unit of volume is the cubic centimeter (cm^3). The **liter** (L) is a unit of volume often used for measuring liquids. A milliliter (mL) is 1/1000 of a liter and is the same size as a cubic centimeter.

To measure the volume of a liquid, a graduated cylinder, or graduate, can be used. The correct way of reading the volume of water in a graduate is shown in Figure 1–12. A graduate has unit markings printed on its side.

SI units of volume are used to mark other kinds of lab equipment. Three types of equipment used for liquids are test tubes, beakers, and flasks. These containers are made in a number of sizes and shapes (Figure 1–13). They are often made of a heat-resistant glass to avoid breaking when heated.

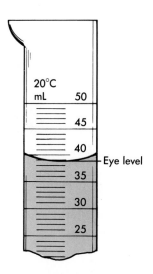

FIGURE 1–12. For accurate volume measurement, read the level of liquid at the lowest point on its curved surface.

What units are used for volume?

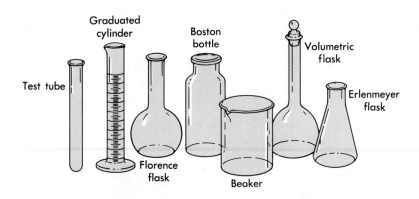

FIGURE 1–13. These are examples of laboratory equipment used to hold and measure liquids.

activity — FINDING AREA

Find the length and width of the two rectangles in Figure 1–14. Record the measurements in millimeters and centimeters. What is the area of each rectangle in square millimeters and square centimeters? How many square millimeters are in a square centimeter?

FIGURE 1–14.

activity
MEASURING LENGTH, AREA, AND VOLUME

Objective: To practice measuring using SI units

Materials

2 boxes, different sizes
drinking glass
dropper
graduated cylinder, 50 mL
meter stick
teacup

Procedure

Part A

1. Measure the volume needed to fill the water glass, dropper, and teacup.
2. Determine the number of drops from the dropper that equals 1 mL. Calculate the number of drops equal to 50 mL.
3. Using the meter stick, find your height in cm.
4. Using the meter stick, measure the length and width of your desk or table top. Find the area in cm².

Part B

1. Label the boxes *A* and *B*.
2. Before measuring the boxes, estimate the volume in cm³ of each box. Record your estimated values in the data table.
3. Measure in cm the length, width, and height of boxes *A* and *B*.
4. Determine the volume in cm³ of boxes *A* and *B* by multiplying length × width × height. Record the volumes in the table.
5. Change the volume of each box in cm³ to mL. Record the volumes.

Observations and Data

Box	Estimated volume (cm³)	Actual volume (cm³)	Volume (mL)
A			
B			

FIGURE 1–15.

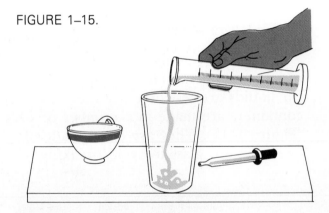

Questions and Conclusions

1. What is your height in meters?
2. What is the area of your desk in square meters?
3. How well did you estimate the volumes of boxes *A* and *B?* How close to the correct volumes were your estimations?
4. If you were to fill your largest box with water using a 10-mL graduate, how many times would you have to fill the graduate?
5. What procedure would you use to find the volume of your classroom in liters?

5. How much water may be added to a dish that is 20 cm long, 10 cm wide, and 5 cm high? Remember, a milliliter is the same as a cubic centimeter.

6. Which has a greater area, a housefly's wing or a bird's wing?

7. Is the area of this page greater or less than 1 cm²?

1:7 Mass

The mass of an object is the amount of matter in the object. For example, there is more matter in a truck than in a bicycle. Thus, a truck has more mass than a bicycle. A sledge hammer has more mass than a tack hammer.

What units are used for mass?

FIGURE 1–16. A truck may have 3000 times more mass than a bicycle.

The **kilogram** (kg) is the base unit of mass in SI. A gram (g) is 1/1000 of a kilogram. A paper clip has a mass of about 1 gram. A stack of 10 "D" size flashlight batteries is about 1 kilogram.

A balance, such as the one in Figure 1–17, can be used to measure mass. An object is placed on the left pan, and objects of known masses or standard masses are placed on the right pan. The pans will balance when the mass of the standard masses on the right pan equals the mass of the object on the left pan.

Hickson-Bender Photography

FIGURE 1–17. With a balance, an unknown mass can be compared to a known mass.

MAKING SURE

8. What procedure would you use to determine the mass of water in a beaker?

9. An object has a mass of 40 580 g. What is the object's mass in kilograms?

Perspectives
frontiers

Make-believe Worlds

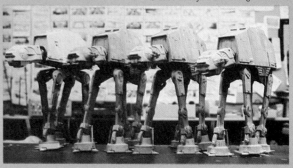

Have you ever left a movie theater wondering how it was done—how the monsters moved and the spaceships flew? The monsters and spaceships did not really exist. Instead, they were special effects. Special effects are used in many movies to create scenes that could not possibly happen in real life. Through special effects, movie makers recreate lost civilizations of the past and create exciting space adventures of the future.

In movies such as "The Empire Strikes Back," as many as 450 special effects were needed. In one scene in the movie, rebel soldiers were attacked by giant snow walkers. The sequence of events in this film combined real actors in Norway with models and paintings in a California studio. The walkers were actually miniature models with moveable parts. Through special effects, the ideas the movie directors, writers, and actors imagined, came to life.

Creating special effects for a single movie requires a team of highly skilled technicians and engineers. Computer operators and photographers work together to produce the desired visual and sound effects. Also, model builders are needed to construct plastic scale models that range from a few centimeters to many meters in height. Each model must be

built to precise specifications down to the smallest detail. Sometimes, eight hours of painstaking work by technicians and artists are needed to film just five or six seconds of action.

Modern special effects studios contain a variety of complex equipment. A flex camera, for example, is used to film a scene consisting of several parts, each filmed separately. A computer linked to the camera allows the camera to "remember" its moves so that each part of the scene is filmed in precisely the same way. An optical printer is another piece of equipment. It combines scenes filmed in separate parts or strips. One strip may show a model of a spaceship. Another may show a background of stars, and another, live actors. The optical printer combines each strip of film like layers in a sandwich to produce a scene that is exciting and believeable.

Special effects is not a new idea. Movie makers have been using them since the first silent movies were introduced. What is new, however, is the way special effects are now being created. Sound engineers, computer operators, and lighting specialists are now used. They work together using advanced equipment in modern special effects studios to produce some of the most exciting movies for your enjoyment.

main ideas

vocabulary

Define each of the following words or terms.

control	International System	mass
cubic meter	of Units (SI)	meter
experiment	kilogram	observation
graduated cylinder	liter	science
hypothesis		

study questions

DO NOT WRITE IN THIS BOOK.

A. True or False

Determine whether each of the following sentences is true or false. If the sentence is false, rewrite it to make it true.

1. Scientific methods are used to solve problems and discover answers to questions.
2. Scientific facts and ideas belong to the product of science.
3. A hypothesis may be tested by an experiment.
4. Scientists always report their discoveries before they do an experiment.
5. A control group is the same as an experimental group.
6. There are 100 g in a centigram.
7. A cubic centimeter is larger than a cubic meter.

8. The prefix *milli-* means 1/1000.
9. A paper clip has a mass of about 1 kg.
10. A liter is equal to 1000 mL.

B. Multiple Choice
Choose the word or phrase that completes correctly each of the following sentences.
1. The way in which an experiment is done is called the *(problem, procedure, observations, conclusion).*
2. The first step in an experiment is to state clearly the *(problem, procedure, observation, conclusion).*
3. A *(meter, dollar, pint, pound)* is an SI unit.
4. To change centimeters to meters you must *(divide by, multiply by, add, subtract)* 100.
5. The abbreviation mm³ stands for *(millimeter, square millimeter, cubic millimeter).*
6. A *(gram, liter, cubic meter)* is a unit of mass.
7. A beam balance is used to measure *(volume, weight, mass, change).*
8. When a dry sponge gets wet its mass *(increases, decreases, stays the same).*
9. The large divisions on a metric ruler are *(millimeters, decimeters, kilometers, centimeters).*
10. A *(m, m², m³, kg)* is a unit of mass.

C. Completion
Complete each of the following sentences with a word or phrase that will make the sentence correct.
1. The _____ is a base unit of mass in SI.
2. The prefix *centi-* means _____.
3. A centimeter is equal to _____ m.
4. There are _____ grams in 2.5 kg.
5. A cubic centimeter is equal to _____ mL.
6. Milliliters of liquid may be measured with a(n) _____.
7. A _____ is used in the laboratory to measure mass.
8. A 1-L flask would be filled by the water in _____ 20-mL test tubes.

9. A square 10 cm on each side has an area of _____.

10. It is easy to change from one SI unit to another because SI units are multiples of _____.

D. How and Why

1. Why is a control group used in some experiments?
2. Name five careers or jobs that are related to science.
3. Describe four steps used by a scientist in solving a problem.
4. Explain how a laboratory balance works.
5. Calculate the volume of a dish 10 cm long, 5 cm wide, and 2 cm high. How many 25-mL graduates of water would be needed to fill this dish?

investigations

1. Arrange for a scientist to talk to your class. If this is not possible, have a member of the class visit a scientist and act as a reporter. Find out why the scientist chose science as a career, what kind of work is required, and what makes the work rewarding.

2. Prepare a "great scientist" report. Through library research obtain information about why a certain scientist is considered important. Make a report to your class.

3. Use a notebook to keep a log of current events in science reported on TV and in newspapers. Make a short summary report of the log to your classmates.

interesting reading

Klein, A. Arthur, *The World of Measurements: Masterpieces, and Muddles of Metrology*. New York, NY: Simon and Shuster, 1974.

Moorman, Thomas, *How to Make Your Science Project Scientific*. New York, NY: Atheneum, 1974.

Norris, Jane, *Metrics and Me*. Indianapolis, IN: Youth Publications, Saturday Evening Post, 1976.

Shapiro, Stanley J., *Exploring Careers in Science*. New York, NY: Richard Rosens Press, 1981.

Granite from a quarry is cut into many sizes and shapes to be used in a variety of ways. Granite is an example of one form of matter. What is matter? What are the characteristics of matter? What are the forms of matter? What are some uses for granite? How is granite different from other forms of matter?

Ruth Dixon

Matter

2:1 Properties

How are snowflakes, hailstones, and ice cubes alike? All three are forms of water that is frozen solid. Each will melt into water again when warmed. Water and ice are two kinds of matter. Air, plastic, gasoline, and soil are other examples of matter.

Anything that has mass and takes up space is **matter.** All matter can be identified by its properties. Color, odor, hardness, and melting point are some properties of matter. The properties of a substance are the features that make it different from other substances. For example, glass is brittle and can be formed easily into many shapes. Can you name some properties of wood that make it different from glass?

The use of a substance depends on its properties. You look for a solid to sit on. You drink liquids such as water and milk. Wool is used in winter clothes because it prevents body heat from escaping rapidly. Airplanes are made of aluminum metal because it is light and strong. Copper, a reddish-brown metal, is used to make electric wires. It is a good electrical conductor and can be stretched to form a wire.

GOAL: You will learn the properties and composition of different kinds of matter.

Define the terms matter and property.

How are properties related to the use of matter?

a

b

FIGURE 2–1. The properties of the special tiles enable the Space Shuttle to withstand very high temperatures (a). Steel's properties make it useful for building structures (b).

FIGURE 2–2.

activity A PROPERTY OF MATTER

Crumple a soft tissue and fit it tightly into the bottom of a paper cup. Push the cup, top down, into a container of water until the whole cup is underwater. Then pull the cup, top still down, out of the water. Is the tissue wet? Punch a small hole in the bottom of the cup. Repeat the procedure. Explain your observations. What property of matter did you observe?

MAKING SURE

1. What properties allow you to tell the difference between each of the following pairs?
   (a) rubber and aluminum
   (b) chalk and snow
   (c) milk and water
   (d) salt and sugar
   (e) wood and plastic
2. Name one use for each substance listed in Question 1

2:2 States of Matter

All matter can be classified by its physical state. These states are solid, liquid, gas, and plasma. A **solid** has a definite volume and a definite shape. Solids include such things as your desk, this book, and most of the objects around you. Some solid substances are used to build things such as furniture, houses, and airplanes.

Water, milk, and oil are examples of matter normally in liquid form. A **liquid** has a definite volume, but it does not have a definite shape. Milk in a bottle will have the same volume after it is poured into a pitcher. But the milk in the pitcher will have a different shape. The shape of a liquid can be changed easily. What shape will the milk take if you spill it on the floor? What will its volume be?

Name four states of matter.

Larry Hamill

FIGURE 2–3. A liquid takes the shape of its container.

FIGURE 2–4. A gas takes up space but has no definite shape.

A **gas** has mass and occupies space, but it does not have a definite shape or volume. A gas fills its container, regardless of the shape or size of the container. The balloon in Figure 2–4 occupies more space than it did before it was blown up. Gas added to the balloon takes up space. When you blow up a balloon, air fills the whole balloon and takes the shape of the balloon. Air is a gas. Hydrogen, helium, oxygen, and carbon dioxide are also gases.

Cameron Balloons U.S.

NASA

FIGURE 2–5. A region of plasma surrounds the sun.

What is the plasma state?

What is density?

Another state of matter, plasma, is formed only when matter is heated to unusually high temperatures. **Plasma** is extremely hot and composed of electrical particles. Its properties are like those of a gas. The hot surface of our sun is made up of plasma. Also, the intense heat from a lightning bolt can change matter into the plasma state.

Table 2–1.
Properties of Matter

State	Properties	Examples
Solid	Definite shape Definite volume	Wood, lead, sugar, sand
Liquid	No definite shape Definite volume	Alcohol, water, milk, molasses
Gas	No definite shape No definite volume	Air, hydrogen, oxygen, nitrogen

Plasma	Similar to a gas
	Composed of electrical
	  particles at high
	  temperatures
		The sun and
		  other stars

MAKING SURE
3. Under normal room conditions, which of the substances below are gases? Which are liquids? Which are solids? Use a dictionary to look up words you do not know.
   (a) carbon dioxide   (c) helium   (e) neon
   (b) gasoline   (d) mercury   (f) steel
4. How is a plasma different from a gas?

2:3 Density

An important measurable property of matter is density (DEN suht ee). **Density** is mass per unit of volume. To find density, you must be able to measure mass and volume. You can measure mass with a balance. To measure volume, you can use a meter stick for solids and a graduated cylinder for liquids. Density can be expressed in grams per

milliliter (g/mL). Since 1 mL = 1 cm³, density is also
expressed in grams per cubic centimeter (g/cm³).

Table 2–2. Densities of Some Common Substances	
Substance	**Density (g/cm³)**
Air	0.0013
Gasoline	0.68
Water	1.0
Iron	7.9
Lead	11.3
Gold	19.3

FIGURE 2–6. The density of a
bowling ball is greater than the
density of a volley ball.

Which would you rather carry up a flight of
stairs—a suitcase filled with lead or the same suitcase
filled with feathers? The suitcase filled with feathers
would be easier to carry. Why? The density of lead is
greater than the density of feathers. The lead has
more mass per volume than the feathers.

To find the density of an object you must first
determine its mass and volume. You must then use
the following equation:

$$\text{density} = \frac{\text{mass}}{\text{volume}} \qquad D = \frac{m}{V}$$

Example

A plastic box has a mass of 12.9 g and a volume
of 15 cm³. Determine the density of the box.

Solution

Step 1: Write the equation for density.

$$D = \frac{m}{V}$$

Larry Hamill

How do you calculate
density?

Step 2: Substitute the values for mass and volume
given in the problem.

$$D = \frac{12.9 \text{ g}}{15 \text{ cm}^3}$$

Step 3: Divide to find the answer.

$$\frac{12.9 \text{ g}}{15 \text{ cm}^3} = 0.86 \text{ g/cm}^3 \qquad D = 0.86 \text{ g/cm}^3$$

activity FINDING THE DENSITY OF WOOD

Find the density of two types of wood: oak and pine. Obtain a block of each wood. Measure the length, width, and height of each block in centimeters. Find the volume of each block. Use a balance to find the mass of each block in grams. Calculate the density. Which type of wood is more dense?

activity FINDING DENSITY USING A GRADUATED CYLINDER

(1) Obtain a rubber stopper and a cork about the same size. (2) Find and record the mass of each with a balance. (3) Fill a graduated cylinder to the 15-mL mark with water. (4) Drop the cork into the water and push it down gently until it is just below the surface. How many milliliters does the water rise? The change in water level is the volume of the cork. Record the volume. (5) Remove the cork and make sure the volume of the water is at the 15-mL mark. (6) Find and record the volume of the rubber stopper. Use the same procedure as Step 4. Calculate the density of the stopper and cork. How do they compare?

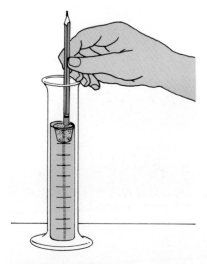

FIGURE 2–7.

MAKING SURE

5. Heavy machinery is made of cast iron. Beverage cans are made of aluminum. How do the densities of these two metals make them suited for these uses?

6. Why is aluminum used to make airplanes?

7. A metal block has a mass of 418.7 g and a volume of 53 cm³. Use Table 2–2 to identify the metal of which the block is made.

8. A block of "gold" has a length of 5 cm, a width of 4 cm, and a height of 3 cm. Its mass is 1 kg. Determine if the block is pure gold. (*Hint:* You will need to use Table 2–2 to determine the answer.)

2:4 Elements

All matter consists of simple substances called elements. An **element** is a substance that cannot be broken down into simpler substances.

Gold, carbon, lead, and oxygen are elements. At least 106 elements have been discovered. At room temperature, most of these elements are solids and some are gases. Two, mercury and bromine, are liquids.

Of the 106 known elements, 88 occur naturally on the earth and the other 18 have been made in experiments. Scientists are still searching for new elements. Thus, the total number of known elements may increase.

Using symbols is a shorthand method for writing the names of elements. Each element has a different symbol containing one or two letters. H is the symbol for hydrogen. Fe is the symbol for iron. Note in Table 2–3 that a symbol has a capital letter. When there are two letters in a symbol, the second letter is a small letter.

What is an element?

How is a symbol used to represent an element?

Univ. of California, Lawrence Radiation Lab, Berkeley

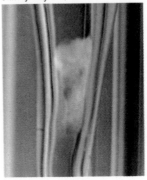

FIGURE 2–8. Einsteinium in the tip of a quartz tube.

Table 2–3.
Some Elements and Their Symbols

Element	Symbol	Element	Symbol
Aluminum	Al	Oxygen	O
Calcium	Ca	Silicon	Si
Carbon	C	Sodium	Na
Gold	Au	Sulfur	S
Lead	Pb	Zinc	Zn
Magnesium	Mg	Californium	Cf
Mercury	Hg	Einsteinium	Es
Nitrogen	N	Plutonium	Pu

MAKING SURE

9. Write the symbols for the following elements: aluminum, gold, carbon, lead, oxygen.

10. List one property of each element in Question 9.

2:5 Atoms

Every element is made of tiny particles called **atoms.** Atoms are so small you cannot see them with a microscope. One part of an atom is the central core, called the **nucleus.** Around the nucleus is a sphere or cloud of negative charges. Inside the nucleus are two types of tiny subatomic particles. A subatomic particle is a particle within an atom. One type of subatomic particle is the **proton** which has a positive charge. Another kind of subatomic particle in the nucleus is the **neutron.** It has the same mass as a proton. A neutron, however, does not have an electrical charge. Both the proton and neutron have a very high density. For this reason, almost all the mass of an atom is in the nucleus.

Name three kinds of particles in an atom.

Outside the nucleus are particles called **electrons**. The number of electrons in an atom is equal to the number of protons in the nucleus. An electron has a negative electric charge and its mass is almost zero. Electrons move about the nucleus at very high speeds. The rapid movement of the electrons creates the cloud of negative electricity that is part of the atom. Locate the parts of an atom in Figure 2–9.

Electrons in an atom are arranged in different energy levels. The first energy level, which is closest to the nucleus, can have no more than two electrons. The second energy level can contain a maximum number of eight electrons. The energy levels for atoms and the number of electrons they can hold are shown in Table 2–4.

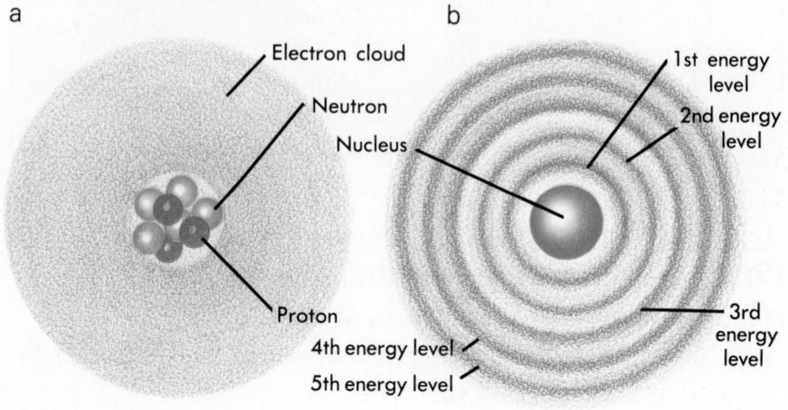

a   b

FIGURE 2–9. Protons and neutrons are found in an atom's nucleus. An electron cloud surrounds the nucleus (a). Electrons are arranged in energy levels (b).

Table 2–4.
Electrons in Energy Levels

Level	Maximum Number of Electrons in Each Level	Maximum Number of Electrons in the Atom
1	2	2
2	8	10
3	18	28
4	32	60
5	50	110

Atoms of different elements have different numbers of protons. For example, a hydrogen atom has one proton in its nucleus. An oxygen atom has eight protons. There are 26 protons in an iron atom. The properties of elements are determined by the number of particles in their atoms.

How is an oxygen atom different from a hydrogen atom?

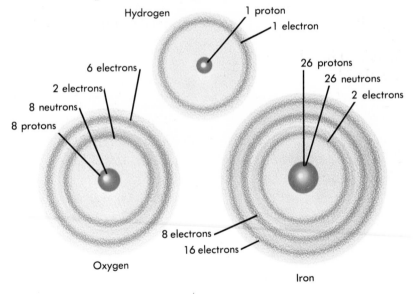

FIGURE 2–10. The properties of hydrogen, oxygen, and iron are determined by the number of particles in their atoms.

MAKING SURE
11. How many electrons are in a hydrogen atom? Oxygen atom? Iron atom?

12. How many energy levels are in an oxygen atom?

13. Select three elements you know and make a chart which shows how their properties are alike and how they are different.

2:6 Compounds

Elements combine to form substances called compounds. A **compound** contains two or more elements joined by a chemical bond. The bond makes it difficult to separate the elements. Water, sugar, salt, soap, and rust are examples of compounds.

How is a compound different from an element?

Tim Courlas

FIGURE 2–11. When atoms of copper (a), sulfur (b), and oxygen are joined by chemical bonds, copper sulfate (c) is formed.

How do atoms bond?

When elements combine to form compounds their atoms gain, lose, or share electrons. The electrons involved in bonding are those in the outermost energy level. For example, sodium combines with chlorine to produce sodium chloride. Table salt is the common name for sodium chloride. In the process of bonding, the sodium atom loses one electron and the chlorine atom gains one electron. An atom that loses one or more electrons gains a positive charge. Why? The atom now has more

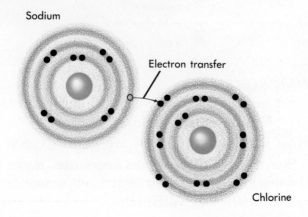

Sodium

Electron transfer

Chlorine

FIGURE 2–12. Sodium chloride (table salt) is formed when one electron from the sodium atom is transferred to an atom of chlorine.

protons than electrons. An atom that gains electrons becomes negatively charged because it has more electrons than protons.

An atom with an electric charge is called an ion. Sodium chloride consists of sodium and chlorine ions held together by chemical bonds. These bonds are called ionic bonds because they are between ions.

A covalent (koh VAY lunt) bond is formed when atoms share electrons. For example, hydrogen and oxygen may combine together to form water. Water consists of particles called molecules. Each molecule contains two hydrogen atoms and one oxygen atom. Each hydrogen is attached to the oxygen by a covalent bond which is a shared pair of electrons.

What is an ion?

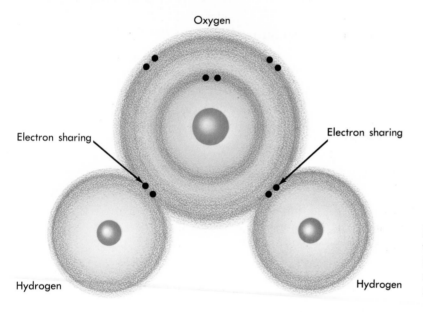

FIGURE 2–13. A molecule of water consists of two covalent bonds. The oxygen atom shares two electrons with two separate hydrogen atoms.

Table 2–5.
Some Compounds and Their Elements

Compound	Elements
Ammonia	Nitrogen, hydrogen
Carbon dioxide	Carbon, oxygen
Rust	Iron, oxygen
Sand	Silicon, oxygen
Sugar	Carbon, hydrogen, oxygen
Sulfuric acid	Hydrogen, sulfur, oxygen

FIGURE 2–14. A molecular model shows the kinds and number of atoms in a molecule.

How is a subscript used in a formula?

Write three formulas.

2:7 Formulas

Just as a symbol is an abbreviation for an element, a **formula** is used to show a compound. A formula may have one or more symbols. For example, NaCl is the formula for sodium chloride. This formula contains the symbol for sodium and the symbol for chlorine. H_2O is the formula for water. What symbols does it contain?

Formulas are also used to show substances like hydrogen gas. The formula H_2 shows that a hydrogen molecule has two atoms of hydrogen. O_2 is the formula for oxygen gas which has two atoms in its molecule. The small numbers, called **subscripts,** show how many atoms are in a molecule of the substance.

Subscripts also show the ratio between elements in a compound. The subscript 2 in H_2O means two parts of hydrogen to one part of oxygen, a ratio of 2:1. CO_2 is the formula for carbon dioxide. What elements are in carbon dioxide? What is the ratio between the elements in this compound?

Table 2–6.
Some Compounds and Their Formulas

Compound	Formula
Ammonia	NH_3
Carbon dioxide	CO_2
Rust	Fe_2O_3
Sand	SiO_2
Sugar	$C_{12}H_{22}O_{11}$
Sulfuric acid	H_2SO_4

activity MOLECULAR MODELS

Models of molecules may be made with clay spheres and toothpicks. Different colors of clay are used to represent different kinds of atoms. Obtain some modeling clay and make models of three of the molecules listed in Table 2–6. Are your models exactly like real molecules? Explain.

14. Each formula below represents one unit of a compound. How many and what kinds of atoms are in each unit?

(a) N_2 (e) CCl_4
(b) Cl_2 (f) N_2O_5
(c) HCl (g) Al_2O_3
(d) H_2S (h) CH_4

15. What is the ratio between the elements in Questions 14c–14h?

2:8   Mixtures

Salt water is a mixture. A **mixture** contains two or more elements or compounds which are mixed together but not chemically joined. The parts of a mixture can be separated by physical means such as sifting, pouring, or evaporating. For example, salt water can be separated into salt and water through the process of evaporation.

How is a mixture different from a compound?

Air and soil are also mixtures. Air is made up of oxygen, nitrogen, and other gases. Soil is made up of rock, sand particles, and decayed plant and animal matter. Can you think of a way to separate soil into its parts?

Doug Martin

FIGURE 2–15. A screen may be used to separate the large and small particles in soil.

One kind of mixture is a solution. In a solution one or more substances are dissolved in another substance. The particles in the solution are so small they cannot be seen with the naked eye. Water solutions are the most common because so many substances dissolve in water. Milk, soft drinks, and soapy water are examples of water solutions.

Another kind of solution occurs when a substance is dissolved in a gas. Air is a solution containing oxygen, nitrogen, carbon dioxide, and other gases.

Name three kinds of solutions.

In a solid solution, solids, liquids, or gases are dissolved in solids. For example, many crystals contain water molecules mixed together with the atoms in the crystal. Most alloys (AL oyz) of metals are also solid solutions. An **alloy** is a mixture of two or more metals. Stainless steel is an alloy of chromium metal in iron. Yellow gold is a solution of gold, silver, and copper.

FIGURE 2–16. Bubbles form when gas that was dissolved in the water escapes (a). An opal consists of crystals that contain water molecules (b).

a   Hickson-Bender Photography   b   Manfred Kage/Peter Arnold, Inc.

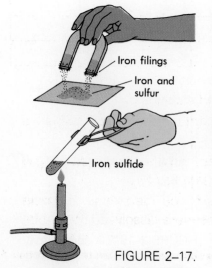

Iron filings

Iron and sulfur

Iron sulfide

FIGURE 2–17.

activity   SEPARATING A MIXTURE

(1) Make a mixture by stirring iron filings and sulfur together. (2) Pass a magnet over the mixture. What happened to the iron filings (Figure 2–17)? (3) Now place a mixture of iron filings and sulfur in a test tube. (4) Heat the mixture until it glows (Figure 2–17). **CAUTION:** Do the heating under an exhaust hood or other place where there is good ventilation. (5) Let the test tube cool. (6) Wrap the cooled test tube in a paper towel and place it on a table. (7) Crack the test tube inside the towel by striking it with a hammer. (8) Open the towel and try to remove the iron filings with a magnet. What happened? Why?

activity

MAKING SOLUTIONS

Objective: To observe properties of different solutions

Materials
alcohol
bromothymol blue
dropper
lime (calcium oxide)
mineral oil
red litmus solution
soda straw
soil
5 test tubes/stoppers
test tube rack

FIGURE 2–18.

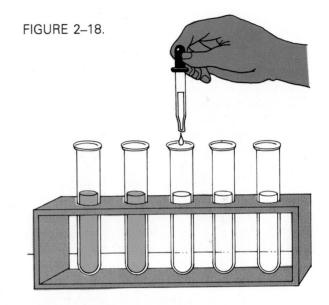

Procedure
1. Label the test tubes *A, B, C, D,* and *E.* Set them in the test tube rack.
2. Fill test tubes *A* and *C* one-half full of water. Add 5 drops of mineral oil to test tube *A* and 3 g of soil to test tube *C.*
3. Fill test tube *B* one-half full of alcohol. Add 5 drops of mineral oil to the alcohol.
4. Fill test tube *D* one-half full of red litmus solution. Add 3 g of lime to the solution.
5. Place the stoppers in test tubes and mix by carefully shaking each test tube. Record any changes that occur.
6. Fill test tube *E* one-half full of bromothymol blue. Place a straw in the test tube and carefully bubble your breath through the liquid for a few minutes. Record any changes that occur.

Observations and Data

Test Tube	Observations
A	
B	
C	
D	
E	

Questions and Conclusions
1. Which test tube(s) did not contain a solution?
2. Which test tube(s) contained a gas dissolved in a liquid?
3. How could you determine if some substances were dissolved in test tube *C*?

Perspectives

Using Tables

Being able to use tables quickly and accurately is important in the study of science. They organize and classify large amounts of scientific information. In this book, tables have the following characteristics: (1) The information is condensed in as few words as possible. (2) Each table is about one kind of information. (3) The information is arranged in columns. (4) Each table is related to the information next to it in the text. The following activities will help you become better at using tables.

Use Table 2–1 to answer the following questions.

1. What type of information does this table present?
2. What two types of information are given for each "state"?
3. Using the table, can you answer Question 4 of Making Sure?

Use Table 2–2 to answer the following questions.

1. What is the density of water?
2. In what order are the substances listed? Does this order seem logical?

Use Table 2–3 to answer the following questions.

1. What type of information is given? Why do you suppose four columns were used?
2. Which would be easier to use in locating the information—Table 2–3 as it is shown or each item of informaion in a separate sentence? Why?

Use Table 2–4 to answer the following questions.

1. Why is it not possible to answer Questions 11 and 12 of Making Sure from the table alone?

2. In order to make use of Table 2–4, what other information do you need? Where do you find the additional information?
3. At what energy level would there be a maximum number of 32 electrons?
4. How could the maximum number of electrons in each atom be 60 when the energy level can only contain 32 electrons?
5. Can you easily see the relationship between the two columns showing the maximum number of electrons in each level and in the atom? Explain.
6. Is the relationship you get from the table made clear in the text? Explain.

Use Tables 2–5 and 2–6 to answer the following questions.

1. What relationship does the table show you between the compounds and elements?
2. What is the relationship between Table 2–5 and Table 2–6?
3. Sugar is a compound and consists of three elements. What element occurs in the greatest amount? Where are you told about how to find this information?

After completing the activities you have probably concluded the following ideas about the use of tables:

(1) Informaion that is listed in column form is easier and quicker to locate.

(2) Columns of related information makes it easer to see the organization and classification of the information.

(3) Many times the information in the text helps to explain information in the table. The opposite is also true. The text and the table used together make the information clearer.

main ideas

vocabulary

Define each of the following words or terms.

alloy	gas	plasma
atom	liquid	proton
compound	matter	solid
density	mixture	subatomic
electrons	neutron	subscript
element	nucleus	symbol
formula		

study questions

DO NOT WRITE IN THIS BOOK.

A. True or False

Determine whether each of the following sentences is true or false. If the sentence is false, rewrite it to make it true.

1. The properties of solids and liquids are the same.
2. Liquids and gases take the shape of their container.
3. Plasma is a state of matter.
4. Density is the mass per unit of volume of a substance.

5. An element is a substance in which two or more compounds are chemically joined.
6. The compound NH_3 contains nitrogen and hydrogen.
7. Matter is made of small particles called atoms.
8. The mass of a proton is greater than the mass of an electron.
9. Both a proton and an electron have a positive charge.
10. Atoms join together to form molecules.

B. Multiple Choice

Choose the word or phrase that completes correctly each of the following sentences.

1. (*Liquids, Gases, Solids*) have a definite volume and a definite shape.
2. The number of electrons in an atom is (*equal to, less than, more than*) the number of protons.
3. (*Fe, O, O_2, Fe_2O_3*) is the formula for rust.
4. (*Water, Carbon dioxide, Hydrogen, Air*) is a mixture.
5. Salt water is a(n) (*element, compound, mixture*).
6. (*H_2, N_2, O_2, H_2O*) is the formula for oxygen gas.
7. In a water molecule (H_2O) there are (*3, 2, 6, 4*) atoms.
8. In a molecule of table sugar ($C_{12}H_{22}O_{11}$) there are (*12, 22, 11, 45*) atoms.
9. (*Protons, Neutrons, Electrons*) move around the nucleus of an atom.
10. The (*proton, neutron, electron*) has a positive electric charge.

C. Completion

Complete each of the following sentences with a word or phrase that will make the sentence correct.

1. The _____ of an atom is almost entirely in its nucleus.
2. There are always the same number of _____ and _____ in an atom.
3. A compound contains two or more _____.
4. _____ is the formula for hydrogen gas.
5. The parts of a _____ can be separated by physical means.
6. The symbol Fe stands for the element _____.
7. The formula NH_3 represents the compound _____.

8. Ammonia contains the elements _____ and _____.
9. Au is the symbol for_____.
10. Carbon dioxide contains _____ oxygen atoms.

D. How and Why
1. Tell whether each of the following substances is an element, compound, or mixture: oxygen, soil, nitrogen, water, carbon dioxide, mercury.
2. How is a gas different from a liquid? How is a liquid different from a solid?
3. What elements are present in $NaCl$, H_2O_2, CaO, $ZnSO_4$?
4. A fluorine atom contains 9 protons, 10 neutrons, and 9 electrons. How many of these particles are in the nucleus?
5. Explain how a molecule is different from an atom.

investigations

1. Obtain small samples of five elements and five compounds. Tape each to a large piece of cardboard. Print the name of each element, its symbol, and three of its properties. List the name, formula, and three properties for each compound.
2. Make a list of five elements you know. Obtain information from a library on how each element was discovered.

interesting reading

Asimov, Issac, *How Did We Find Out About Atoms?* New York, NY: Walker and Company, 1976.

Gallant, Ray A., *Explorers of the Atom.* Garden City, NY: Doubleday, 1974.

side roads

GLASS IS . . . .

Lightning flashes! It strikes a sand beach. Slender tubes of natural glass, known as fulgarites, form. Natural glass is also formed by volcanic action. This type of glass is black and transparent. Natural glass is made when silica, found in sand and rock particles, is heated. Humans discovered how to use natural glass before written history. Volcanic glass, for example, was chipped or flaked to make arrows, spear points, and knives.

About the year 5000 B.C., people learned how to produce glass. They also discovered more uses for glass. Early Egyptians made ornamental beads and small bottles. Glassblowing became an art with the Babylonians about 250 B.C. By the 12th century, windows in some European churches were constructed with colorful bits of stained glass.

© Alan Benoit

Glass is hard to the touch and seems to be a solid. It is not a solid, however. It is one of a group of substances called "supercooled liquids." The particles of a true solid, such as diamond, have a repeating order called crystals. Supercooled particles are trapped in random order during cooling. They have no crystals. This order is demonstrated in the way glass breaks—randomly and jaggedly.

The optical properties of glass vary greatly. Glass may be transparent—you can see through it, which makes it useful for windows, mirrors, and lenses. Glass may also be translucent—you can see light through it but objects cannot be identified. Glass may also be opaque—no light passes through it.

Rich Brommer

Today, glass has a wide variety of uses—from cooking utensils to tiny threads that carry telephone messages. The use of glass became so popular because of its special properties. What are some of the properties that enable us to use glass in so many ways?

Larry Hamill

Other useful properties include glass's resistance to most chemical attacks. This is the reason why many acids are stored in glass bottles. Glass is smooth and nonporous, which allows for the storage of medicines and foods. Glass is an excellent electrical insulator, but it can be treated to conduct electricity. Glass absorbs heat which makes it useful for ovenware. Some insulation for houses and buildings consists of glass that is spun into thin fibers, called fiberglass.

Glass is composed of three substances found in nature—sand, soda, and lime. Silica, or silicon dioxide, in sand gives glass its transparency. Silica is changed to glass by heating it to extreme temperatures.

National Bureau of Standards

Doug Martin

When soda is melted with sand, it permits the sand to melt at a much lower temperature. A material such as soda is called a flux. The soda and silica melted together form sodium silicate which is glass. This type of glass, however, dissolves in water. Lime is added to insure that the glass will not be affected by moisture or acids. Lime also makes glass easier to handle while it is hot. The many properties of glass depend on the type and amount of materials that are used to make glass. By varying the ingredients or adding certain substances such as lead, aluminum, and boron compounds, new properties may be obtained.

chapter

3

Energy is used in many ways. In the photograph, the welder is using energy to produce a change. The welder uses chemical energy of a gas to produce heat. Light is also produced. Heat and light are two of many forms of energy. What is energy? How is energy related to changes in matter? What changes in the picture are the result of energy?

Joe DiChello, Jr.

Energy and Changes in Matter

3:1 Energy

Everything you do requires energy. Reading, running, throwing, climbing, and eating are all activities that use energy. Energy is also needed for travel and industry and to warm our homes, schools, and factories. Energy is used in refrigeration, lighting, and cooking. **Energy** is the ability to do work. In science, work means to move something.

GOAL: You will learn the sources and forms of energy and how energy is related to changes in matter.

What is energy?

Table 3–1.
Major Uses of Energy in the United States

Use	Percent
Industry	36
Transportation	27
Homes	21
Business	16
Total	100

Energy can be divided into two kinds—potential and kinetic. **Potential energy** is energy of position, or stored energy. **Kinetic energy** is energy of motion. For example, moving water in a river has

How is potential different from kinetic energy?

FIGURE 3–1. Much energy is needed for transportation.

Name five forms of energy.

kinetic energy. This kinetic energy becomes potential energy as the water reaches a dam. When the water falls over the dam the potential energy changes back to kinetic energy. Another example of energy change is found in a wind-up toy. The wound spring in the toy has potential energy. The potential energy changes to kinetic energy as the spring unwinds.

Energy has many forms. Light and heat are two forms of energy. Some others are electric, chemical, nuclear, and mechanical energy. Energy can be changed from one form to another. In a light bulb, electric energy is changed to light and heat. In a battery, chemical energy is changed to electric energy. In a solar water heater, light energy is changed to heat. All forms of energy can be changed to heat.

Remember that one kind of energy can be changed to another kind of energy. For instance, potential energy can be changed to kinetic energy. Kinetic energy can be changed to potential energy.

FIGURE 3–2. The potential energy of the water behind the dam changes to kinetic energy as the water falls over the dam.

Energy can be released from matter and stored in matter. When a match burns, energy is released as heat and light. When water is heated to boiling, steam is formed. Energy is stored in the steam as potential energy. Energy is released when the steam cools and changes back to liquid water. Energy is gained or lost as matter changes from one form to another.

activity   KINETIC ENERGY AND HEAT

Obtain two paper cups. Fill one cup one-third full of dry sand. Place the end of a thermometer in the sand and record the temperature. Remove the thermometer and invert the second cup over the first cup. Seal the cups with a piece of tape. Shake the sand back and forth inside the cup. Insert the thermometer. Did you observe a change in temperature? Explain.

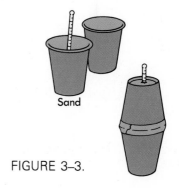

Sand

FIGURE 3–3.

MAKING SURE

1. Do the following have potential energy or kinetic energy?
(a) wound-up spring   (c) stretched rubber band
(b) ocean wave   (d) rotating windmill

3:2 Heat and Temperature

If you hammer a nail into a block of wood, the nail becomes warm because it gains heat energy. When your hands are cold, you may try to warm them by rubbing your hands together. In the winter, people keep comfortable indoors by heating their homes. Heat for homes is often produced by burning fuels such as oil or natural gas.

Heat is the kinetic and potential energy of molecules within a substance. At the same temperature, which has more heat, a glass of milk or a pitcher of milk? The amount of heat in an object depends on both its temperature and mass. Since the pitcher contains a greater mass of milk, it contains more heat. If you have a pitcher of cold milk and one of warm milk, which has the most heat? Both the warm and cold milk have the same mass. Therefore, the pitcher with the higher temperature has the most heat.

Define the terms heat and temperature.

FIGURE 3–4. The frozen pond (a) contains more heat than the boiling water (b) since the pond contains a greater mass of water.

Temperature is an indicator of heat. It tells how hot an object is and the direction heat will travel. Does your body gain or lose heat to the air around you? Usually, it loses heat because your body has a higher temperature than the air. If you heat a kettle of water on a gas stove, the water gains heat. The heat comes from the fire beneath the kettle. Heat travels from regions of higher temperature to regions of lower temperature.

Temperatures are measured using the Celsius temperature scale. On this scale, water freezes at zero degrees (0°) and boils at 100 degrees (100°). There are 100 degrees between the freezing and boiling points. Some common Celsius temperatures are listed in Table 3–2.

Table 3–2.
Some Celsius Temperatures

Boiling point of water	100°C
Human body (average)	37°C
Pleasant room temperature	21°C
Freezing point of water	0°C

How is temperature measured?

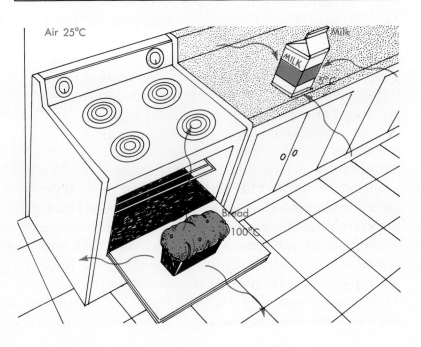

FIGURE 3–5. Temperature determines the direction of heat travel. Eventually, the loaf of bread, the air, and the milk will have the same temperature.

activity

GAINING AND LOSING HEAT

Objective: To determine the movement of heat by measuring temperature

Materials
balance
beaker, 250 mL
clock or watch with second hand
ice cube
stirring rod
thermometer

Procedure

1. Determine the mass of the empty beaker.

2. Fill the beaker with 125 mL of water. Find the total mass of the beaker and the water. Determine the mass of the water by subtracting the mass of the empty beaker from the total mass of the beaker and water. Record the mass of the water.

3. Carefully place the thermometer into the water and record the temperature of the water. Note: Be certain that the thermometer does not touch the sides or bottom of the beaker.

4. Add the ice cube to the water and stir for 1 min. **CAUTION:** Use the stirring rod and not the thermometer to stir the water. After 1 min, measure and record the temperature of the water.

5. Continue stirring the water and ice and measuring the temperature for 5 min. Record the temperature after each minute.

6. After 5 min, remove any ice that is left. Stir the water gently again and measure

the temperature each minute until the water returns to room temperature.

7. Find and record the mass of water in the beaker.

Observations and Data

Mass of the water before ice was added: ____ g

Mass of the water after the ice melted: ____ g

Time (min)	Temperature (°C)
0	
1	
2	
3	

Questions and Conclusions

1. What was the lowest temperature to which the water cooled in the beaker?

2. How was the temperature of the water changed by the loss and gain of heat?

3. Where did the heat go when the water was cooled and warmed?

4. How did the rate in which the water cooled compare to the time it took for the water to return to room temperature?

5. How did the change in the mass of water affect the rate in which the water returned to room temperature?

FIGURE 3–6. A metal is melted to a liquid so it can be easily formed into different shapes.

What is a physical change?

Give two examples of physical change.

3:3 Freezing and Melting

When a liquid freezes, it changes to a solid. Water inside a freezer changes to ice. Just the opposite happens when something melts. During melting, a solid changes to a liquid. Freezing and melting are two kinds of physical changes.

Boiling, crushing, tearing, and grinding are also examples of physical change. A **physical change** occurs when a substance changes from one form to another without a change in its composition. Both ice and liquid water are composed of water molecules. Ice molecules are slightly farther apart and in a rigid solid position. The molecules in water can slide over and around each other. Energy may be gained or lost by a substance during a physical change.

At very high altitudes, ice particles in clouds are formed directly from water vapor. The water vapor forms solid ice without going through a liquid state. When carbon dioxide gas is cooled to a low temperature or placed under high pressure, it turns into a solid called dry ice. Dry ice is used to cool food and other things. When warmed, dry ice turns back into a gas without forming a liquid. The physical change in which a substance changes directly from a solid to a gas or gas to a solid is called **sublimation** (sub luh MAY shun).

FIGURE 3–7. Through the process of sublimation, solid iodine at the bottom of the container, changes to a gas. The gas returns to a solid at the top of the container.

2. Does a substance gain or lose heat when it condenses?

3. How is freezing different from sublimation?

4. Why is boiling an example of a physical change?

5. Frost consists of small ice crystals that form on windows and blades of grass. Explain the process by which frost forms during cold mornings.

3:4 Evaporation and Boiling

How do wet clothes dry when they are hung on a washline? The liquid water changes into water vapor which enters the air. This change from a liquid into a gas is called evaporation. Heat energy is needed to evaporate a liquid. This explains why wet clothes should dry faster on warm days than on cold days.

What happens to a liquid as it evaporates?

Condensation is the opposite of evaporation. You have seen the effect of condensation many times. Clouds contain tiny drops of water formed when water vapor changes to a liquid. Water forming on kitchen windows during the winter is a result of condensation. Gases lose heat energy as they become liquids. You can see the condensation of water vapor in your breath if you exhale on a mirror.

How is condensation different from evaporation?

Tim Courlas

FIGURE 3–8. Heat is gained or lost when water undergoes physical changes.

When a liquid is heated to its boiling point, the change from a liquid to a gas occurs rapidly. Just as in evaporation, heat is gained by a substance when it boils. If the heat source, such as a burner flame is turned off, the boiling will stop. To keep a liquid boiling, heat must continually be applied.

How is boiling different from evaporation?

FIGURE 3–9.

activity SEPARATING PURE WATER FROM SALT WATER.

Soak a piece of sponge with salt water and set it in a small glass inside a glass jar. Place a plastic bag in the jar as shown in Figure 3–9. Set the jar in sunlight or under a lamp. After a few hours, note the changes. Where does evaporation occur inside the jar? Where does condensation occur? How is the water changed?

activity THE RATE OF EVAPORATION

(1) Label three beakers A, B, and C. (2) Fill beaker A with 10 mL of water. Place the beaker outdoors where it will not be disturbed. (3) Fill beaker B with 10 mL of water and place it inside the classroom. (4) Fill beaker C with 10 mL of rubbing alcohol and set it next to beaker B. (5) Observe the beakers. Determine and record the amount of liquid that evaporates each day until all the water and alcohol is gone. (6) Draw a graph showing how much liquid evaporated from each beaker each day. In which beaker was evaporation the fastest? The slowest? Explain why there was a difference. What factors affect the rate at which a liquid evaporates?

MAKING SURE

6. Does water vapor gain or lose heat when it condenses on a cool window?

7. Why does alcohol placed on the skin feel cool?

3:5 Chemical Change

What happens in a chemical change?

In a **chemical change,** new substances with different properties are produced. Elements and compounds may combine to form the new substance. A substance may break down into two or more elements or compounds. Rust is produced when iron combines with oxygen. A type of acid is formed when milk sours. Gases and ashes are produced when wood burns. The new substances formed are no longer iron, milk, or wood. A chemical change has taken place in each case.

The bright light from a photo flashbulb is the result of a chemical change. Try to look at a flashbulb before and after the flash. You will see that the fine metal wire in the bulb changes to a white powder. In most flashbulbs, the fine wire is made of magnesium and the bulb is filled with oxygen. When the flashbulb is used, the magnesium (Mg) combines with the oxygen (O_2) and forms a white powder. The white powder is magnesium oxide (MgO) that forms during a chemical change.

Burning also involves a chemical change. When a substance burns in air, atoms of the substance combine with atoms of oxygen. Heat is always given off during burning. Thus, burning is a means of obtaining energy.

FIGURE 3–10. Magnesium oxide is formed during a chemical change when the flashbulb is used.

Name two examples of a chemical change.

activity CHANGES IN A BURNING CANDLE

Place a small candle on a watch glass and light it. Invert a glass jar over the candle and watch glass (Figure 3–11). What happened to the candle? Explain. Note the drops of water and the black substance on the inner surface of the jar. How can you explain these? Why did the candle stop burning?

FIGURE 3–11.

MAKING SURE

8. Which of the following chemical changes release energy?
   (a) burning of wood
   (b) decaying of cut grass
   (c) discharging a battery
   (d) charging a battery

3:6 Chemical Equations

When a chemical change occurs, new substances are formed. That is, there is a change in the arrangement of atoms. In some cases, atoms join to form molecules. In other cases, molecules break apart into atoms. These atoms may join together to form different molecules. However, atoms are never gained or lost in a chemical change. There is the same number of each kind of atom at the end as there was at the start.

A chemical change may be shown by a word equation. A word equation shows both the substances that react and those that are formed. For instance, when hydrogen burns in air it combines with oxygen to form water. The word equation for the change is

hydrogen + oxygen ——→ water

The symbol (+) means plus and the arrow (——→) means yield or produce. This word equation is read, "Hydrogen plus oxygen yield water."

A chemical change may also be shown by a balanced chemical equation. In a balanced chemical equation, symbols and formulas are used in place of words. The equation for the formation of water is

$$2H_2 + O_2 \longrightarrow 2H_2O$$

In this reaction hydrogen combines with oxygen to form water.

A number in front of a symbol or formula shows the number of atoms or particles in the chemical change. In the equation above, two molecules of hydrogen (H_2) combine with one molecule of oxygen (O_2). These substances are written to the left of the arrow. They are called reactants.

How is a chemical equation used to show a chemical change?

What is a balanced chemical equation?

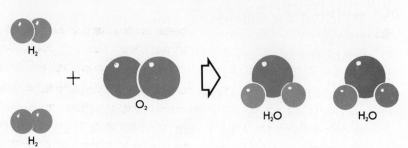

FIGURE 3–12. Two molecules of water are formed when four atoms of hydrogen react with two atoms of oxygen.

To the right of the arrow, symbols and formulas stand for the new substances that are formed. They are called products of the reaction. The $2H_2O$ in the equation shows that two molecules of water are formed. Water is the product of the reaction.

The word equation for the rusting of iron is

$$\text{iron} + \text{oxygen} \longrightarrow \text{iron oxide (rust)}$$

This can be read, "Iron plus oxygen yield iron oxide." Rust (iron oxide) is a compound of iron and oxygen.

The balanced chemical equation for rusting is

$$4Fe + 3O_2 \longrightarrow 2Fe_2O_3$$

This equation shows that four atoms of iron ($4Fe$) combine with three molecules of oxygen ($3O_2$) to form two molecules of rust ($2Fe_2O_3$). When iron rusts, millions of atoms of iron combine with millions of molecules of oxygen. The equation shows the ratio of atoms of iron, molecules of oxygen, and molecules of rust.

Don Parsisson

FIGURE 3–13. Rust forms in the presence of moisture.

MAKING SURE

9. If 4 billion iron atoms rusted, how many molecules of oxygen did it take to make the change? How many atoms of oxygen did it take?

10. Write a chemical equation for each reaction:
    (a) carbon + oxygen $\longrightarrow$ carbon dioxide
    (b) water $\longrightarrow$ hydrogen + oxygen
    (c) iron + sulfur $\longrightarrow$ iron sulfide

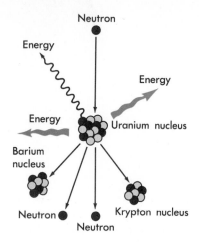

FIGURE 3–14. In nuclear fisson, a large nucleus splits to form two smaller nuclei.

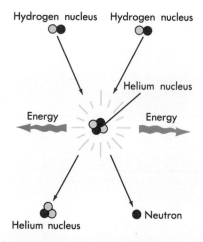

FIGURE 3–15. In nuclear fusion, small nuclei join together to form a larger nucleus.

What is a nuclear change?

List five sources of energy.

3:7 Nuclear Change

A nuclear change differs from a chemical or a physical change. In a nuclear change, an element is changed into a different element. That is, the nucleus of an atom is changed. Energy is always released during a nuclear change.

There are two types of nuclear change—fission and fusion. Fission means to divide. In **nuclear fission,** a single, large nucleus splits into smaller nuclei. A uranium nucleus, for instance, may split into two nuclei—barium and krypton. Much energy is released during this change. A piece of uranium about the size of a golf ball can provide as much energy as 1 million kg of coal.

In nuclear fission, one or more neutrons are released along with the smaller nuclei. These neutrons can cause other atoms to split, thus producing a nuclear chain reaction. Since a chain reaction provides a steady supply of energy, it can serve as the energy source for an electric power plant.

Fusion is the opposite of fission. To fuse means to join. In **nuclear fusion,** two or more nuclei join to form one larger nucleus. For instance, hydrogen nuclei may fuse to form one helium nucleus. One gram of hydrogen can provide as much energy as 8 million grams of coal. Nuclear fusion takes place in the sun and stars.

3:8 Sources of Energy

Many people in modern countries depend upon a plentiful supply of energy at a reasonable cost. Most of the energy we use comes from the sun, fossil fuels, hydroelectric dams, and nuclear power plants. New sources of energy being developed include geothermal (jee oh THUR mul) and alcohol.

Solar energy is energy that comes from the sun. It is produced by the nuclear fusion reactions of the hot gases that make up the sun. Solar energy may someday become a major energy resource. It is present in an almost endless supply, and it does not cause pollution. It presents no danger of accident. One problem in the use of solar energy is collecting a large amount of it. One way is to use large curved mirrors that focus the sun's energy on a small area. Another way is through the use of a large surface area for collecting the energy.

Bruce M. Wellman/Tom Stack & Assoc.

FIGURE 3–16. Some homes use solar panels on the roof to collect the sun's energy for heating.

Solar energy is absent at night and greatly reduced when the sky is cloudy. Thus, there must be a means of storing solar energy. One way to store solar energy is by heating water or rocks. Another way is to use solar cells that convert light into electric energy which is stored in batteries.

How is solar energy stored?

Solar energy is now being used in some places for cooking, heating, and cooling. Heating water for homes is an important practical use. Some buildings are being built with panels for collecting solar energy. Often the panels are placed on the roof.

Coal, oil, gasoline, and natural gas are fossil fuels. They are called fossil fuels because they were formed from plants and animals that died many, many years ago. Fossils are the preserved remains of once living things.

When a fossil fuel such as coal is burned, light and heat are released. The burning of fossil fuels is an example of chemical change. Energy stored in the

FIGURE 3–17. Fossil fuels may be burned to produce electrical energy.

fuel is released as light and heat. When fossil fuels burn, carbon dioxide and water are formed.

Hydroelectric power is produced by moving water. Water from a river is trapped in a lake behind a dam. The water from the lake is allowed to fall through a shaft in the dam to a stream below. As the water falls, it flows through a turbine. The kinetic energy of the falling water is transferred to the moving turbine blades. As the turbine rotates, it turns an electric generator (JEN uh ray tur) which produces the electricity.

Geothermal energy refers to heat energy within the earth. In some areas, wells can be drilled into water heated by hot rock deep below the surface. Steam or very hot water is forced up the well and is used to generate electricity.

A nuclear power plant has a nuclear reactor (ree AK tur) that contains a radioactive fuel element such as uranium. Fission reactions in the nuclear fuel produce heat. This heat is carried out of the nuclear reactor by a water cooling system and is used to produce steam. The steam is used to produce electricity.

What is hydroelectric power?

How is geothermal energy obtained?

FIGURE 3–18. In a nuclear power plant, energy released during nuclear fission is used to generate electricity.

U.S. Dept. of Energy

No way has yet been found to control nuclear fusion. Many problems must be solved before nuclear fusion can provide us with a steady supply of energy. For example, scientists must learn how to create a temperature of several million degrees. Nuclear fusion may someday provide an almost endless supply of energy.

activity HEAT FROM THE SUN

Obtain two glass bottles. The bottles should be the same size and have a narrow neck. One should be clear glass and the other dark, colored glass. Attach a balloon over the neck of each bottle. Place the bottles in direct sunlight. What changes did you observe? What caused these changes?

activity COLLECTING SOLAR ENERGY

Tie a piece of thread to a thumbtack. Push the tack into the bottom of a cork that will fit tightly in the mouth of a clear glass bottle. Put the cork in the top of the bottle so that the thread hangs inside. Use a magnifying glass to focus the sunlight onto the thread. What happened? Will you get the same results if you set the bottle in the sun and do not use the magnifying glass? Explain.

FIGURE 3–19.

MAKING SURE

11. Name three sources of energy you used today.
12. What sources of energy are used most for transportation?
13. Why are solar and hydroelectric power called "clean" sources of power?
14. What can people do to reduce their use of energy?

A Special Clock

It looks like a blue tube with a warm rosy glow coming from the bottom. The blue tube is a special glass cylinder. The glow is from hydrogen atoms traveling at great speed inside the cylinder. How is this strange cylinder used? It is the main part of a clock—the hydrogen maser clock. In this clock, the movement of a pendulum is replaced by the movement of hydrogen atoms. Apart from the flow of atoms, there are no moving parts in this clock.

Accurate time measurement has been needed since before the 18th century. Ship navigators needed a clock that measured fractions of a second to find their position. Position was found by comparing local time with the time at Greenwich, England. Since clocks were imprecise during the 1700's, there were many navigational problems.

The British Parliament offered 20 000 pounds for a practical ship's clock. John Harrison claimed the reward when he built the first accurate marine timekeeper. It ran for thirty-eight hours on one winding. Today, atomic clocks run five years on 1 liter of hydrogen. They measure trillionths of seconds.

How do these clocks work? The hydrogen maser clock is started by a radio signal sent into a glass bottle filled with hydrogen. The signal splits the molecules into two kinds of hydrogen atoms. Some are in a high energy state, and the rest are in a low energy state. The high energy atoms move into a quartz container. These atoms are unstable. Eventually, one atom drops to the low energy state, becoming stable. This process triggers other atoms to do the same. The stable atoms then leave the quartz container and are replaced by new unstable atoms. Each time this cycle occurs, it is counted. The atoms move

through the cycle about 1.4 billion times each second. Because of the number of cycles, a second can be split into a trillion parts.

Who needs to measure time in trillionths of a second? Geologists use atomic clocks for measuring very small land movements. The ability to measure these movements is valuable in studying earthquakes.

Another use for atomic clocks is tracking spacecraft. Time is converted to distance for locating the spacecraft and making critical course corrections. Any small error in timing can result in a mistake of hundreds of kilometers. The spacecraft would be far off course, a space program disaster!

Adapted from *Popular Mechanics* © 1980 by The Hearst Corporation.

NASA

main ideas

vocabulary

Define each of the following words or terms.

burning
chain reaction
chemical change
chemical equation
energy

fossil fuel
geothermal
hydroelectric
kinetic energy
nuclear fission

nuclear fusion
physical change
potential energy
sublimation

study questions

DO NOT WRITE IN THIS BOOK.

A. True or False

Determine whether each of the following sentences is true or false. If the sentence is false, rewrite it to make it true.

1. Potential energy can be changed to kinetic energy.
2. In a physical change, new and different substances are formed.
3. Water and ice both have the same chemical formula.
4. A chemical change takes place when a substance combines with oxygen.

5. Electric energy can be changed to heat energy.
6. Potential energy is energy of motion.
7. Water behind a dam has potential energy.
8. A liquid absorbs heat when it evaporates.
9. Water boils at 37°C.
10. When iron rusts, it combines with nitrogen.

B. Multiple Choice

Choose the word or phrase which completes correctly each of the following sentences.

1. When a substance burns in air, it combines with *(nitrogen, oxygen, carbon, hydrogen)*.
2. In a chemical equation the symbol ⟶ means *(yield, plus, balanced)*.
3. In a *(chemical, physical, nuclear)* change, hydrogen combines with oxygen to form water.
4. *(Coal, Oil, Natural gas, Uranium)* releases nuclear energy.
5. Nuclear *(fission, burning, fusion)* occurs in the sun.
6. An element is changed into another element during a *(chemical, physical, nuclear)* change.
7. *(Potential, Chemical, Solar)* energy may be collected with large curved mirrors or through the use of large surface areas.
8. In a battery, chemical energy is changed to *(electrical, solar, chemical)* energy.
9. One example of a fossil fuel is *(hydrogen, oxygen, uranium, coal)*.
10. *(Hydroelectric, nuclear, geothermal)* energy is produced by falling water.

C. Completion

Complete each of the following sentences with a word or phrase which will make the sentence correct.

1. Rusting is a(n) _____ change.
2. A(n) _____ change takes place when a mixture is separated into its parts.
3. Freezing is caused by the _____ of heat.
4. In a balanced chemical equation, _____ and _____ are used to represent the reactants and products.

5. Burning is an example of a(n) _____ change.
6. A(n) _____ reaction can provide a steady supply of energy.
7. Hydroelectric power is produced by falling _____.
8. _____ is an example of a fossil fuel.
9. Geothermal energy comes from within the _____.
10. Falling water has _____ energy.

D. How and Why
1. Explain the difference between a chemical change and a physical change.
2. List three examples of a chemical change and three examples of a physical change.
3. When hydrogen burns, it combines with oxygen to form water. Write a word equation and a balanced chemical equation for this change.
4. What is the difference between potential and kinetic energy? Give one example of each.
5. Why must we find new sources of energy to replace fossil fuels?

investigations

1. Collect free educational materials from power and utility companies in your area. Use these materials to make an energy conservation bulletin board display.
2. The use of nuclear energy is a controversial issue. Do library research on this topic and prepare a report for your class. List the pros and cons of nuclear power plants.
3. Fossil fuels are limited in supply. How much coal, petroleum, and natural gas are believed to be in the earth? How long will these fuels last? Through library research, prepare a report on this problem.

interesting reading

Coombs, Charles, *Coal in the Energy Crises.* New York, NY: Morrow, 1980.
Davis, George, *Your Career in Energy-Related Occupations.* New York, NY: Arco, 1980.
Hoke, John. *Solar Energy.* rev. ed., New York, NY: F. Watts, 1978.

unit
2

Mechanics

In the days of sailing ships, the wind provided the energy to move the ships. People provided the energy to move the cargo. Today, large machines are used to power the ships as well as load and unload cargo. From where does the energy for these machines come? What forces enable the large steel ships to float? How can machines help us move? What are the forces that affect us?

John Youger

A gondola is one way to transport people and materials over a rugged landscape. This gondola is being pulled up the face of a steep cliff. Work is being done in moving the gondola up the cliff. What is work? How is energy being used to do this work? What is necessary for work to be done? How are work and energy related?

Work and Energy

4:1 Force

Every time you walk, jump, or pedal a bicycle, you use a force. When you walk or jump your body moves. When you push on the pedals of a bicycle, your force sets you and the bicycle in motion. The harder you push, the greater the force, and the faster you go.

A **force** is any push or pull on an object. The pull of a car on a trailer being towed is a force. So is the push of your hand against a ball when you throw it. When two people arm wrestle, they clasp each other's hand and push hard. The person who pushes with the most force wins.

You can measure force with a spring scale. Attach the spring scale to an object. Then pull the object up or sideways. The amount of force used will be indicated in newtons on the scale. The **newton** (N) is the unit of force. Forces may range from very small to very large.

GOAL: You will gain an understanding of forces, work, and the use of energy to do work.

List five examples of a force.

FIGURE 4–1. A large force is needed to lift a heavy object.

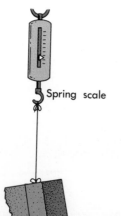

Spring scale

FIGURE 4–2.

activity MEASURING FORCES

(1) Obtain a spring scale and a piece of cord about 1 m in length. (2) Tie one end of the cord around a brick, wooden block, or other object of similar mass. (3) Tie a small loop in the other end of the string. Attach the spring scale to the loop. (4) Drag the object across your desk top. Note and record the readings on the spring scale when the object starts to move and after it is moving. (5) Using the spring scale lift the object off the desk. Again note and record the reading on the scale. Compare the amount of force needed to start, drag, and lift the object.

MAKING SURE

1. Make a list of forces. Which force do you think is largest? Smallest?

4:2 Weight

Define the terms weight and gravity.

You can use a spring scale to find the weight of something. **Weight** is the amount of force (pull) which the earth exerts on an object. This force is the earth's gravity. Gravity is a property of all matter. It is a force that every object exerts on another object. The earth exerts a force of gravity on every object on or near its surface. Since weight is a force, it is measured in newtons like other forces.

Weight and mass are different. Weight is a force and mass is the amount of matter in an object. Suppose you weigh a 1-kg sack of potatoes with a scale. The mass of the potatoes is 1 kg. The weight of the potatoes is 9.8 N. A size "D" battery has a mass of about 102 g. It weighs about 1 N. How much force would you use to lift a size "D" battery?

Gravity is not the same all over the world. The force of gravity is less near the equator than at the North and South Poles. This is so because the earth's diameter at the equator is greater than at the poles. Gravity is also less at high altitudes than at the earth's surface. Therefore, an object weighs less when it is near the equator or on a high mountain. If you move a sack of potatoes from the North Pole to the equator it loses weight. It does not lose mass, however. The mass of an object does not change with a change in location.

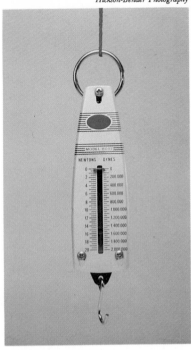

FIGURE 4–3. This spring scale measures the weight of an object in newtons.

How is mass different from weight?

FIGURE 4–4. Although the astronaut's mass remains the same, weight decreases as the force of gravity decreases.

Table 4–1.
Some Weights in Newtons

Boeing 747 jet	3.3×10^6 N
Elephant	6.9×10^4 N
Average person	735 N
Desk telephone	20 N
Slice of bread	0.25 N
Postage stamp	2.0×10^{-4} N

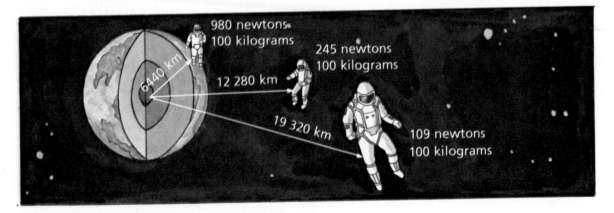

2. How is weight different from mass?
3. How can an object be weightless but not massless?
4. According to *The Guinness Book of World Records,* R. E. Hughes reached a record weight of 4763 N. What was his mass in kilograms?

4:3 Friction

Forces are used to move objects. Cars, roller skates, bicycles, and airplanes all depend on forces for their motion. As an object is pushed by a force, it must overcome friction. **Friction** is a force that slows down or prevents motion. The three types of friction are sliding, rolling, and fluid. Sliding friction exists when solid objects slide over each other. Rolling friction occurs when an object such as a ball or wheel rolls across a surface. Fluid friction occurs when things move across or through a fluid, such as water, oil, or air.

When a brick slides across a surface, a friction force opposes its motion. A spring scale can be used to measure the force needed to slide the brick. This force is equal to the friction force. The amount of friction force depends on the weight of the object and the type of surfaces that rub together.

In general, the smoother the surface between two objects, the less the friction. When you walk on a

What are the three types of friction?

waxed floor, there is little friction between the floor and your feet. If there is too little friction, your feet may slide from under you. Accidents sometimes occur when one car slides into another on icy streets. When a driver applies the brakes, there may not be enough friction between the tires and the icy surface to stop the car.

A rolling object has less friction than a sliding object. A ball bearing and a roller bearing are examples of this principle. The bearing between a wheel and an axle is used to reduce friction.

FIGURE 4–5. Examples of sliding friction (a), rolling friction (b), and fluid friction (c).

a
Bureau of Reclamation

b
Larry Hamill

c
Ruth Dixon

Friction causes moving surfaces that are in contact with each other to wear. Friction gradually strips away tiny particles from the surfaces. As a result, the moving parts of machines may wear down and break. Friction between moving parts also produces heat. You can find this out for yourself if you rub your hands together very rapidly. You will feel the heat in your palms. Heat from friction also causes the moving parts of machines to break down.

Lubricants (LEW brih kunts), such as oil and grease, are used to reduce friction between moving parts of machines. For example, the bearings of bicycles and roller skates are oiled and greased. Lubrication reduces wear and makes roller skating and bicycle riding easier. Proper lubrication extends the life of machinery and reduces the need for costly repairs.

How can friction be reduced?

a
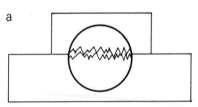

b
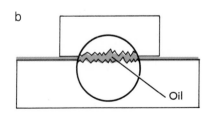
Oil

FIGURE 4–6. Friction between two surfaces (a) may be reduced by using a lubricant (b).

activity

FORCE OF FRICTION

Objective: To compare sliding and rolling friction

Materials

board, (smooth) 1 m × 20 cm
brick
cord
spring scale
6 wooden dowels, 10 cm

Procedure

1. Tie the cord around the brick. Attach the spring scale to the other end of the cord.

2. Pull the brick slowly across a rough concrete surface such as a sidewalk. Determine the force needed to keep the brick moving (Figure 4–7). Record the force in the data table.

3. Place the brick on the pieces of dowel. Pull the brick with the spring scale so that the dowels roll underneath it (Figure 4–8). In the data table, record the force needed to keep the brick moving.

4. Measure the amount of force needed to keep the brick moving across the smooth board. Record the force.

5. Repeat Step 4 with the brick on top of the dowels. Record the force.

FIGURE 4–7.

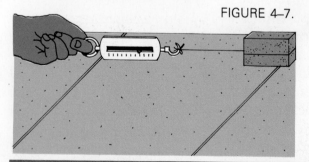

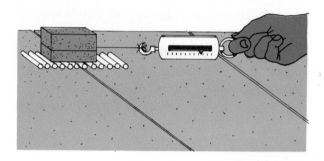

FIGURE 4–8.

Observations and Data

Type of surface	Type of motion	Amount of force
Rough concrete	Sliding	
	Rolling	
Smooth board	Sliding	
	Rolling	

Questions and Conclusions

1. Compare the forces needed to keep the brick sliding over the smooth and rough surfaces. Which required more force? Why?

2. How much more force was needed to keep the brick sliding than to keep it rolling over the rough surface?

3. Would more force be required to keep the brick rolling using two wooden dowels rather than using the six dowels? Test your hypothesis and explain your results.

5. List the type of friction in the following situations.
    (a) A submarine moves through the ocean.
    (b) A bowling ball rolls down a bowling alley.
    (c) The Space Shuttle reenters the earth's atmosphere.
    (d) A person skates on a sidewalk.
    (e) A skier waxes skis and then glides down a slope.

6. Why is sandpaper used to smooth rough wood?

4:4 Work

If a force causes an object to move, work is done. In science, **work** is defined as a force acting through a distance. Work is done whenever something is moved by a force.

The girl in Figure 4–9 is lifting a box. To lift the box, she must exert a force to overcome the pull of gravity on the box. As she lifts the box upward, work is done. If she had not been able to lift the box, no work would have been done.

Note that the definition of work includes distance. When forces do not move objects, they do not produce work. Your body exerts a force on a chair when you are sitting, but no work is done. The chair does not move through a distance. When you push down on a desk top with your hand, you apply a force. Again, no work is done. The force does not move through a distance. Work is done only when a force is applied through a distance.

FIGURE 4–9. Work is done when force is exerted through a distance.

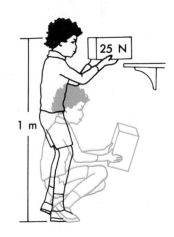

FIGURE 4–10. Although a force is exerted, no work is done on the car (a). Work is done only when the force causes the car to move (b).

a

b

Young/Hoffhines

Work is force multiplied by the distance through which the force is applied. To calculate work, use the equation

$$\text{Work} = \text{Force} \times \text{distance} \qquad W = F \times d$$

The force of 1 N exerted through a distance of 1 m is a newton-meter (N·m) The **joule** (J) is equivalent to 1 N·m. The joule is a unit of work.

Example

The girl in Figure 4–9 uses a force of 25 N to lift the box 1 m off the floor. How much work is done?

Solution

Step 1: Write the equation for work.

$$W = F \times d$$

Step 2: Substitute the values for force and distance given in the problem.

$$W = 25 \text{ N} \times 1 \text{ m}$$

Step 3: Multiply to find the answer.

$$25 \text{ N} \times 1 \text{ m} = 25 \text{ N·m} \qquad W = 25 \text{ J}$$

MAKING SURE

7. In which of the situations is work done?
   (a) a ball hitting a brick wall
   (b) a breeze pushing a kite into the air
   (c) a small child trying to push a car
   (d) a hand turning the handle of an eggbeater
   (e) a power shovel lifting a load of soil
   (f) a hand holding a 10-N object

8. A boy was helping his parents move some stones to another part of the backyard. He hauled them in a wagon. The boy moved the stones 20 m and had to apply a force of 65 N to move the wagon. How much work did he do?

9. A girl was collecting newspapers for a recycling project. She hauled some newspapers from a garage to a truck. A force of 30 N was required to move the newspapers 10 m. How much work was done?

4:5 Work and Energy

To do work, energy is needed. Energy is the ability to do work. It is needed to move a car, to lift a skier up a slope, or to push a roller coaster up a hill.

When work is done, energy changes from one form to another. The potential energy of a skier at the top of a slope changes into kinetic energy as the skier moves down the slope. The kinetic energy of a roller coaster changes into potential energy as the roller coaster moves up a hill.

Energy can change forms, but *energy cannot be created or destroyed under ordinary conditions.* This statement is known as the **law of conservation of energy.** It is considered a law because it has been tested many times and has always been true. Though energy can be changed from one form to another, the total amount of energy always stays the same. When work is done, energy is used, but the energy is never destroyed or used up.

FIGURE 4–11. As a roller coaster moves down a slope, potential energy changes to kinetic energy.

State the law of conservation of energy.

MAKING SURE

10. You do work when you rub your hands together briskly. What energy change occurs?
11. Why does a bulldozer use more energy than a garden tractor when work is done?
12. How does the law of conservation of energy apply to the burning of coal?

4:6 Power

Power is the rate at which work is done. It is the amount of work per unit of time. A large engine is more powerful than a small one. It can do more work per hour than the small one. This means it can move larger forces through greater distances in less time. The **watt** (W) is the unit of power. One watt is equivalent to 1 joule per second (J/s).

Define the terms power and watt.

Eric Hoffhines

Dick Smith

FIGURE 4–12. The power shovel is more powerful than the person because it can do more work in less time than the person.

How is power calculated?

The following equation is used to find power:

$$\text{power} = \frac{\text{work}}{\text{time}} \qquad P = \frac{W}{t}$$

Example

A 450-N person walked up a flight of stairs 10 m high in 30 s. What power was used?

Solution

Step 1: Determine the amount of work done by the person climbing the stairs.

$$W = F \times d$$

$$W = 450 \text{ N} \times 10 \text{ m} = 4500 \text{ N·m} = 4500 \text{ J}$$

Step 2: Write the equation for power.

$$P = \frac{W}{t}$$

Step 3: Substitute the values for work and time given in the problem.

$$P = \frac{4500 \text{ J}}{30 \text{ s}}$$

Step 4: Divide to find the answer.

$$\frac{4500 \text{ J}}{30 \text{ s}} = 150 \text{ J/s} \qquad P = 150 \text{ W}$$

activity USING POWER TO CLIMB STAIRS

Find the height of a flight of stairs. To do this, measure the height of one step and multiply by the total number of steps. Have a classmate clock the time it takes you to walk up the steps. Determine your weight using 1 lb. = 4.5 N. Find the power (in watts) used to climb the stairs.

FIGURE 4–13.

MAKING SURE

13. In 2 s, a person lifts a box that weighs 500 N to a height of 4 m. Find the power in watts.

4:7 Engines

At one time much of the world's work was done by horses, mules, and oxen. In the United States today, engines have replaced most of these work animals. Engines are machines that produce mechanical power. One example of an engine is the gasoline engine. It burns gasoline and thereby uses the energy in gasoline to do work. Gasoline engines are used to run cars, trucks, boats, lawn mowers, and other machines.

What is an engine?

How does a gasoline engine produce power? A gasoline engine has one or more round tubes called cylinders. In each cylinder is a piston that moves back and forth. Each piston is attached to a rod. The rod is a piece of metal that connects to the crankshaft. When gasoline is burned inside a cylinder an explosion occurs. The explosion creates the force that moves the piston. As the pistons move back and forth, they cause the crankshaft to rotate and produce power. In a vehicle such as a car, the crankshaft is connected to the driveshaft. The driveshaft turns the car's wheels. A driveshaft can also be used to supply power for machinery such as a chain saw, a winch, or a snow blower.

How does a gasoline engine operate?

A gasoline engine burns gasoline and produces waste gases. Gasoline is fed into the cylinders from a device called a carburetor. Inside the carburetor, liquid gasoline pumped from the fuel tank is changed to a vapor. Gasoline vapor is then mixed with air drawn in through an air filter. The gasoline-air mixture enters the cylinder through an opening called an intake valve. A sparkplug in the cylinder creates an electric spark that ignites the gasoline. Waste gases produced in the burning are forced out of the cylinder through the exhaust valve.

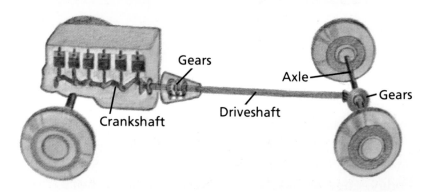

FIGURE 4–14. Automobiles are run by gasoline or diesel engines which produce mechanical power.

A diesel engine is similar to a gasoline engine. It is different in that it does not have spark plugs and burns a fuel called diesel oil. The fuel-air mixture is ignited by the heat produced when the mixture is compressed by the motion of a piston inside a cylinder. Both diesel and gasoline engines waste most of the fuel they use. Only about 12 percent of the energy in the fuel a gasoline engine burns is used for power. Most is lost as waste heat. However, a diesel engine is more efficient in that it uses a greater proportion of the energy in fuel to produce power. There is less wasted energy.

FIGURE 4–15. Operation of most gasoline engines involves four steps. Fuel mixture enters cylinder (a). The mixture is compressed (b). Sparkplug ignites mixture (c). Waste gases are forced out of cylinder (d).

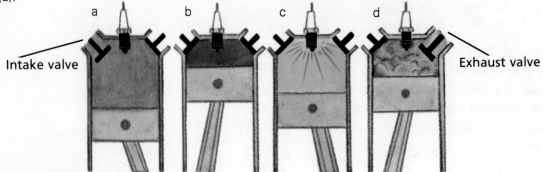

main ideas

1. A force is a push or pull on an object.   4:1
2. Force is measured in newtons.   4:1
3. Weight is the amount of force exerted by gravity on an object.   4:2
4. Friction force opposes the movement of objects. Three kinds of friction are sliding, rolling, and fluid friction.   4:3
5. Work is done when a force moves an object through a distance.   4:4
6. The joule is the unit of work.   4:4
7. Energy can be changed from one form to another, but energy cannot be created or destroyed.   4:5
8. Power is the work done per unit of time.   4:6
9. Power may be measured in watts.   4:6
10. An engine uses the energy obtained in burning a fuel to do work.   4:7

vocabulary

Define each of the following words or terms.

conservation of	friction	power
energy	joule	watt
force	newton	weight
		work

study questions

DO NOT WRITE IN THIS BOOK.

A. True or False

Determine whether each of the following sentences is true or false. If the sentence is false, rewrite it to make it true.

1. A person does work by pushing against a solid brick wall.
2. The newton is a unit of force.
3. The joule is a unit of work.
4. If a 5-N force moves a box 10 m, 15 J of work is done.
5. Weight and mass are the same.
6. You can measure your weight in newtons.
7. A rolling object has more friction than a sliding object.
8. When you lift a chair, you do work.

9. Adding oil to an engine increases the friction between the moving parts.
10. Work is the amount of power per unit of time.

B. Multiple Choice

Choose the word or phrase that completes correctly each of the following sentences.

1. The definition of work includes (*force, distance, force and distance*).
2. (*Friction, Power, Weight*) is the force that opposes the motion of a sliding object.
3. An anchor being pulled up through water is an example of (*rolling, sliding, fluid*) friction.
4. Power is equal to (*work, force, distance*) per unit of time.
5. When a person lifts a 200-N sack of feed 2 m, (*100, 4, 400, 40*) J of work are done.
6. A metric spring scale measures weight in (*grams, newtons, ounces*).
7. Your (*weight, mass, action, work*) is the amount of force that gravity exerts on your body.
8. As gasoline burns inside a gasoline engine the (*spark plugs, cylinders, pistons*) move back and forth.
9. When work is done, energy is (*created, changed, destroyed*).
10. (*Rolling, Fluid, Sliding*) friction occurs when an object moves across water.

C. Completion

Complete each of the following sentences with a word or phrase that will make the sentence correct.

1. _____ can be measured with a spring scale.
2. Lubrication _____ friction force.
3. The smoother the surface between two objects, the less the _____.
4. Ball bearings are used to reduce _____.
5. The _____ of a gasoline engine supplies the mixture of gasoline and air.
6. Work is the application of a(n) _____ through a distance.
7. The equation for work is _____.

8. When _____ is done, energy changes form.
9. A(n) _____ is a push or pull on an object.
10. The law of _____ states that energy cannot be created or destroyed.

D. How and Why
1. How does work differ from force?
2. What is the difference between sliding, rolling, and fluid friction? Give one example of each.
3. Why do the wheel bearings of a car sometimes need to be checked and repacked with grease?
4. Make a list of all the forces produced when a person rides a bicycle.
5. What is the law of conservation of energy? Give one example.

investigations

1. Use a spring scale to measure friction force. Compare the friction force of sliding, rolling, and fluid friction for the same object.
2. Devise an experiment to show the advantage of ball bearings.
3. Models of engines can be purchased in hobby stores. Obtain a kit for a model engine and put the parts together. Display the model in your classroom.

interesting reading

Feldman, Anthony and Bill Gunston, *Technology at Work*. New York, NY: Facts on File, 1980.

Lefkowitz, R. J., *Forces in the Earth: A Book About Gravity and Magnetism*. New York, NY: Parent's, 1976.

Vergara, William C., *Science in Everyday Life*. New York, NY: Harper and Row, 1980.

An industrial arts class is a busy place. Students in the class use a variety of common tools. Tools such as a saw, screwdriver, and drill consist of one or more machines. Machines help you do work. How do they make tasks easier? How is the efficiency of a machine measured? Why is efficiency important?

Hickson-Bender Photography

Machines

5:1 Machines

When you use a machine you may do work faster and easier. Mowing a large lawn is much faster and easier with a power mower than with a hand mower. Washing clothes in a washing machine is easier than washing them by hand. Cutting firewood with a chain saw goes faster than chopping it with an ax.

A **machine** is a device that can make work easier by changing the direction or amount of a force. For example, a bicycle can move you from place to place faster than you can walk. You can use a pulley to lift a heavy object. The pulley changes the direction and amount of the force needed to lift the object. A wrench can be used to loosen a bolt. The wrench increases the amount of force applied to the bolt.

All machines can be classified as either simple or compound machines. Simple machines produce work with one movement. There are six simple machines. They are the lever, pulley, wheel and axle, inclined plane, screw, and wedge. As you will see, the pulley and the wheel and axle are forms of a lever. The screw and the wedge are forms of an inclined plane.

Compound machines are composed of two or more simple machines. To understand compound machines, you should first be familiar with simple machines.

GOAL: You will gain an understanding of the use of simple and compound machines to do work.

What is a machine?

Name the six simple machines.

5:2 Levers

A **lever** is a bar that is free to move about a fulcrum. The **fulcrum** is the point at which a lever rotates. A seesaw is one kind of lever. When people ride a seesaw it rotates around a fulcrum. The fulcrum supports the seesaw at the center.

A lever may be used to do work. When a lever is used, a force is applied through a distance. The force applied to a lever is called the **effort force.** The force that is overcome when work is done is called the **resistance force.** In a lever such as a crowbar, the effort force is applied at one end. The resistance force is overcome at the opposite end. Between the two forces is the fulcrum. The distance from the effort force to the fulcrum is called the effort arm. The distance from the resistance force to the fulcrum is the resistance arm. Every lever has two arms, the effort arm and the resistance arm. Identify the parts of a lever in Figure 5–1.

Define the terms lever, fulcrum, effort force, and resistance force.

Name the two arms in a lever.

Effort force   Resistance force

— Effort arm —   — Resistance arm —

Fulcrum

FIGURE 5–1. Diagram of a lever.

Levers are classified as first, second, or third class levers. The class of lever is based on the relative positions of the effort force, resistance force, and fulcrum. Examples of first, second, and third class levers are given in Figure 5–2.

What are the three classes of levers?

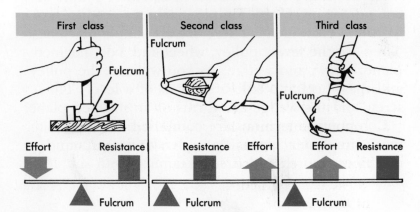

First class	Second class	Third class
Fulcrum	Fulcrum	Fulcrum
Effort Resistance	Resistance Effort	Effort Resistance
Fulcrum	Fulcrum	Fulcrum

FIGURE 5–2. The three classes of levers.

Two things affect the action of a lever—the amount of force at both ends and the length of both arms. Remember, every lever has two forces, the effort force and resistance force. Every lever has two arms, the effort arm and resistance arm.

When the effort arm is longer than the resistance arm, the effort force is less than the resistance force. Thus, a lever can be used to multiply the effort force.

It is easier to pry open a can of paint with a long screwdriver than with a short one. Why? The long screwdriver has a longer effort arm. Thus, it takes less effort force to produce a large resistance force. The can is more easily opened because the effort force has been multiplied.

activity   USING A RULER AS A LEVER

Place a book on the edge of a table or desk. Insert about 5 cm of a wooden ruler under the edge of the book. The remainder of the ruler should extend out beyond the table. Pull up on the end of the ruler so it raises the book. Where are the fulcrum and the effort forces? Now put a pencil on the table in front of the book. Place one end of the ruler under the book. Place the center of the ruler over the pencil. Push down on the ruler with your hand. Where are the resistance force, effort force, and fulcrum?

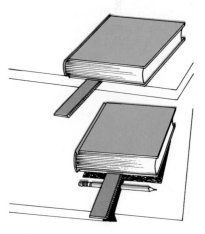

FIGURE 5–3.

MAKING SURE

1. Where is the fulcrum in each of these levers?
   (a) crowbar   (d) scissors
   (b) seesaw   (e) bottle opener
   (c) shovel

2. Name the lever(s) from Question 1 in which the resistance force is greater than the effort force.

3. Name the lever(s) from Question 1 in which the effort force moves through a greater distance than the resistance force.

4. What is the practical use of each lever mentioned in Question 3?

5:3 Mechanical Advantage

A lever is often used to multiply an effort force. The number of times that a machine multiplies the effort force is called the **actual mechanical advantage** (A.M.A.). The actual mechanical advantage is found by dividing the resistance force by the effort force.

What is the equation for A.M.A.?

$$A.M.A. = \frac{\text{resistance force}}{\text{effort force}}$$

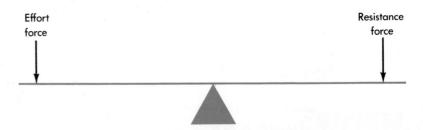

Effort force

Resistance force

FIGURE 5–4. Divide resistance force by effort force to find the A.M.A. of a lever.

Example

An effort force of 10 N is applied to a lever in lifting a 200-N load. What is the A.M.A.?

Solution

Step 1: Write the equation for A.M.A.

$$A.M.A. = \frac{\text{resistance force}}{\text{effort force}}$$

Step 2: Substitute the values for effort force and resistance force given in the problem.

$$A.M.A. = \frac{200 \text{ N}}{10 \text{ N}}$$

Step 3: Divide to find the answer.

$$\frac{200 \text{ N}}{10 \text{ N}} = 20 \qquad A.M.A. = 20$$

Note that the value for mechanical advantage has no units. The division of newtons by newtons cancels the units. The answer is the number 20. Thus, the effort force is multiplied 20 times. Each newton of effort moves 20 N of weight.

You have found the actual mechanical advantage of a lever. Sometimes it is useful to know the **ideal mechanical advantage** (I.M.A.) of a lever or other machines. Ideal means that friction and weight of the lever are not considered. In actual practice, friction reduces the mechanical advantage. Thus, the ideal mechanical advantage of a machine is greater than its actual mechanical advantage.

To find a lever's I.M.A., divide the effort arm length by the resistance arm length.

How is the A.M.A. of a machine different from the I.M.A.?

$$I.M.A. = \frac{\text{effort arm}}{\text{resistance arm}}$$

What is the equation for I.M.A.?

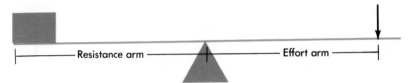

FIGURE 5–5. The I.M.A. of a lever is found by dividing effort arm length by resistance arm length.

Example

Find the I.M.A. for a lever that has a resistance arm 1 m long and an effort arm 2 m long.

Solution

Step 1: Write the equation for I.M.A.

$$I.M.A. = \frac{\text{effort arm}}{\text{resistance arm}}$$

Step 2: Substitute the values for effort arm and resistance arm given in the problem.

$$I.M.A. = \frac{2 \text{ m}}{1 \text{ m}}$$

Step 3: Divide to find the answer.

$$\frac{2 \text{ m}}{1 \text{ m}} = 2 \qquad I.M.A. = 2$$

How long are the arms of a lever with an I.M.A. of 2? They can be any length. The effort arm of this lever, however, is two times longer than the resistance arm. What if the I.M.A. is 3? Then the effort arm is three times longer than the resistance arm. When the I.M.A. of a lever is 1, the effort force is equal to the resistance force. A lever with an I.M.A. of 1 does not change the amount of force.

The I.M.A. is also equal to the effort movement divided by the resistance movement.

$$I.M.A. = \frac{\text{effort movement}}{\text{resistance movement}}$$

Here the word movement refers to the distance traveled by a force acting on a rotating lever. For example, you may use the tip of a screwdriver to open a can of paint. You put the tip under the can's lid. Then, you push down on the handle. The distance your hand pushes the handle of the screwdriver is the effort movement. Resistance movement is the distance the tip of the screwdriver moves up as it pushes the lid open.

FIGURE 5–6. The effort movement of a lever divided by the resistance movement determines the I.M.A. of a lever.

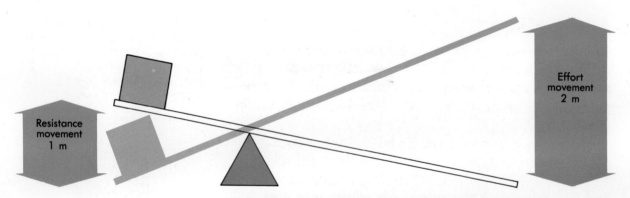

Resistance movement 1 m

Effort movement 2 m

Example

In a certain lever, the effort force moves 4 m and the resistance force moves 2 m. Find the I.M.A. of this lever.

Solution

Step 1: Write the equation for I.M.A.

$$I.M.A. = \frac{\text{effort movement}}{\text{resistance movement}}$$

Step 2: Substitute the values for effort movement and resistance movement given in the problem.

$$I.M.A. = \frac{4 \text{ m}}{2 \text{ m}}$$

Step 3: Divide to find the answer.

$$\frac{4 \text{ m}}{2 \text{ m}} = 2 \qquad I.M.A. = 2$$

MAKING SURE

5. A person applies an effort force of 65 N to raise a 325-N stone. What is the A.M.A. of this lever?
6. A 150-N log is shifted with an effort force of 25 N. Find the A.M.A. of the lever. How many newtons of weight did each newton of effort move?
7. What is the I.M.A. of a seesaw if a person 3 m from the fulcrum moves a person who is 1 m from the fulcrum?

5:4 Pulleys

A **pulley** is a wheel that turns on an axle. It is used with a rope, chain, or belt to change the amount or the direction of a force. A pulley can be either fixed or movable. There are single and double pulleys.

Figure 5–7a shows a rope and a single, fixed pulley. An effort force of 125 N is used to raise a 125-N metal block. The effort force equals the resistance force. Thus, the mechanical advantage is 1. What is the practical value of this pulley? The pulley changes the direction of force to make lifting easier. With a single, fixed pulley, the effort force pulls down and the weight goes up.

The pulley in Figure 5–7b has an I.M.A. of 2. In finding the I.M.A., the friction between the pulley and the rope is ignored. Two strands of a single rope support the 100-N weight. The total number of support strands of a movable pulley is always equal to the I.M.A. The number of support strands is determined by considering each part of the long rope as a separate strand. Then, count the number of strands that support the movable pulley. Since there are two support strands, the I.M.A. is 2.

What is a pulley?

FIGURE 5–7. The I.M.A. of the pulley system is 1 because only one rope strand supports the weight (a). The I.M.A. is 2 because two rope strands support the weight (b).

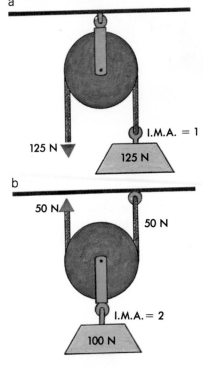

activity

USING PULLEYS

Objective: To measure the I.M.A. of three pulley systems

Materials

double pulley
object (rock or large bolt)
ring stand
2 single pulleys
spring scale
string, 1 m

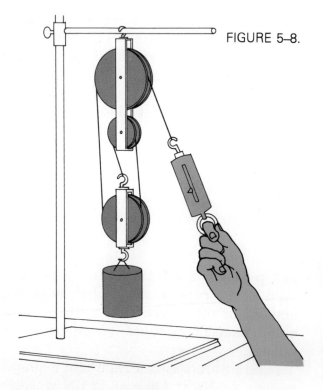

FIGURE 5–8.

Procedure

1. Determine the weight of the object using the spring scale. Record the weight in the data table.

2. Set up the single pulley, the string, and the object to make a machine with an I.M.A. of 1. Use Figure 5–7 as a guide.

3. Attach the spring scale to the effort end of the string. Measure the force needed to raise the object. Record the force in the data table.

4. Set up the pulleys to make a machine with an I.M.A. of 2 (Figure 5–7). Measure the force needed to raise the object. Record the force in the data table.

5. Make a sketch and label the I.M.A. and effort force for each pulley system.

6. Using the double pulley, repeat Step 3 for a pulley system with an I.M.A. of 3 (Figure 5–8). Be sure to make a sketch of this system. Record the force in the data table.

Observations and Data

I.M.A.	Weight	Force
1		
2		
3		

Questions and Conclusions

1. How did friction force affect the force needed to raise the weight?

2. Draw a diagram of a pulley system with an I.M.A. of 4. (*Hint:* Use 2 double pulleys.)

5:5 Wheel and Axle

Bikes, cars, trucks, and trains have two or more wheels and axles. A **wheel and axle** works on the same principle as the lever and pulley. The wheel always turns through a greater distance than the axle. The smaller force on the wheel moves through a greater distance than the larger force on the axle. A force applied to the wheel is increased at the axle.

To find the I.M.A. of a wheel and axle, divide the diameter of the wheel by the diameter of the axle. Suppose a wheel has a diameter of 1 m. Its axle has a diameter of 10 cm. What is the I.M.A.?

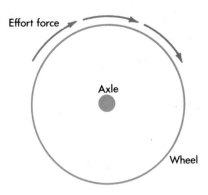

FIGURE 5–9. Effort force applied to a wheel is increased at the axle.

How is the I.M.A. of a wheel and axle calculated?

MAKING SURE

8. When a bicycle wheel turns, is the force greater at the wheel or axle? Explain why.

9. What is the benefit of this change in force in a bicycle?

5:6 Inclined Plane

An **inclined plane** is a slanted surface which may be used for raising objects to higher places. A mountain road and a ramp are examples of inclined planes. Less effort force is needed with an inclined plane. This is because an object is moved through a longer distance on the slanted surface. When the same object is lifted straight up, a large effort force must be applied through a short distance.

What is an inclined plane?

Doug Martin

FIGURE 5–10. A ramp allows less force to be used in going to different levels.

activity

USING INCLINED PLANES

Objective: To determine the I.M.A. and A.M.A. of inclined planes

Materials

board, (smooth) 1 m × 20 cm   meter stick
5 books   spring scale
brick   string

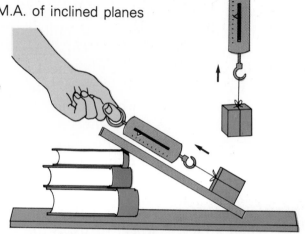

Procedure

1. Tie the string to the brick. Attach the free end of the string to the spring scale and measure the weight of the brick. Record the weight in the table.

2. Place one end of the board on a book to form an inclined plane. Measure the length and height of the inclined plane. Record the measurements in your data table.

3. Pull the brick up the inclined plane at a constant speed. Do not jerk the brick. Read the spring scale while the brick is moving. Record the force needed to pull the brick up the inclined plane in your data table.

4. Change the angle of the inclined plane by adding a second book. Measure the length and height of the inclined plane. Record the measurements in your data table.

5. Repeat Step 3 and record the force used in the data table.

6. Change the height of the inclined plane by adding more books. Record the length and height of the inclined plane in your data table.

7. Repeat Step 3 and record the force used in the data table.

FIGURE 5-11.

Observations and Data

Weight of brick:_____ N

Number of books	Height of plane (cm)	Length of plane (cm)	Force (N)
1			
2			

Questions and Conclusions

1. Determine the I.M.A. for each inclined plane using the following equation.

$$I.M.A. = \frac{\text{length of plane}}{\text{height of plane}}$$

2. Use your data and the following equation to calculate the A.M.A. for each inclined plane.

$$A.M.A. = \frac{\text{weight of brick}}{\text{effort force}}$$

3. Compare the A.M.A. to the I.M.A. for each inclined plane. Why did they differ?

10. The I.M.A. of an inclined plane is its length divided by its height. Find the I.M.A. for the inclined planes in Figure 5–12. Then find the effort force needed to move the object up each of the inclined planes. Ignore the effect of friction when solving these problems.

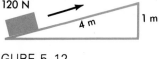

FIGURE 5–12.

5:7 Wedge

A **wedge** is a type of inclined plane. It consists of a piece of material, such as wood or metal, that is thicker at one edge than at the other. Examples of wedges are a knife, axe, needle, and can opener. The length of the wedge divided by its thickness determines its I.M.A. A long, narrow wedge requires a small effort force to overcome a great resistance force.

When you sharpen a knife, you are decreasing its thickness at the cutting edge. This increases its mechanical advantage. You need less force to cut with a sharp knife than to cut with a dull knife.

MAKING SURE
11. Determine the I.M.A. of two wedges that have the following dimensions.
   (a) thickness of 5 cm; length of 36 cm
   (b) thickness of 3 cm; length of 42 cm
12. Which wedge in Question 11 requires the least effort force to do work? Explain.

FIGURE 5–13. Some common examples of wedges include a razor blade, chisel, and nail.

How is the I.M.A. of a wedge calculated?

5:8 Screw

A **screw** is a circular inclined plane. It looks like an inclined plane wound around a center to form a spiral. Turning a screw requires a small effort force to overcome a large resistance force. The small effort force turns through a large distance. It produces a large resistance which turns through a small distance.

List five examples of a screw.

FIGURE 5–14. These household objects show some common uses of screws.

MAKING SURE

13. Which simple machine is present in each of the following items:

(a) automobile jack

(b) door knob

(c) ax

(d) pliers

(e) snowplow

(f) block and tackle

(g) eggbeater

(h) loading ramp

(i) bow of a boat

(j) faucet

(k) screwdriver

(1) broom

5:9 Efficiency

Do you think of machines as gadgets that do work? Actually, machines must use energy to do work. A machine can do work only if work is done on it. The work done on the machine is effort force times the distance the effort force moves. It is called the work input.

work input = effort force × effort distance

$$W_i = F \times d$$

A machine also has a work output. The work output is the resistance force times the distance through which the resistance force moves.

work output = resistance force × resistance distance

$$W_o = F \times d$$

What is the difference between work input and work output?

Example

The effort force used with a certain set of pulleys is 50 N. When this effort force moves a distance of 3 m, 120 N of resistance moves 1 m. What is the work input for this machine? What is the work output for this machine?

Solution

Step 1: Write the equation for work input.

$$W_i = F \times d$$

Step 2: Substitute the values for effort force and effort distance given in the problem.

$$W_i = 50 \text{ N} \times 3 \text{ m}$$

Step 3: Multiply to find the answer.

$$50 \text{ N} \times 3 \text{ m} = 150 \text{ J} \qquad W_i = 150 \text{ J}$$

Step 4: Write the equation for work output.

$$W_o = F \times d$$

Step 5: Substitute the values for resistance force and resistance distance given in the problem.

$$W_o = 120 \text{ N} \times 1 \text{ m}$$

Step 6: Multiply to find the answer.

$$120 \text{ N} \times 1 \text{ m} = 120 \text{ J} \qquad W_o = 120 \text{ J}$$

Rohn Engh

FIGURE 5–15. A gasoline engine provides the energy for this log-splitting machine to do work.

In an ideal machine, the work output would equal the work input. Since no machine is ideal, some force must always be used to overcome friction. Thus, the work output of a real machine is always less than the work input. The work output for the pulleys in the example is 120 J. The work input is 150 J.

Some machines are more efficient than others. The **efficiency** (ih FIHSH un see) of a machine is a comparison of the work output to the work input. Efficiency is measured in percent. An ideal machine, if it could exist, would have an efficiency of 100 percent. However, some work is always used to overcome friction. No machine can have an efficiency of 100 percent. You can never get as much work out of a machine as you put into it.

The efficiency of a machine is found by dividing the work output by the work input and then multiplying by 100%. The equation is

$$\text{efficiency} = \frac{\text{work output}}{\text{work input}} \times 100\%$$

$$E = \frac{W_o}{W_i} \times 100\%$$

How is the efficiency of a machine calculated?

Example

Find the efficiency of the pulleys whose work input is 150 J and work output is 120 J.

Solution

Step 1: Write the equation for efficiency.

$$E = \frac{W_o}{W_i} \times 100\%$$

Step 2: Substitute the values for work input and work output given in the problem.

$$E = \frac{120 \text{ J}}{150 \text{ J}} \times 100\%$$

Step 3: Divide, and then multiply to find the answer.

$$\frac{120 \text{ J}}{150 \text{ J}} \times 100\% = 80\% \qquad E = 80\%$$

b

FIGURE 5–16. Regular tuning of a car engine (a) can maintain the efficiency listed on the EPA sticker (b).

a

Efficient machines help conserve resources. They also help save money. Machinery of low efficiency wastes work input. For example, a car that gets low gas mileage is not efficient. It wastes fuel.

MAKING SURE

14. Find the work input, work output, and efficiency of the machines in Table 5–1.

Table 5–1.
Input and Output for Some Machines

Machine	Effort force	Effort distance	Resistance force	Resistance distance	Efficiency
A	2 N	15 m	8 N	3 m	? %
B	100 N	20 m	200 N	5 m	? %
C	10 N	5 m	40 N	1 m	? %
D	125 N	4 m	200 N	1.5 m	? %
E	480 N	7 cm	840 N	3 cm	? %
F	80 N	5 m	53 N	4 m	? %

15. How does lubrication increase the efficiency of machines?

16. Why do efficient machines help to save energy?

17. Why is it impossible to have an ideal machine?

5:10 Compound Machines

What is a compound machine?

A compound machine contains two or more simple machines. The simple machines are connected so that the work each does is combined to do the job performed by the compound machine. One example of a compound machine is a mechanical pencil sharpener. The handle of the pencil sharpener is a wheel and axle. It rotates when someone applies a force to turn it. Connected to the axle are blades that shave the end of the pencil. Each of these blades is a wedge. The force applied to the handle is carried through the wheel and axle to the blades that do the work.

One kind of mechanical can opener has three simple machines. The simple machines are the wedge, the lever, and the wheel and axle. The blade of the opener is a wedge. A lever on the handle is used to force the blade into the top of a can. The force needed to open the can is applied to the wheel and axle part of the opener. As the wheel and axle rotates on the edge of the can, the blade cuts around the top of the can. Working together the three simple machines make a compound machine that opens the can easily and efficiently.

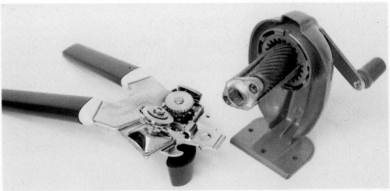

Kevin Fitzsimons

FIGURE 5–17. A pencil sharpener and a can opener contain simple machines.

Another example of a compound machine is a typewriter. Paper is fed into a typewriter by a long, round, hard rubber wheel called a platen. Inside the platen is an axle. Axle and platen are rotated by turning knobs located on each end of the axle. The inked ribbon used to print on the paper is connected to two spools, one on each side of the machine. These spools feed the ribbon across the surface of the paper at the point where the printing takes place. Each spool is a wheel and each wheel rests on an axle. As the axles turn the wheels, the ribbon is fed out from one spool and wound up on the other. Some typewriters have anywhere from 45 to 50 levers in the center of the typewriter in front of the ribbon. These levers are metal bars that strike the ribbon to print letters, numerals, and other symbols. Each lever is connected to a typewriter key. At the top end of the bar is the type that prints the letter or numeral. At the opposite end or bottom, the bar connects to the typewriter. The point of connection is the fulcrum. Here the bar rotates when its key is depressed, causing it to strike the ribbon. Each bar is attached to a spring that snaps it back in place after the key is released.

Eric Hoffhines

FIGURE 5–18. A typewriter contains a number of levers and wheels and axles.

MAKING SURE

18. What simple machines in a mechanical pencil sharpener are in a mechanical can opener?
19. Name two simple machines that make a typewriter work.
20. Why might a compound machine not work if one of its simple machines is broken?

Perspectives

Organizing Notes in Outline Form

Outlining the information you read will help you to organize and remember it. Outlining is a way of taking notes. Taking notes leads you to think about what you have read. The outline form assists you in arranging the information in a sensible order. The outline of a chapter shows very quickly the relationship of the main ideas of the chapter and the smaller but important details.

A framework for an outline for part of Chapter 5 is shown below. Some of it has been done for you. For practice, complete the remainder of the outline. Note that many of the principal headings of the outline follow the section titles of the chapter. The section titles in heavy black print are part of the author's outline for the chapter.

I Machines (Note this is Section 5:1.)
  A. Definition: a device that can change the speed, direction, or amount of force.
  B. Types
    1. simple
    2. compound

II Simple Machines
  A. Levers (Note this is Section 5:2.)
    1. Definition: a bar that is free to move about a fulcrum
    2. Parts
      a. Fulcrum: the point at which a lever rotates
      b. Effort arm: the distance from the end of the bar to the fulcrum
      c. Resistance arm: the distance from the opposite end of the bar to the fulcrum.
    3. Working with levers
      a. Effort force: the force applied to a lever
      b. Resistance force: the force that is overcome to do work
    4. Mechanical advantage of a lever (Section 5:3)
      a. Definition: the relationship of the force and the length of arm of the effort and the resistance
      b. Actual mechanical advantage (A.M.A.)
        (1) Definition: the number of times that a machine multiplies the effort force
        (2) Equation:

$$\text{A.M.A.} = \frac{\text{resistance force}}{\text{effort force}}$$

      c. Ideal mechanical advantage
        (1) Definition:
        (2) Equations:

  B. Pulley (Section 5:4)
    1. Definition:
    2. Types
    3. Mechanical advantage

  C. Wheel and axle (Section 5:5)

  D. Inclined plane (Section 5:6)

The form of your outline may vary depending on the type of information found in the chapter. One variation has been introduced to you in the partial outline given above—using section titles as the main headings of your outline. This variation makes it easier to refer to specific sections if you need to do so. Another variation might be to draw each simple machine and label the parts. Remember, taking notes in outline form should help you to (1) put the important information in your own words and (2) enable you to easily obtain the information when reviewing it.

main ideas

1. Machines can change the amount, speed, or direction of a force.

   5:1

2. A lever is a bar that is free to move about a fulcrum. Levers can be classified as first, second, or third class levers.

   5:2

3. The actual mechanical advantage (A.M.A.) of a machine is the number of times the machine multiplies an effort force.

   5:3

4. Ideal mechanical advantage (I.M.A.) does not include friction and weight.

   5:3

5. A pulley is a wheel that rotates on an axle.

   5:4

6. A wheel and axle works on the same principle as a lever. The wheel turns with the axle.

   5:5

7. An inclined plane is a slanted surface which may be used for raising objects to higher places.

   5:6

8. The work output of a machine is always less than the work input. Efficiency is found by comparing these two values.

   5:9

vocabulary

Define each of the following words or terms.

actual mechanical advantage (A.M.A.)
efficiency
effort force
fulcrum

ideal mechanical advantage (I.M.A.)
inclined plane
lever
machine

pulley
resistance force
screw
wedge
wheel and axle

study questions

DO NOT WRITE IN THIS BOOK.

A. True or False

Determine whether each of the following sentences is true or false. If the sentence is false, rewrite it to make it true.

1. Machines have no practical value.

2. A machine can change the direction of a force.

3. Every lever has two arms.

4. Levers are classified as first, second, and third class.

5. The wheel and axle and the wedge are forms of the lever.

6. The I.M.A. of a machine is usually greater than its A.M.A.

7. A short, thick wedge has a greater mechanical advantage than a long, narrow wedge.
8. The work output of a machine is usually more than the work input.
9. No machine is 100% efficient.
10. Mechanical advantage is expressed in newtons.

B. Multiple Choice

Choose the word or phrase that completes correctly each of the following sentences.

1. Every lever has *(one, two, two or more)* arms.
2. A gear is an example of a(n) *(wheel and axle, wedge, inclined plane)*.
3. A lever with the fulcrum between the resistance force and effort force is a *(first class, second class, third class)* lever.
4. If the I.M.A. of a machine is 1, the effort force is *(multiplied, decreased, unchanged)*.
5. To find the I.M.A. of a machine *(size, movement, friction)* is not considered.
6. The total number of support strands is equal to the I.M.A. in a *(lever, wheel and axle, pulley)*.
7. A circular inclined plane is called a *(wedge, screw, pulley)*.
8. The work output divided by the work input is equal to the *(power, speed, efficiency)* of a machine.
9. Efficiency is measured in *(J, J/s, percent)*.
10. The effort arm in a lever with an I.M.A. of 4 is *(2 times, 3 times, 4 times)* longer than the resistance arm.

C. Completion

Complete each of the following sentences with a word or phrase that will make the sentence correct.

1. The pivot point of a lever is called the _____.
2. The effort arm of a lever is 4 m long, the resistance arm is 2 m long. The I.M.A. is _____.
3. A block and tackle has four support strands. The I.M.A. is _____.
4. When the resistance force for the pulleys in Question 3 moves through 5 m, the effort force moves through _____ m.

5. A shovel is an example of a(n) ———.
6. A wedge is a type of ———.
7. Work input of a machine is always ——— work.
8. The efficiency of a machine is always ——— 100%.
9. When the effort force is equal to the resistance force in a lever, the I.M.A. is ———.
10. In a can opener, a(n) ——— forces the blade into the top of a can.

D. How and Why
1. In what three ways are lever, pulley, and wheel and axle alike?
2. Make a list of the six simple machines. Give an example of each simple machine and state its practical value.
3. Draw a diagram of a set of pulleys with an I.M.A. of 3. The effort force on the rope moves 2 m. How far will the resistance force move?
4. The work input of a machine is 200 J. The output is 50 J. Find the efficiency of the machine.
5. Make a list of five compound machines. Name one simple machine present in each of the compound machines.

investigations

1. Collect a variety of small hand tools. Examine each one to find how many simple machines it contains.
2. Find out how new cars are being designed to improve their efficiency. Obtain information on federal standards for improving gasoline mileage in the future. Make a report to your class.

interesting reading

Kerrod, Robin, *The Way It Works: Man and His Machines*. New York, NY: Octopus, 1980.
Kleiner, Art, *Robots*. Milwaukee, WI: Raintree, 1981.
Solomon, Stephen, "Amazing Machines." *Science Digest*. Nov./Dec. 1980, pp. 56–61.
Weiss, Harvey, *How to Be An Inventor*. New York NY: Crowell, 1980.

THE VERSATILE ROBOT

Robot—the word is becoming more common all the time. What is a robot? What can it do? A robot is similar to an automatic machine. It can do a specific task such as welding auto parts over and over. It never gets tired and does not need a lunch break. A robot is not an automatic machine. The difference is that an automatic machine can do only one task. A robot can be taught to do many different tasks. The control center or brain of a robot is a computer (Figure A). If you want to teach a robot to pick up an object, you program its computer brain. If you want the robot to do some welding, you change the program.

A

Doug Martin

Currently there are about 20 000 robots working in industry. They perform dangerous or often-repeated tasks. The automobile industry uses many robots (Figure B). Besides welding, robots transport engines and doors from one place to another. Since robots are computer controlled, each weld, each movement is the same as the first.

When you think of a robot, you may think of a shiny metal body on wheels. It may have arms with pincers and flashing lights. Or, you may think of a shiny metal body with arms, legs, and head. It may talk to you. Neither idea describes today's robots. Most robots consist of an arm with one or two joints and a two-or three-fingered hand. The arm is attached to a big box or cylinder that stands on the floor. The box contains the robot's brain and the machines that move the arm and hand.

B

Alan Nogues/Sygma

These robots are limited to simple tasks because they cannot see and have no sense of touch. Another kind of robot looks like a motorized cart. This robot can deliver mail and papers between offices in a building. Some of these robots can even bring a person's morning coffee.

Today's robots can accomplish many tasks. Many scientists, however, are working to make robots even more useful.

For example, robots could do more jobs if they could see. Scientists are connecting television cameras to the robot computers. The computers analyze the pictures from the cameras and then match the pictures with shapes stored in their memories. Once robots recognize the shapes, they can perform the proper tasks. The ability to see also helps robots move. Robots that see can avoid obstacles.

C

Gayle Curtis, Veterans Administration Medical Center, Palo Alto, CA

Another improvement is robots that obey voice commands. These robots are taught new tasks using voice commands. Voice controlled robots are especially useful for the physically handicapped. A person who cannot use either arm can talk to a robot arm (Figure C). The arm can be instructed to pick up a glass of milk or a newspaper. It can even be told to turn the pages of a book. Voice controlled robots are already used to make "smart" wheelchairs. The physically handicapped person tells the chair in which direction to move and the chair moves.

For a robot hand to pick up a delicate piece of glass or turn a page, another sense must be added—the sense of touch.

Scientists are working on robot hands that have plastic fingertips to hold objects. Within the fingers, are pressure plates. The plates tell the robot's computer how tight an object is held.

As robots improve, they continue to do more dangerous or boring jobs. For example, they work in nuclear reactors. In the future, robots may work in fast food restaurants or run cash registers at neighborhood supermarkets. You may have a robot butler to take your coat when you get home. The butler may even look a little like a person.

D

The spacecraft Columbia has just been launched. Watching the launch of a spacecraft can be exciting. There is a feeling of great power and motion. What indications of motion are present? You experience motion in many ways. What is motion? What kinds of motion do you observe every day?

NASA

Motion

6:1 Inertia

When something is moving, it is in motion. The movies you see in a theater show motion because the film moves steadily through a film projector. You can hear the music on a tape when it is moving through a tape player. Without motion the hands of a clock would not indicate the time of day. For every motion there is a force that causes it.

A force is needed to start something moving or to change its direction. A force is also needed to stop motion. The tendency of matter to stay at rest or in motion, unless acted on by a force, is called **inertia** (ihn UR shuh).

A person riding in a car has inertia. Think of a car moving at a speed of 50 km/h. How fast is the person inside going? The person is moving with the car and is not left behind; therefore, the person must also be moving at 50 km/h. If the brakes are applied suddenly, what happens to the person in the car? The person continues to move forward even though the car is stopping. If the seat belt is unfastened, the dashboard or windshield may stop this forward motion.

If you are standing in a bus, you may be thrown off balance when the bus starts to move. Your body has inertia. It tends to remain in place as the bus

GOAL: You will gain an understanding of how forces produce, change, and stop the motion of objects.

What causes motion?

Define the term inertia.

FIGURE 6–1. Passengers standing in a bus fall backward when the bus starts (a) and fall forward when the bus stops (b).

a Starting bus

b Stopping bus

begins to move. If the bus goes forward too fast, you may fall backward.

All matter has inertia. Inertia is a property of matter. The amount of inertia an object has depends upon its mass. The greater the mass of an object, the greater its inertia. A sofa of large mass has more inertia than a kitchen chair. It takes more force to move a sofa than to move a kitchen chair. It takes a larger force to start and stop a bus than to start and stop a small sports car.

FIGURE 6–2.

activity DEMONSTRATING INERTIA

Set a drinking glass on a desk or table. Lay a flat playing card on top of the glass. Place a coin on the center of the card. Pull the card away quickly with your fingers so it flies out from under the coin. Can you pull the card out fast enough so that the coin falls into the glass? How did this activity illustrate inertia?

activity INERTIA OF BOOKS

Tie a long, thin string around five books. Place the books on the floor. Raise the books by pulling upward very slowly on the string. Lower the books back to the floor. Pull up on the string with a sharp, jerking movement. Compare the effect of pulling slowly and suddenly. What did inertia have to do with your observation?

1. How can seat belts help protect a passenger in a car?

2. Which has more inertia, a golf ball or a Ping-Pong ball? Explain.

3. A person is standing next to the first seat in a train moving at 150 km/h. The person jumps high in the air. Where will the person land? Why? Figure 6–3 will help you discover the answer.

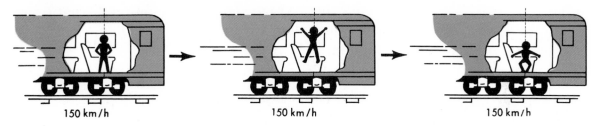

150 km/h   150 km/h   150 km/h

FIGURE 6–3.

6:2   Speed

One property of motion is speed. **Speed** refers to how fast an object is moving. It is defined as the distance an object travels per unit of time. For example, a car may travel at 88 km/h on a highway. At this speed the car will go 88 km in 1 h.

If a car moves at a steady 50 km/h, its speed is constant. It goes 50 km each hour it travels. In two hours the car will move a distance of 100 km. How far will it go in three hours?

Frank Lerner

FIGURE 6–4. The speed of a softball can be determined by measuring the time it takes for the ball to travel the distance between the pitcher and the batter.

A car is more likely to change speeds than to move at a constant speed. Thus, the speed of a car during a trip is really an average speed. Average speed is the total distance traveled divided by the time it takes to go that distance. The following equation is used to find average speed.

How is average speed calculated?

$$\text{speed} = \frac{\text{distance}}{\text{time}} \qquad S = \frac{d}{t}$$

Example

Find the average speed of a motorcycle that travels 16 km in 8 min. Give the speed in km/h.

Solution

Step 1: Write the equation for speed.

$$S = \frac{d}{t}$$

Step 2: Substitute the values for distance and time given in the problem.

$$S = \frac{16 \text{ km}}{8 \text{ min}}$$

Step 3: Divide to find the answer.

$$\frac{16 \text{ km}}{8 \text{ min}} = 2 \text{ km/min} \qquad S = 2 \text{ km/min}$$

Step 4: Change the answer to km/h by multiplying by 60 min/h.

FIGURE 6–5. Comparing speeds.

$$\frac{2 \text{ km}}{\text{min}} \times \frac{60 \text{ min}}{\text{h}} = 120 \text{ km/h} \qquad S = 120 \text{ km/h}$$

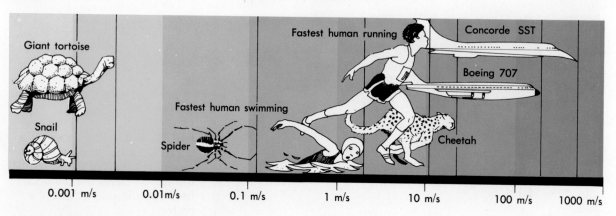

Giant tortoise

Snail

Spider

Fastest human swimming

Fastest human running

Cheetah

Concorde SST

Boeing 707

0.001 m/s   0.01 m/s   0.1 m/s   1 m/s   10 m/s   100 m/s   1000 m/s

MAKING SURE

4. Find the average speed of an airplane that flies 4500 km coast to coast in 5 h 15 min.

5. A motorcycle goes around a 1 km track 10 times in 2 min. Find its average speed.

6:3 Change in Speed

Every car has a gas pedal. This pedal is also called an accelerator. When a driver steps on the gas pedal, the speed of the car increases. The car accelerates. **Acceleration** (ak sel uh RAY shun) is the rate at which speed changes. An object accelerates whenever it starts, stops, changes speed or changes direction. A force is necessary to cause these changes.

What happens when an object accelerates?

To find the acceleration of an object, divide its change in speed by the time it takes for the speed to change. The equation for acceleration is

$$\text{acceleration} = \frac{\text{final speed} - \text{initial speed}}{\text{time}}$$

$$a = \frac{S_2 - S_1}{t}$$

Write the equation for acceleration.

Example

A car goes from rest to 70 km/h in 10 s. What is the acceleration of the car?

Solution

Step 1: Write the equation for acceleration.

$$a = \frac{S_2 - S_1}{t}$$

Step 2: Substitute the values for final speed, initial speed, and time given in the problem.

$$a = \frac{70 \text{ km/h} - 0}{10 \text{ s}}$$

Step 3: Subtract, then divide to find the answer.

$$\frac{70 \text{ km/h} - 0}{10 \text{ s}} = 7 \text{ km/h/s} \qquad a = 7 \text{ km/h/s}$$

The rate of acceleration depends on both the mass of an object and the force acting on it. An empty truck can accelerate faster than a loaded truck because it has less mass. A race car can accelerate faster than an average small car because it has a more powerful engine.

Which accelerates faster, a truck or a sports car? A truck may have a powerful engine, but it may also have a heavy load to move. The less powerful engine in a small sports car can accelerate the car faster because there is less mass to move.

FIGURE 6–6. A small race car can accelerate rapidly because of its low mass and powerful engine.

When an object that is moving comes to a stop, it decelerates. Deceleration is the rate at which the speed of an object decreases. A driver decelerates a moving car by applying the brakes. The brakes produce a force on the wheels that slows them down. As a result the speed of the car decreases.

FIGURE 6–7. A drag chute is used to decelerate a race car.

Deceleration (dee sel uh RAY shun) means negative acceleration. You can use the acceleration equation to calculate deceleration. The deceleration you calculate is always a negative number. Why?

How is deceleration calculated?

Example

A sled traveling at 6 m/s slows to a stop in 3 s. Find the deceleration.

Solution

Step 1: Write the equation for acceleration.

$$a = \frac{S_2 - S_1}{t}$$

Step 2: Substitute the values for final speed, initial speed, and time given in the problem.

$$a = \frac{0 - 6 \text{ m/s}}{3 \text{ s}}$$

Step 3: Subtract, then divide to find the answer.

$$\frac{0 - 6 \text{ m/s}}{3 \text{ s}} = -2 \text{ m/s}^2 \qquad a = -2 \text{ m/s}^2$$

To stop or slow a moving object, force must be applied. The rate of deceleration depends on mass and force. The greater the force applied in stopping something the faster it decelerates. The greater the mass of an object, the more slowly it stops. In the example problem above, friction and gravity were the two forces that caused the sled to stop.

MAKING SURE

6. In which of the following does acceleration occur? Explain your answers.
   (a) Air rushes out of an inflated balloon.
   (b) A clock's second hand moves in a circle.
   (c) An ocean current flows at 3 km/h.

7. What is the acceleration of a skateboard whose speed changes from 5 km/h to 10 km/h in 5 s?

8. A parachute on a drag racer is opened. It slows the racer's speed from 260 km/h to 130 km/h in 10 s. Find the deceleration.

Action force

Reaction force ➡

Action force 4 N

Reaction
force
4 N

FIGURE 6–8. Every action
force has a reaction force.

Describe one example of
action and reaction forces.

FIGURE 6–9. In a Hero's
engine, escaping steam causes
the engine to spin.

6:4   Action and Reaction Forces

What happens to the person and chair when the
person in Figure 6–8 pushes against the desk? The
push on the desk is called an **action force.** As the
desk is being pushed in one direction, the person
and chair move in the opposite direction. This
movement is caused by a force on the person called
a **reaction force.** A reaction force is always equal in
size and opposite in direction to an action force. In
this case, the action force pushes against the desk.
The reaction force makes the person and chair move
away from the desk. Action and reaction always
occur together. Every force has an equal and
opposite force.

When a 4-N book rests on a table it exerts a
downward action force of 4 N. The table pushes up
on the book with a reaction force of 4 N (Figure
6–8). Action and reaction forces are always equal and
in opposite directions.

In a Hero's engine (Figure 6–9), water is heated to
steam. Then the steam moves out of the engine. As
the steam escapes, it exerts a reaction force on the
engine. This reaction force causes the engine to spin.
It spins in a direction opposite to the direction in
which the steam escapes.

In principle the operation of a rocket engine is
somewhat like a Hero's engine. Hot gases escape
from the rocket engine. These gases exert a reaction
force on the engine. The reaction force is the push
that makes the rocket move.

activity   USING SPRING SCALES TO MEASURE ACTION AND REACTION FORCES

Tie a spring scale to the leg of a desk or table. Connect
the hook of the spring scale to the hook of a second
spring scale. Exert a force on the second spring scale.
Keeping the force constant, read both scales. Repeat with
different amounts of force. What did you observe?

activity   AN ACTION AND A REACTION

Inflate a toy balloon with air. Hold it tightly at the neck. Then release it. What happened to the balloon? Explain your observations.

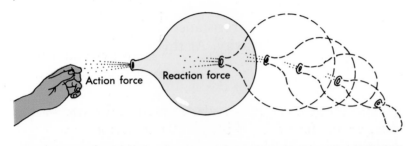

Action force   Reaction force

FIGURE 6–10.

MAKING SURE

9. Explain the following:
   (a) A person tries to jump from a boat to the dock. The boat moves away from the dock.
   (b) A water sprinkler rotates when the water is turned on.

6:5 Falling Objects

Falling is caused by gravity. Near the earth a falling object accelerates at a rate of 9.8 m/s^2. That is, its speed increases by 9.8 m/s each second. After 2 s, it is moving at 19.6 m/s. After 3 s, it is moving at 29.4 m/s. The value 9.8 m/s^2 is called the acceleration of gravity. All falling objects near the earth

What is the acceleration of a falling object?

Table 6–1.
Speed of a Falling Object

Time of fall (s)	Speed (m/s)
1	9.8
2	19.6
3	29.4
4	39.2
5	49.0
6	58.8

accelerate at the same rate in a vacuum. Because there is no air or other matter in a vacuum, there is nothing to slow the fall of an object.

An object falling from a great height eventually stops accelerating. Its speed becomes constant. This point is called terminal speed. **Terminal speed** is reached when the air resistance against the object equals the pull of gravity. At this point, the force on the object is zero.

J. Irwin/Alpha

FIGURE 6–11. Skydivers in free fall reach terminal speed when air resistance equals the force of gravity.

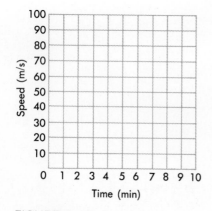

FIGURE 6–12.

activity
GRAPHING TIME VS SPEED

On a sheet of graph paper make a graph using the data given in Table 6–1. Label the time on the horizontal axis from 0–10 s. Label the speed on the vertical axis from 0–100 m/s. (If graph paper is not available, use notebook paper. Allow 2 cm of space between each second. Use 1 cm of space between each 5 m/s of speed.) Plot the speed for each second of time as given in the table. Draw a line to connect the points you have plotted. How could you use your graph to find the speed at 8 s? What is the speed at 8 s and 10 s?

activity
MEASURING THE SPEED OF FALLING OBJECTS

Motion along an inclined plane can be studied to learn something about falling objects. **(1)** Nail two boards, measuring 15 cm wide and 4 m long, together to form a trough. **(2)** Paste a 5-cm strip of aluminum foil on one side of the trough. **(3)** Paste 1-cm square pieces of foil along the opposite side as shown in Figure 6–13. The pieces of foil must be 2.5 cm apart. **(4)** Connect each foil piece to a wire and then connect one end of the wire to a battery. **(5)** Connect the battery to a bell and then connect the bell to the aluminum strip. "Liquid" or "cold" solder can be used to attach the wire to the foil. Tape may also be used. **(6)** Stand the trough up and tilt it at a slight angle. Run a metal ball down the trough. **(7)** Use a stopwatch to time the speed of the ball. Why did the bell ring more often as the ball got close to the bottom of the ramp? At what point was the ball's speed greatest?

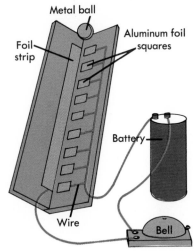

FIGURE 6–13.

MAKING SURE

10. How does air friction affect the speed of a falling object?

11. Why might a sheet of paper fall more slowly than the same sheet crumpled into a ball?

12. The force of gravity on the moon is less than Earth's gravity. How is the speed of falling objects different on the moon?

6:6 Circular Motion

The motion of an object along a curved path is called circular motion. For example, a person riding on a merry-go-round rides in a circle. In order to keep an object moving in a circular path, a force must act toward the center of the circle. This force is called centripetal (sen TRIHP ut ul) force. A **centripetal force** keeps an object moving in a circular path.

How does a centripetal force keep an object moving in a circle?

FIGURE 6–14. Centripetal forces cause people on this amusement park ride to move in a curved path.

List three examples of circular motion and centripetal force.

What happens when the car in which you are riding makes a fast turn around a corner? You may feel your body sliding toward the outside of the curve. The inertia of your body tends to keep you moving in a straight line while the car is turning. There must be a centripetal force acting toward the center of the circle to keep you moving around the curve. The door of the car prevents you from traveling in a straight line. The car door provides the centripetal force.

A bicycle rider leans inward on a curve to increase the centripetal force and make the bike move in a circle. Because of inertia, the bike tends to go in a straight line rather than in a curve. On a sharp curve, the inertia may cause the bike to tip over.

Most roads are banked on the curves. A banked road is higher on the outside edge than on the inside edge. Banked curves increase the centripetal force which pushes inward on a car as it moves around the curve.

Some washing machines use circular motion. After the laundry is washed, the wet clothes are spun to remove most of the water. Because of inertia, the water goes out through holes in the tub as the clothes are spun around.

Gerry Cranham/Photo Researchers, Inc.

FIGURE 6–15. The banked curved of this bicycle track increases the centripetal force on the bicycles as they move around the curve.

activity CIRCULAR MOTION

CAUTION: This activity is to be done under the direct supervision of the teacher. Attach a ball to a string and swing it in a circle. Notice the motion your hand makes. Did you keep pulling on the string to keep it taut? Did you at the same time move the ball forward around the circle? If someone cut the string while the ball was moving, what would happen?

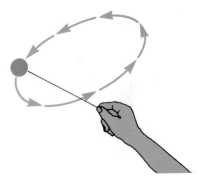

FIGURE 6–16.

activity AN EFFECT OF INERTIA

Obtain a thin metal pie pan. Cut out a 1/5 slice of the pan with sheet metal shears. Place a large marble along the inner edge of the pan. Move the marble swiftly in a circle toward the cut-out section. Which direction did the marble travel when it left the pan? Explain your observation.

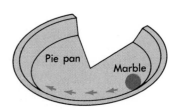

FIGURE 6–17.

13. How does a banked road improve highway safety?
14. Why might a car slide off an icy road when the car rounds a curve?
15. What keeps the moon traveling in a curved path around the earth?
16. How does inertia affect the path of a moving object?

6:7 Momentum

What is momentum?

Every object in motion has momentum. **Momentum** is the product of the mass of an object and its speed. The more mass and speed, the greater the momentum. Which has more momentum, a truck moving at 60 km/h or a motorcycle moving at the same speed? The larger mass of the truck gives it more momentum. Does a fast-pitched or a slow-pitched softball have more momentum? The greater speed of the fast-pitched ball gives it more momentum. Momentum increases as either the mass or speed increases.

FIGURE 6–18. Both the car and truck are traveling at the same speed. The truck has a greater momentum because it has more mass.

Janet Adams

The momentum of one object can change. But whenever one object gains momentum, another object loses an equal amount of momentum.

The law of conservation of momentum states that momentum cannot be created or destroyed. When one object gains momentum another object loses it. For instance, if two roller skaters push against each other they will roll away in opposite directions. The skater with the larger mass moves slower than the skater with the smaller mass. The momentum for the two skaters is equal and opposite. When two billiard balls collide, there is no gain or loss of momentum. The speed of each ball may change. But the total momentum for the two balls does not change.

FIGURE 6–19. Momentum is transferred as the billiard balls collide.

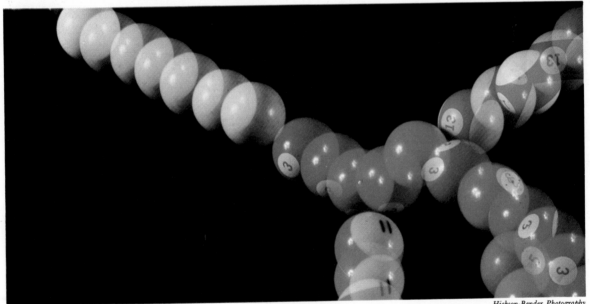

Hickson-Bender Photography

MAKING SURE

17. A student throws a Ping-Pong ball and a tennis ball as hard as possible. Which has more momentum? Why?

18. Why will a bullet shot from a gun have more momentum than an arrow shot from a bow?

19. Why is it harder to stop a loaded truck than an unloaded truck?

20. It takes more than a kilometer for a heavily-loaded freight train to stop. Why?

Perspectives

people

Breaking the Speed of Sound

It was a crisp December morning. The place was the desert test track at Edwards Air Force Base, California. It had been 32 years since an aircraft first broke the sound barrier over this desert. This morning brought another attempt at breaking the sound barrier. It was not an aircraft making the attempt, it was a car.

Hollywood stunt man, Stan Barrett, hit the throttle of his 12-m long rocket car. He slammed back against the cockpit seat with a force six times his own weight. In 14 seconds, the engine, fed by both liquid and solid fuel, hurled the car nearly 1.6 km down the track.

Decades ago pilots and researchers found a real, unseen barrier when aircraft reached the speed of sound. Violent forces thwarted their attempts to break the sound barrier. In some cases, the planes crashed. In searching for solutions to the problem, the researchers found that a narrow dart-shaped craft with small wings could break the sound barrier. To avoid the problems caused by those forces, a dart-shaped, wingless car that was only 90 cm wide was designed.

At the moment the car's engine pushed the car to its maximum speed, Stan Barrett triggered a rocket. For the extra kick needed to push the car through the sound barrier, a Navy Sidewinder missle had been added. The missle was basically the same as those used on Navy fighters, except there was no warhead.

The jolt from the rocket set the car's wheels spinning at 150 times per second. Since rubber tires would fall apart at this speed, the wheels were made from forged aluminum. After firing the rocket, Stan radioed exuberantly, "That's some passing gear."

The speed of sound in the cold desert air that morning was 1180 km/h. Just 20 seconds after its standing start, the rocket on wheels reached 1190 km/h. It was the first time any land vehicle had traveled faster than the speed of sound.

Unfortunately, the record was unofficial because the fuel ran out 330 m from the timing lights. But, Air Force radar clocked the car at Mach 1.01. Mach is the term used when a vehicle's speed is compared to the speed of sound. For example, a car traveling at 80 km/h hour is moving at Mach 0.07. Mach 1.01 is 1.01 times the speed of sound.

"As far as we're concerned," says the car's owner, Hal Needham, "we were supersonic."

Adapted by permission of *Science 82* magazine © The American Association for the Advancement of Science.

George Long/Long Photography

main ideas

1. The greater the mass of an object the greater its inertia.
2. Average speed is found by dividing distance by time.
3. Acceleration occurs when an object changes speed or direction.
4. It takes a force to change the motion of an object.
5. Deceleration is negative acceleration.
6. Speed of a falling object increases until it reaches terminal speed.
7. A centripetal force is needed to keep an object moving in a curved path.
8. The momentum of an object changes as either its mass or speed changes.
9. Momentum cannot be created or destroyed. When one object loses momentum, another object gains it.

vocabulary

Define each of the following words or terms.

acceleration
acceleration of gravity
action force
centripetal force
circular motion

conservation of
    momentum
deceleration
inertia

momentum
reaction force
speed
terminal speed

study questions

DO NOT WRITE IN THIS BOOK.

A. True or False

Determine whether each of the following sentences is true or false. If the sentence is false, rewrite it to make it true.

1. It takes a force to stop something that is moving.
2. Your body has inertia.
3. A basketball has more inertia than a tennis ball.
4. Centripetal force acts on a marble moving in a curved path.
5. The acceleration of gravity is 9.8 m/s^2.
6. Banked roads decrease the centripetal force acting on cars.
7. Every object has inertia.

8. On a trip, a car always moves at its average speed.
9. When a driver steps on the brakes the car decelerates.
10. When you start to run, your body accelerates.

B. Multiple Choice
Choose the word or phrase that completes correctly each of the following sentences.
1. The acceleration of a car moving at a constant speed of 30 km/h is *(30 km, 30 km/h, 0).*
2. A centripetal force acts on a person *(at rest, running in a straight line, on a merry-go-round).*
3. To find the average speed of a bicycle, divide distance traveled by *(acceleration, speed, time).*
4. The speed of a falling object *(increases, decreases, does not change)* until it reaches terminal speed.
5. *(5 km, 5 km/h, 5 km/h/s)* is a speed.
6. *(Force, Inertia, Momentum)* is needed to stop a freight train.
7. As a moving van is loaded, its inertia *(increases, decreases, remains the same).*
8. The speed of a ball *(increases, decreases, remains the same)* as it rolls down a 1-m ramp.
9. The acceleration of a ball *(increases, decreases, remains the same)* as it rolls down a 1-m ramp.
10. A falling object reaches terminal speed when it *(increases in speed, stops falling, no longer increases in speed).*

C. Completion
Complete each of the following sentences with a word or phrase that will make the sentence correct.
1. An object remains at rest unless a(n) _____ acts on it.
2. The amount of inertia an object at rest has depends on its _____.
3. A banked road is _____ on the outside than the inside.
4. If a car accelerates from rest to 50 km/s in 5 s, its acceleration is _____.
5. A _____ force exists when an object moves in a circle.
6. If you swing a ball attached to a string, the string exerts a(n) _____ force on the ball.

7. A car that travels 240 km in 4 h has an average speed of
_____.

8. A moving object that is slowing down is _____.

9. A parachute decelerates a drag racer by exerting a(n)
_____ on the racer.

10. Momentum decreases when either the mass or the _____
decreases.

D. How and Why

1. An injury in an auto accident may be caused by the
"second collision" of a person riding in the car. How?

2. Explain how inertia enables a clothes washer to spin water
out of clothes.

3. How does the speed and acceleration of a parachute
jumper change during a jump?

4. Give three examples of acceleration. What force produces
each acceleration?

5. Why do all falling objects in a vacuum accelerate at the
same rate?

investigations

1. Make a poster about motion using pictures from old
magazines that show something moving. Beside each picture
list the energy source that is used to produce motion. For
example, gasoline is the energy source for a car. Organize
the pictures into groups based on their energy source.

2. Obtain information from a library, auto club, or insurance
company on automobile safety. Prepare a bulletin board
poster that illustrates the connection between motion,
forces, and automobile accidents.

interesting reading

Aylesworth, Thomas G., *Cars, Boats, Trains, and Planes of Today and
Tomorrow.* New York, NY: Walker and Co., 1975.

Drake, S., "Galileo and The Rolling Ball; except from Galileo at
Work." *Science Digest,* October 1978, pp. 74–76.

chapter

7

Wind surfing combines sailing and surfboarding. The properties of fluids are important in a sport like wind surfing. How many fluids can you find in this picture? The wind surfer uses differing fluid pressures to control the craft. How do you use the properties of fluids in your life?

Steve Lissau

Fluids and Pressure

7:1 Fluids

Liquids and gases are fluids. Both of these forms of matter are shapeless and can flow from place to place. Water and petroleum are the only liquids which occur in large quantities on the earth. The most plentiful gases in the air are nitrogen and oxygen.

Fluid means a substance can move and change shape without separating. These properties are due to the spaces and forces between particles in liquids and gases. In a solid, the particles are in fixed, rigid positions. In liquids and gases, the particles are farther apart and can move about each other. Fluids flow downhill, pulled by the force of gravity, and can be pumped through pipes.

When a liquid boils and turns into a gas, it may expand to many times its original volume. For example, boiling water may expand more than 1500 times as it forms water vapor. This expansion creates a force that can drive a steam engine. A gas can expand to a large volume or it can be compressed into a small space. When a gas expands the spaces between its particles increase. Particles in a liquid are packed closer together than the particles in a gas. Therefore, a liquid cannot be compressed like a gas.

GOAL: You will gain an understanding of fluids and how they affect motion.

What are fluids?

127

Particles in a liquid are held together by forces. These forces among the particles on the liquid's surface create a **surface tension.** You can observe surface tension. Rub some grease on a needle and set it gently on the surface of water in a glass or dish. The needle floats because the forces between the water molecules keep them from spreading and allowing the needle to sink. The force or tension between the molecules is greater than the force of the needle pushing down. Water forms spherical drops when sprinkled on a waxed surface. Forces between the water molecules on the surface of a drop cause the molecules to pull together. The formation of spherical drops is a result of surface tension.

a
Sharon M. Kurgis

b
Ethyl Corporation

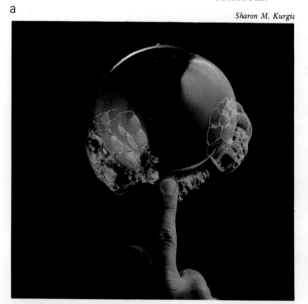
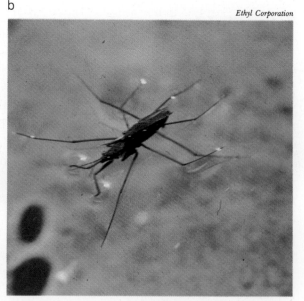

FIGURE 7–1. Soap bubbles form because of surface tension (a). Surface tension allows a water strider to stand on the surface of water (b).

Some fluids are used in machines for cooling. The cooling occurs when fluids carry heat away from an area that is hot. One way to cool an object is to blow air over it. Most automobile engines are cooled by pumping water through the engine. Water is also used to cool the fuel in a nuclear reactor so it does not melt. Oil and liquid sodium are two fluids used in some kinds of cooling devices.

activity   WATER SEEKS ITS OWN LEVEL

Obtain a piece of rubber tubing about 2 m long and two funnels. Insert a funnel into each end of the tubing. Hold each funnel at the same level. Pour water into one funnel until it fills the other funnel halfway. Take turns slowly raising and lowering each funnel. What happened to the water levels in the funnels when they were moved?

FIGURE 7–2.

MAKING SURE

1. Name three fluids that are transported through pipes.
2. How does a hydroelectric dam use the fluid properties of water?
3. Why might drops of water appear on the surface of a newly waxed car?

7:2 Pressure in Liquids

Pressure is the amount of force per unit area. Force is measured in newtons and area is expressed in square meters (m^2). The unit for pressure is the pascal. One pascal (Pa) is equivalent to 1 N/m^2. A kilopascal (kPa) is equal to 1000 pascals. Pressure in an automobile tire is about 196 kPa.

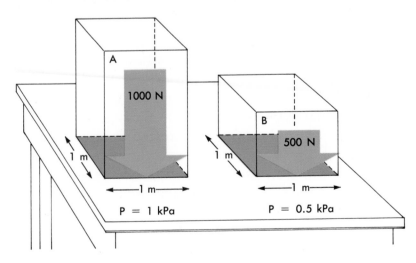

FIGURE 7–3. Block B weighs one-half as much as Block A and therefore, exerts one half the pressure of Block A.

To find pressure you must determine the force that is exerted on a surface. You must also determine the total surface area on which the force is exerted. The following equation is then used to find pressure.

How is pressure calculated?

$$\text{pressure} = \frac{\text{force}}{\text{area}}$$

$$P = \frac{F}{A}$$

Example

A liquid in a container exerts a force of 500 N on the bottom of the container that has an area of 2 m². Determine the pressure on the bottom of the container.

Solution

Step 1: Write the equation for pressure.

$$P = \frac{F}{A}$$

Step 2: Substitute the values for area and force given in the problem.

$$P = \frac{500 \text{ N}}{2 \text{ m}^2}$$

Step 3: Divide to find the answer.

$$\frac{500 \text{ N}}{2 \text{ m}^2} = 250 \text{ N/m}^2 \qquad P = 250 \text{ Pa}$$

Pressure in a liquid is directly related to the depth and density of a liquid. Any one who has dived to the bottom of a swimming pool or lake knows water pressure increases with depth. Submarines have been crushed when they descended too far below the ocean's surface. The pressure exerted at any depth is equal in all directions. This means the pressure is the same at any point, up, down, and sideways.

When pressure is applied at any point on a confined liquid, it is transmitted equally through the liquid. For example, suppose a jug is filled with water and corked. Then someone pushes down on

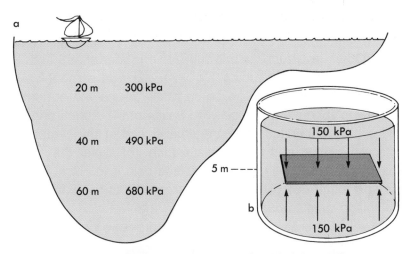

FIGURE 7-4. Water pressure within a lake increases with depth (a). Pressure exerted on a flat object placed in water will be the same on both the upper and lower surface (b).

the cork and exerts a pressure of 100 kPa. The pressure will be increased this amount at every point in the liquid. If the pressure of the cork becomes great enough the jug will break. Why?

Hydraulic lifts and other hydraulic equipment are based on the use of the pressure transmitted through liquids. Suppose two pistons are connected to a closed container of liquid. One piston has a small area and the other has a large area. A small force is exerted on the small piston. The force on the small piston causes pressure which is transmitted equally through the liquid. The pressure on the large piston creates a large total force because the surface area of the piston is so much greater. What if the area of the small piston is 1 cm² and the area of the large piston is 100 cm²? The area of the large piston is 100 times greater than that of the small piston. Therefore, the increase in force from the small piston to the large piston is 100 times.

How does a hydraulic lift work?

Ted Rice

FIGURE 7-5. In hydraulic equipment, pressure transmitted through a liquid is used to do work.

FIGURE 7-6. A force of 10 N exerted on the small piston will exert a force of 100 N on the large piston.

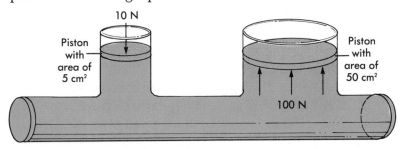

activity ― MEASURING PRESSURE IN A LIQUID

(1) Obtain a U-tube, thistle tube, thin rubber sheet, and small piece of rubber tubing 1 m long. (2) Add some ink or colored water to the U-tube so it fills the curved bottom part. (3) Support the U-tube with a clamp. (4) Attach one end of the rubber tubing to the smaller end of the U-tube. Attach the other end to the thistle tube. (5) Cover the thistle tube with the rubber sheet and hold it in place with a rubber band. (6) Fill a tall cylinder with water. (7) Insert the thistle tube to different depths in the water. How did the level of liquid in the U-tube show pressure change?

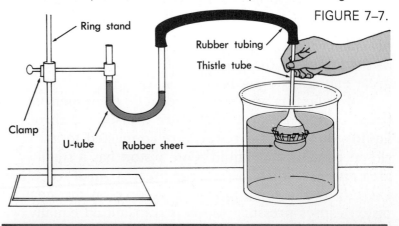

FIGURE 7–7.

MAKING SURE

4. Water has a density of 1 g/cm³ and mercury has a density of 13.6 g/cm³. In which liquid would the pressure be greater at a depth of 1 m. Why?

5. Why would a hydraulic lift not work if it was filled with air?

6. What is the pressure exerted by a force of 3200 N on an area of 3.2 m²? What is the pressure on each square centimeter?

7. A liquid in a container exerts a force of 270 N on the bottom of the container which has an area of 750 cm². Determine the pressure exerted on the bottom of the container.

8. Why is a concrete dam along a deep river thicker at the bottom than at the top?

7:3 Gas Laws

If you could see molecules in a gas, what would you observe? You would see gas molecules in constant motion. The molecules move about rapidly in all directions because they have kinetic energy. When a gas is in a closed container, the gas molecules strike the walls of the container. The gas molecules exert pressure on the container walls. If you opened the container, the molecules would escape into the air.

What happens when you heat a closed container of gas? As the temperature of the gas increases, the molecules of the gas gain kinetic energy. The increase in kinetic energy causes the molecules to strike the walls of the container with more force. The pressure of the gas increases. If the container of the gas expands like a balloon, the increased pressure changes the volume. A hot air balloon, for example, is blown up by heating the air within it.

Charles' law explains the relationship between temperature and volume of a gas. According to **Charles' law,** the volume of a gas increases when it is heated. What happens to the volume if the gas is allowed to cool?

State Charles' law.

a  b

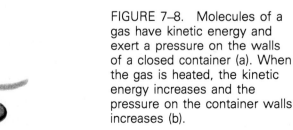

FIGURE 7–8. Molecules of a gas have kinetic energy and exert a pressure on the walls of a closed container (a). When the gas is heated, the kinetic energy increases and the pressure on the container walls increases (b).

If you push down on the handle of a tire pump, you are decreasing the volume of air inside the pump. The air in the pump cylinder is squeezed or compressed. What happens to the particles of air inside the pump? Since the particles have less space in which to move, they strike the cylinder walls more frequently. The pressure inside the pump increases if there is no change in the temperature of the air. The relationship between pressure and volume for a gas is explained in **Boyle's law.** The law states that the pressure of a gas increases as its volume decreases.

State Boyle's law and describe one example.

MAKING SURE

9. Explain each observation.
   (a) An automobile tire has a blowout on a very hot day.
   (b) Pressure increases when you heat water in a pressure cooker.
   (c) A tea kettle whistles when the water in it boils.
   (d) An inflated balloon decreases in size when held in ice water.
   (e) The gas discharged from a fire extinguisher feels cold.
   (f) Heavy steel tanks are used to store compressed gas.

7:4 Buoyancy

If you drop a piece of metal such as a coin into water it sinks. Yet you know that large ships are made of steel. Why do some things float? An object floats when the force pushing up on it is equal to the object's weight. The force that pushes up on a floating object is called **buoyancy.** Solids having a low density will float on water. For example, cork, some kinds of wood, and certain plastics float on water.

Floating is also related to the volume of liquid displaced by an object. When an object is placed in a liquid, it pushes the liquid aside. Have you noticed

FIGURE 7–9. A block of wood floats on water because the upward buoyant force of the water equals the weight of the block.

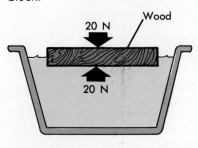

how the level of the water in a bathtub rises when you sit down in it? Your body displaces the water. When an object floats in water only part of it displaces the water. The other part of the object remains above the water. A definite amount of water is displaced before the object floats.

When the mass of the displaced liquid is equal to the mass of the object, the object floats. This law was discovered by Archimedes, an early Greek philosopher. The law is sometimes referred to as Archimedes' principle. When a block of wood is placed in water, it begins to sink. It sinks until it displaces a mass of water just equal to the mass of the block. The water beneath the wood exerts a force to hold it up. The upward force is buoyancy.

Each of the objects in Figure 7–10 sinks through the different liquids until it displaces a mass of liquid equal to its own mass. At this point the object floats. The liquid underneath exerts a force that is able to support it.

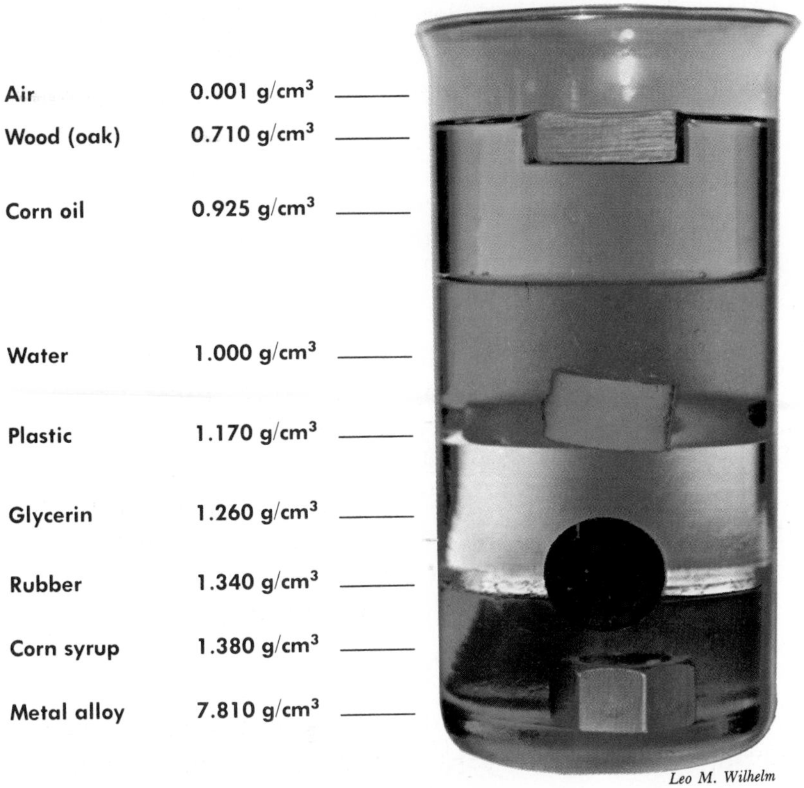

Define the term buoyancy.

Why does a ship float?

Air	0.001 g/cm³
Wood (oak)	0.710 g/cm³
Corn oil	0.925 g/cm³
Water	1.000 g/cm³
Plastic	1.170 g/cm³
Glycerin	1.260 g/cm³
Rubber	1.340 g/cm³
Corn syrup	1.380 g/cm³
Metal alloy	7.810 g/cm³

Leo M. Wilhelm

FIGURE 7–10. Floating objects and liquids of different densities illustrate Archimedes' principle—matter sinks until it displaces its own weight.

7:4 Buoyancy   135

The buoyancy of a fluid depends on its density. A more dense fluid has a greater buoyancy than a less dense fluid. For example, a block of aluminum sinks in water. The same block floats in mercury which has more than 13 times the density of water. Because ocean water is more dense than fresh water, it supports floating objects better. The density of fresh water is 1 g/mL, while the density of ocean water is 1.03 g/mL.

A block of iron will never displace enough water to equal its own mass. It is too dense. The iron block has more mass than an equal volume of water. If the iron block is placed in water, it will sink. If the same block of iron is stamped into the shape of a pan, however, it may float. The pan, displaces more water than the block. The pan sinks until it displaces a volume of water equal to its mass and then it floats. Can you explain why a steel ship floats?

Why does a balloon containing helium float in air? Helium is a very light gas whose density is much less than air. A helium-filled balloon weighs less than the volume of air it displaces. As a result, the force of buoyancy pushes the balloon upward. A balloon filled with hot air also rises. Why? The air inside the balloon expands in volume when heated. Therefore, the density of the hot air inside the balloon is less than the density of the outside air. Since the volume of hot air weighs less than an equal volume of cooler air, the balloon rises.

Why does a hot air balloon rise?

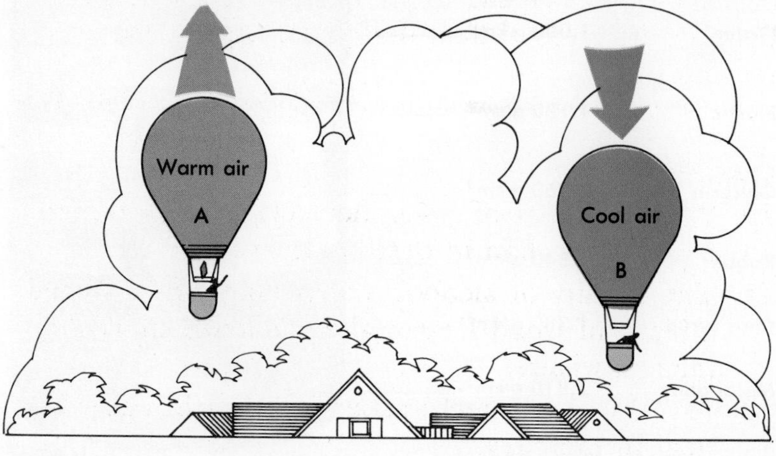

FIGURE 7–11. Balloon A rises because the warm air inside the balloon is less dense than the outside air. Balloon B sinks because the densities of the cool air and the balloon are greater than the outside air.

activity BUOYANCY AND DENSITY

Pour 15 mL of water into a 25-mL graduated cylinder. Tie one end of a piece of string tightly around a small stone. Hold the opposite end of the string and lower the stone into the water until it is completely submerged (Figure 7–12). What is the volume of the stone? Find the mass of the stone on a balance and then calculate its density. Compare it to the density of water (1 g/mL). Did the stone sink because it was more dense or less dense than water?

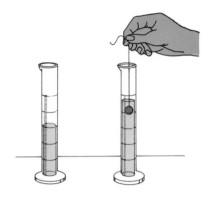

FIGURE 7–12.

activity FLOATING OBJECTS

(1) Place a displacement can on a table or desk top. Set a small beaker under the arm of the can. (2) Fill the can with water until water begins to run into the beaker. Empty water from the beaker and set it back under the arm of the filled can. (3) Fold a piece of heavy aluminum foil into the shape of a saucer. Place several small coins or washers in the saucer. (4) Find the mass of the saucer and contents on a beam balance. (5) Then put the saucer in the displacement can (Figure 7–13). What happened to the saucer? Catch the displaced water in the small beaker. Measure the volume of the displaced water in a graduated cylinder. (6) Then find the mass of the water (1 mL = 1 g). (7) Now fold the aluminum saucer tightly around the coins. Put it into the refilled displacement can. What happened? (8) Find the volume and mass of the displaced water. Compare the mass of the water to the mass of the saucer.

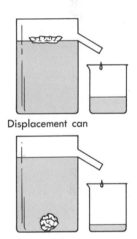

Displacement can

FIGURE 7–13.

MAKING SURE

10. Would a block of wood float higher or lower in fresh water than in ocean water?

11. The density of alcohol is about 0.8 g/mL. Would a block of wood float higher or lower in alcohol than in water?

12. Explain why a steel washer will sink in water but float in mercury.

7:5 Bernoulli's Principle

Here is a simple activity you can do. Fold a piece of notebook paper in half lengthwise. Tear it along the crease. Take one piece of paper and insert about 4 cm of it between the pages at the top of this book. Hold the book upright in front of your mouth with the paper hanging down and away from you. Blow hard across the top of the book over the paper. What do you observe? What happens when you stop blowing?

How can you demonstrate Bernoulli's principle?

The activity described above illustrates **Bernoulli's principle.** This principle states that the pressure in a moving stream of fluid is less than in the fluid around it. The paper rises when you blow because air pressure in the stream of breath is less than in the air around it. The harder you blow the lower the pressure. The air pressure under the paper is greater than the pressure above the paper. The paper is pushed up into the moving air above it. Whenever there is a flowing stream within a fluid, the fluid around it is forced into the stream.

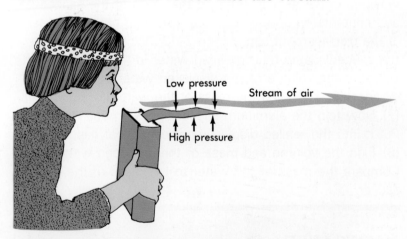

Low pressure

Stream of air

High pressure

FIGURE 7–14. Blowing a stream of air across a piece of paper demonstrates Bernoulli's principle.

Bernoulli's principle explains how an atomizer works. When someone squeezes the rubber bulb of the atomizer, a spray of liquid comes out of it. Squeezing the bulb forces air through the tube attached to the bulb. This causes liquid in the container underneath to be pushed up into the stream of air and sprayed out of the atomizer.

How does an atomizer work?

DEMONSTRATING BERNOULLI'S PRINCIPLE

Hold a funnel with the spout down and place a Ping-Pong ball in the funnel. Hold the funnel over your head. Keeping the funnel vertical, lower it to your mouth and blow hard through the stem. Try to blow the ball out. Did you succeed? Where was the air pressure greater when you blew hard, under the ball or on top? How does this fact explain your observation.

7:6 Lift

An airplane can fly even though it is heavier than air. An upward force on the wings, called lift, keeps it up. Lift is created by the shape of the wing. A wing is round in front and thickest in the middle. It tapers to a narrow edge at the back. When an airplane moves forward, air flows over the wing and lifts the airplane (Figure 7–15).

The shape of the wing causes air to flow faster over the top than the bottom of the wing. This difference in the speed of the air flow causes air pressure to be greater on the bottom wing surface than on the upper surface. The unequal pressure pushes upward causing the lift that makes the airplane fly.

What causes an airplane wing to produce lift?

How does lift make an airplane fly?

FIGURE 7–15. A wing splits the air into two streams. The stream above the wing moves faster than the stream below it (a). Lift results because greater air pressure below the wing exerts an upward force (b).

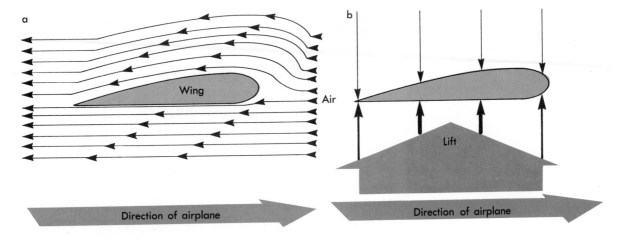

139

7:7 Flight

In order for an airplane to take off, it must overcome the force of gravity. In other words, the lift must be greater than the weight of the airplane. When the airplane is in level flight, the lift force on the wings is equal to the weight of the airplane.

a

b

FIGURE 7–16. Wings differ in size and shape. The wings of the glider are designed for soaring (a). Wings of jet aircraft are designed for high-speed flight (b).

How is the flight path of an airplane controlled?

Recall that for lift to occur, air must be moving across the wings. Therefore, the airplane must be in motion. During takeoff, the airplane accelerates until there is enough lift to force it upward. A propeller is used on some airplanes to drive them forward. A gasoline engine may be used to turn the propeller. A propeller is shaped like a screw. As it turns it exerts a force against the air and pulls the airplane forward. Many airplanes use jet engines. Burning gases escaping from the rear of the engine push the airplane forward.

Once the airplane is in the air, the pilot must be able to control its path. The pilot directs the path using ailerons (AY luh rahnz), elevators, and rudder. Moving these separate parts cause the amount of lift on the wings and tail to change. Ailerons are movable sections on each wing that enable the airplane to tilt from side to side. Elevators on the tail cause the nose of the airplane to go up or down. Turning right and left is controlled by the rudder on the tail. When taking off or landing, the pilot uses

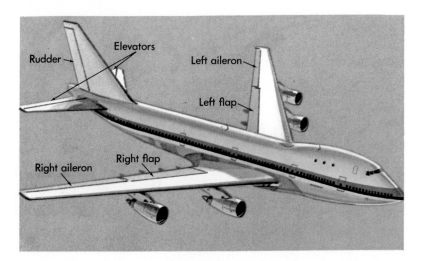

FIGURE 7–17. A pilot controls an airplane by using the movable parts on the wings and tail.

Rudder
Elevators
Left aileron
Left flap
Right aileron
Right flap

the elevators and ailerons. When turning in flight, the rudders and ailerons are used.

If you try running while holding a large piece of cardboard, you can feel air pushing against the cardboard. The faster you run the harder the air pushes against the cardboard. The pushing you feel is called **drag.** Drag is the name given to the force of air against any object that moves through it. A moving airplane experiences drag. The amount of drag increases as the speed of the airplane increases. A large drag slows down an aircraft or makes it necessary to use more fuel per kilometer traveled.

Airplanes are streamlined to reduce drag. The bodies and parts are shaped to allow a smooth flow of air to pass. Streamlined aircraft are pointed in the front and have a thin tail. How many things can you name that have streamlined bodies that reduce drag?

FIGURE 7–18. Wind-tunnel tests are done to determine the effects of drag on an aircraft.

PHOTRI

MAKING SURE

13. Why would ailerons, elevators, and rudders not work on a spacecraft?
14. How is a jet engine similar to a rocket engine?
15. What is the best shape for a submarine? Why?
16. Why are some airplanes tied down during strong winds?
17. Why are high-speed aircraft more streamlined than slower aircraft?

Perspectives

First Flight

Doug Martin, Courtesy of TWA

Bob entered the plane. It was about one hour before take-off. This flight was his first as a flight attendant. The other flight attendants were arriving. They checked all passenger areas and areas for passenger services. Everything and everyone had to be ready and sparkling clean for the passengers' arrival. Bob remembered that every passenger should be treated as he would treat a guest in his home.

As he worked, Bob thought about how his training began. First, he talked with his college counselor about applying for the position with an airline. He asked about the skills and personal qualities needed to be a flight attendant. The most important thing was liking people and relating to them. Enjoying travel was important, too. Organizing his thoughts and communicating them clearly was necessary. Excellent physical health and a well-groomed appearance were also important.

Before he entered the training school, Bob was interviewed by airline personnel. He had to meet certain height and weight requirements. He also needed a high school diploma and two years of college or business training. Bob met all of the requirements. He prepared carefully for the interview, thinking through possible answers to questions he would be asked.

After talking with the interviewer, Bob talked with several flight attendants. He asked what they found most enjoyable about their work. Traveling and meeting new people was their answer. He asked what seemed most difficult about their work. They felt that working irregular hours such as 2:00 A.M. flights was difficult. Feeling lonely was also

difficult. The loneliness was a result of never staying in one place very long.

Bob had gone to the school sponsored by his airline six weeks ago. The airline paid for his training, room, and food while he was there. Classes began at 7:00 A.M. and ended at 5:00 P.M. each day. The training was intensive. At times he wondered how he would remember everything. The classes involved many areas–psychology, safety and first aid procedures, how to prepare and serve food, and parts of an airplane. Bob had to maintain good grades.

Suddenly, Bob realized that the First Flight Attendant was demonstrating safety procedures for the passengers. After checking the passengers, the flight attendants sat down and fastened themselves in. Bob sat back, he was really looking forward to his career as a flight attendant.

main ideas

1. Liquids and gases take the shape of their containers.   7:1
2. The pressure at any point in a fluid is the same in all directions.   7:2
3. The pressure of a gas in a container increases when its temperature increases.   7:3
4. As the pressure of a gas increases its volume decreases.   7:3
5. Buoyancy causes certain objects to float in liquids and gases.   7:4
6. The pressure in a moving stream of fluid is less than in the fluid around it.   7:5
7. Air pressure produces the lift force on an airplane.   7:6
8. Air pressure on the control surfaces of an airplane directs its path in flight. 7:7

vocabulary

Define each of the following words or terms.

Archimedes'   Boyle's law   fluid
  principle   buoyancy   lift
Bernoulli's   Charles' law   pressure
  principle   drag   surface tension

study questions

DO NOT WRITE IN THIS BOOK.

A. True or False

Determine whether each of the following sentences is true or false. If the sentence is false rewrite it to make it true.

1. Water and petroleum are two liquids that occur in large quantities.
2. Nitrogen and helium are plentiful on the earth.
3. Molecules in a liquid are closer together than in a gas.
4. When water boils, its volume decreases.
5. Surface tension is a property of gases.
6. Fluids are seldom used to cool things.
7. Water expands when it changes into a gas.

8. One newton per square meter = 1 pascal.
9. Pressure in a liquid increases as the depth increases.
10. When you blow up a balloon, the pressure inside increases.

B. Multiple Choice
Choose the word or phrase that completes correctly each of the following sentences.
1. The (*elevator, rudder, propeller*) of an airplane is used to increase or decrease altitude.
2. When you squeeze the bulb of an atomizer, you are using (*Charles' law, Boyle's law, Bernoulli's principle*).
3. An increase in the drag force on an airplane causes an (*increase, decrease, no change*) in the amount of fuel needed to fly it.
4. When a gas is heated in a closed container, its pressure (*increases, decreases, stays the same*).
5. Surface tension is caused by the (*size, number, forces*) of molecules.
6. A pressure of 1 Pa is (*1 N, 1 N/m, 1 N/m², 1 N/m³*).
7. The force of a hydraulic lift is produced by an increase in (*volume, pressure, temperature*) in the cylinder.
8. The density of air in a hot air balloon is (*less, the same as, greater*) than in the air around it.
9. (*Buoyancy, Lift, Drag*) is the force that makes an object float.
10. A solid piece of plastic will float if its density is (*greater, less than,*) the density of water.

C. Completion
Complete each of the following sentences with a word or phrase that will make the sentence correct.
1. If a gas in a sealed container is cooled, its pressure _____.
2. Pressure _____ when you heat water in a pressure cooker.
3. A floating block of wood displaces water equal to its own _____.
4. Ocean water is _____ dense than fresh water.
5. Objects float _____ in salt water than in fresh water.
6. The _____ of the water displaced by a boat is equal to the weight of the boat.

7. Pressure in a moving stream of air is _____ than in the air around it.
8. _____ is the upward force on an airplane in flight.
9. Lift on an airplane is caused by _____ pressure on the lower surface of the wing.
10. The _____ on an airplane's tail is used to make it turn right and left.

D. How and Why
1. How can a gas be compressed?
2. How does a hydraulic lift work?
3. Why does a ship float?
4. Draw a cross section of an airplane wing and explain how it produces lift.
5. How is the altitude and direction of an airplane controlled?

investigations

1. Have a paper airplane contest. Devise and agree on a set of rules for making airplanes and flying them. Conduct tests to find out which paper airplane flies farthest.
2. Obtain an atomizer and study its workings. Make a poster size drawing of an atomizer and label its parts. Add information that shows how it operates.
3. Obtain a kit for building a model airplane. Learn how its parts fit together and make it fly.
4. Obtain information on the design of cars to reduce drag and decrease the amount of fuel used. Make a report to your class.
5. Research and report on the operation of a helicopter.

interesting reading

Azarin, Beverly, "Return of The Clipper Ship." *Science 81,* March 1981, pp. 80–87.
Cook, Brian, *Gas.* New York, NY: Watts, 1981.
Earle, Sylvia, "The Descent of Man." *Science 81,* September 1981. pp. 44–53.
Joss, John, "The Wright Stuff." *Science 81,* April 1981. pp. 54–61.

A volcano erupts throwing ash into the atmosphere. Rocks fall and lava flows. The wind picks up some ash and blows it around the world. The ash can affect the weather. Eruptions have occurred throughout Earth's history. What causes an eruption? What can we learn about Earth from the volcanic eruption?

147

8

Earth as viewed from a space shuttle looks far different from Earth as you see it. Both viewpoints can be important in observing and learning about Earth. What are Earth's different movements? What causes the seasons? How can you locate a specific place on the earth's surface?

NASA

The Earth

8:1 Earth's Shape and Size

Most people have seen pictures of the earth taken by astronauts who traveled to the moon. These pictures show the earth as a round ball with large continents and oceans. Although the earth as viewed from space appears to be a sphere, it is not perfectly round. The earth's circumference through the North and South Poles is about 43 km less than around the equator. Also, the Southern Hemisphere is slightly larger than the Northern Hemisphere. In other words, the earth is slightly fatter in the middle and somewhat pear-shaped.

About 200 B.C. a Greek astronomer, Eratosthenes, made the first measurements of Earth's size. He compared the angles at which sunlight strikes the earth at noon in two cities in Egypt. The cities were 925 km apart. In one city, sunlight struck the earth at an angle and created a shadow for a stick placed in the ground. In the second city, the sun shone directly into a deep well and did not cast a shadow. There was no shadow because the sunlight was perpendicular to the earth's surface. Eratosthenes reasoned that the angle of sunlight in the first city was caused by the earth's curved surface. If the earth was flat, there would be no shadow in either city.

GOAL: You will learn some of the surface characteristics of Earth and how maps are used to show them.

Describe the shape of the earth.

FIGURE 8–1. Eratosthenes determined the size of the earth by measuring the angles that sunlight strikes the earth at two cities in Egypt.

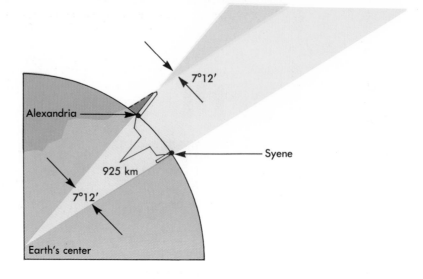

Eratosthenes measured the angle of the sunlight. He used this value to determine the earth's circumference. His answer was close to the correct value of 40 074 km.

What is the mass of the earth? There is no way to put the earth on a balance to measure its mass. The answer must come through indirect measurements using gravity.

All matter has gravity. The gravity of an object is directly related to its mass. The more mass an object has the greater its gravity.

How was the mass of the earth measured?

One of the first attempts to measure the earth's mass using gravity occurred during the nineteenth century. Two objects of the same mass were placed on a special kind of balance. The objects were in balance because the force of Earth's gravity was the same on both objects. A lead weight was placed under one of the objects. The force of gravity of the lead attracted the object and caused the two objects to become unbalanced (Figure 8-2a). The force of gravity of the lead was determined by measuring the mass needed to balance the objects again (Figure 8-2b). By comparing the gravity of the earth with the gravity of the lead, the mass of the earth was calculated. The earth's mass was found to be about 6×10^{24} kg. Today, measurements are made using satellites.

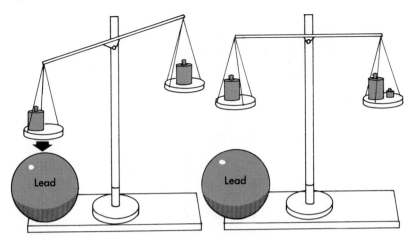

FIGURE 8–2. The experiment used to find the earth's mass.

8:2 Earth's Motions

How do we know the earth moves? One way to find out is through the use of a Foucault pendulum. This kind of pendulum consists of a heavy weight suspended from a wire. The wire, which may be as long as 60 m, is attached so it is free to rotate and swing back and forth. The path of the swinging pendulum is marked as a straight line on the floor as in Figure 8–3. One hour later, the path is marked again. It is observed that the second path is different from the first. Even though the pendulum is swinging in the same direction, its path on the floor has changed. The path changed during the hour because the earth moved slowly beneath the pendulum. This movement demonstrates the earth's rotation.

Rotation is the turning of the earth about its axis. The axis is an imaginary line that runs through the center from pole to pole. The earth rotates slowly from west to east. It takes one day or about 24 h for one complete rotation. You can judge the passing of time by observing the position of the sun in the sky during the day. The sun appears to rise in the east in the morning and to set in the west in the evening. The earth's rotation causes the sun to rise and set at different times in different parts of the world. When the sun is setting in Chicago, it is not setting in San Francisco. The sun has already set in New York and will set about two hours later in Los Angeles.

How does a Foucault pendulum indicate Earth's rotation?

Define the terms rotation and revolution.

FIGURE 8–3. The path of the swinging pendulum along the floor changes as the earth rotates (a). Night and day are caused by Earth's rotation (b).

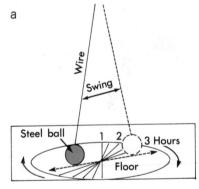

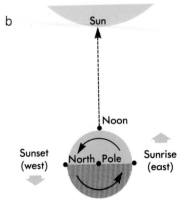

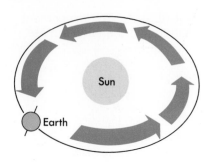

FIGURE 8–4. The earth revolves in a curved path around the sun.

The earth also moves in a curved path or orbit around the sun. This movement is called **revolution.** It takes 365.25 days or one year to complete one revolution. As the earth revolves, the distance between the earth and the sun changes. On January 4, the earth is closest to the sun. On July 5, it is the farthest from the sun. The average distance between the earth and the sun is about 150 000 000 km.

Table 8–1.
Facts About the Earth

Mass	6×10^{27} g
Circumference	41 500 km
Diameter	12 750 km
Time of rotation	23 h 56 min
Time of revolution	365.25 days
Average density	5.52 g/cm³
Average distance from the sun	1.49×10^8 km

activity CHANGING SHADOWS

Obtain a stick about 1 m long. In the morning of a bright, sunny day, push the stick into the ground so it stands perfectly straight. Place three pebbles or a small stick on the shadow to mark its location. Return every hour to observe any changes in the position, direction, and length of the stick's shadow. For each observation, mark the location of the shadow. Draw a diagram that shows the stick and the positions of the shadows you observed.

8:3 Seasons

Many regions have major changes in climate from season to season. Winter is cold. Summer is warm. Spring and fall are mild.

Seasonal changes depend on two factors. These factors are the number of daylight hours and the angles at which the sun's energy strikes the earth. Both factors change throughout the year because the earth's axis is tilted at a 23 1/2° angle.

As the hours of daylight increase from winter to summer, the total solar radiation per day increases. During summer days in the Northern Hemisphere, the sun shines for a long period of time. The sunlight also strikes the earth more vertically. Thus more radiant energy reaches the earth. In the winter, the Northern Hemisphere is tilted away from the sun. The sunlight strikes the surface less vertically and the energy is spread over a larger area (Figure 8–5).

On June 21, the noon sun is directly above the Tropic of Cancer, an imaginary line 23 1/2° north of the equator. June 21 is the beginning of summer in the Northern Hemisphere. There are more daylight hours in the Northern Hemisphere on June 21 than on any other day.

September 22 is the first day of fall. At noon on this day, the sun is directly above the equator. The earth's axis is tilted neither toward nor away from the sun. There are exactly 12 hours of daylight and 12 hours of darkness at every place on the earth except at the North and South Poles.

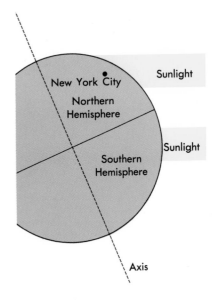

FIGURE 8–5. During winter, solar radiation strikes the Southern Hemisphere more vertically than the Northern Hemisphere.

What causes the seasons?

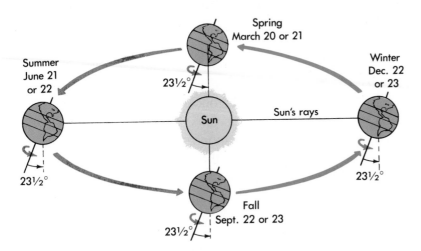

FIGURE 8–6. Four distinct seasons are caused by the 23½° tilt of the earth on its axis.

Winter in the Northern Hemisphere begins on December 21. On this date, the noon sun is directly above the Tropic of Capricorn. This is an imaginary line 23 1/2° south of the equator. In the Northern Hemisphere, there are fewer hours of daylight on December 22 than any other day.

Bill O'Connor/Peter Arnold, Inc.

FIGURE 8-7. During spring and summer the sun may never set for people living near the North Pole.

March 21 is the first day of spring. On this date, the earth is directly opposite its position on September 22. The earth's axis is tilted neither toward nor away from the sun. Again there are 12 hours of daylight and 12 hours of darkness at every place on the earth except at North and South Poles.

activity DEMONSTRATING EARTH MOTIONS

(1) Obtain a sphere such as a classroom globe or a large rubber ball and a flashlight. (2) In a darkened room, hold the lighted flashlight about 2 m from the sphere. (3) Observe that one side of the globe is bright and one side is dark. How is the difference related to night and day on Earth? (4) Have someone turn the sphere slowly on its axis. Did the portion of the sphere that was in light change when it was rotated? (5) Tilt the top of the sphere away from the light so its axis is at a 23 1/2° angle. (6) Have someone move the sphere in a path circling around the light while keeping the flashlight pointed directly at it. How did this motion show the change in seasons on Earth?

8:4 Latitude and Longitude

Different places on the earth's surface are located using imaginary lines. On a map or globe of the earth, these lines cross each other. Lines of **latitude** (LAT uh tewd) run east and west parallel to the equator. Lines of **longitude** (LAHN juh tewd) run north and south through the poles. The location of a particular place in the earth is identified by the point at which lines of latitude and longitude cross.

Lines of latitude are measured in degrees north and south of the equator. The equator is 0° latitude and lies halfway between the poles. The North Pole is 90° north latitude and the South Pole is 90° south latitude. The city of Paris, for example, lies at about 49° north latitude.

Each degree of latitude is further divided into 60 minutes and each minute is further divided into 60 seconds. The distance between two lines of latitude 1° apart is about 111 km. A difference in latitude of 1 minute equals about 1.9 km.

Lines of longitude are often called **meridians** (muh RIHD ee unz). Longitude is measured in degrees east and west from the prime meridian. The **prime meridian** passes through Greenwich, England and is 0° longitude. A place halfway around the world on the other side of the earth from the prime meridian lies at 180° longitude. In the United States, lines of longitude are west of the prime meridian.

What are latitude lines?

What are longitude lines?

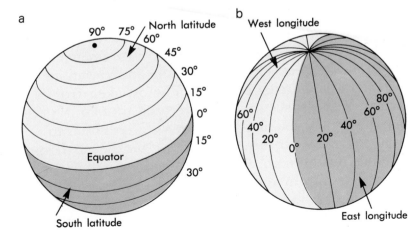

FIGURE 8–8. Lines of latitude are parallel to the equator (a). Lines of longitude pass through the poles (b).

FIGURE 8–9.

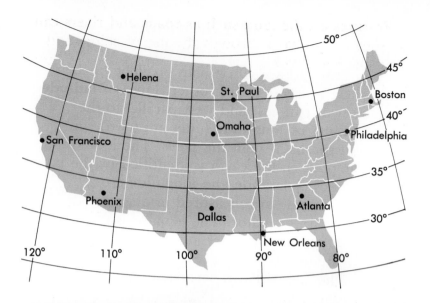

LOCATING CITIES ON A MAP

Identify the lines of latitude and longitude in Figure 8–9. What is the latitude and longitude for each city?

MAKING SURE

1. What is the degree of latitude for a place exactly halfway between the equator and the North Pole?

8:5 Mapping the Earth's Surface

Maps are small scale pictures of all or part of the earth's surface. A map is drawn to a scale that represents each part of the earth at a smaller size. Maps are made from information gathered by scientists and technicians. Careful measurements of the distances between certain points and elevations of different places must be made. Photos taken from airplanes and space satellites are used in map making. When making a map, a scale is chosen to show the ratio between the distance on the earth and distance on the map. For example, a scale of 1 cm = 1 km may appear on a map. On this scale, each centimeter on the map is equal to one kilometer on the earth's surface. How many kilometers equal 4.7 cm on the map?

FIGURE 8–10. Satellite images are often used to make maps.

EROS Data Center

Features on the land such as roads and rivers can be shown on a map through the use of colors and symbols. The color green, for example, may be used to show a forest. Small symbols on the map sometimes show the location of hospitals and schools. An airport is frequently indicated by a small airplane symbol.

One type of map, called a **topographic** (tahp uh GRAF ihk) **map** also shows the landscape. Topographic maps include heights of mountains and depths of valleys. The height above or below sea level is called elevation. Contour lines are used to show elevation. A **contour line** is a line drawn on a map joining all points of the earth's surface having the same elevation. A contour line is indicated in numbers and units. Study Figure 8–12. Contour lines representing a mountain are drawn through points of the mountain that have the same elevation. Contour lines spaced close together represent a steep slope. In the same way, contour lines widely spaced represent a gradual slope.

FIGURE 8–11. Symbols on a map are used to show roads and other features.

How do contour lines show elevation on a topographic map?

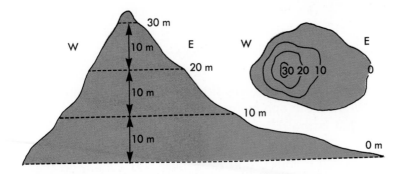

FIGURE 8–12. On topographic maps, contour lines connect points of equal elevation.

activity CONSTRUCTING A MAP SCALE

Make a scale that could be used in constructing a map of your state. The scale should be of the proper ratio so the map will fit on a piece of paper the size of this page. How many kilometers would equal 5 cm on the map? Make a scale to use in constructing a map of your neighborhood. Calculate the number of meters that equal 5 cm on the map. Why did you choose two different scales? Which map would have the most detail?

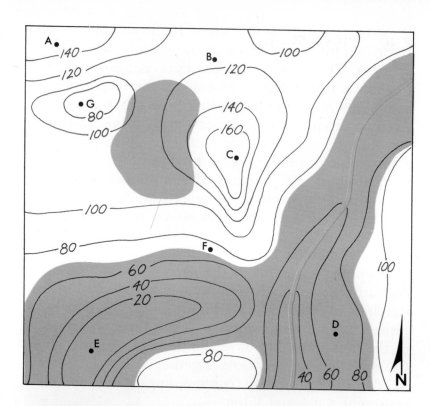

FIGURE 8–13. Topographic map.

activity
USING A TOPOGRAPHIC MAP

Use Figure 8–13 to answer the following questions.
(1) What point is the highest elevation shown on the map? **(2)** What point is the lowest elevation? **(3)** In which direction does the stream flow? How can you tell? **(4)** What is the approximate elevation of Point *D?* **(5)** What is the difference in elevation between Points A and *G?* **(6)** Is the slope steeper between Points *C* and *F* or between Points *C* and *B?* Explain. **(7)** Where on the map might a stream once have been located? **(8)** Point *G* sometimes is flooded during a heavy rainfall. Explain why this is so. **(9)** What is the difference in elevation between Points *F* and *D?*

MAKING SURE

2. How can you tell the difference between a valley and a hill on a topographic map?

8:6 Time Zones

People flying across the United States from coast to coast must reset their watches. Otherwise, they will have the wrong time when they land. The United States is divided into four standard time zones. These zones are pacific, mountain, central, and eastern. Time differs by one hour between each zone. If you travel east you lose one hour as you cross into another time zone. Going west you gain one hour. For example, when it is 5:00 P.M. in New York City, it is 4:00 P.M. in Chicago, 3:00 P.M. in Denver, and 2:00 P.M. in San Francisco.

What are time zones?

FIGURE 8–14. Time zones of North America.

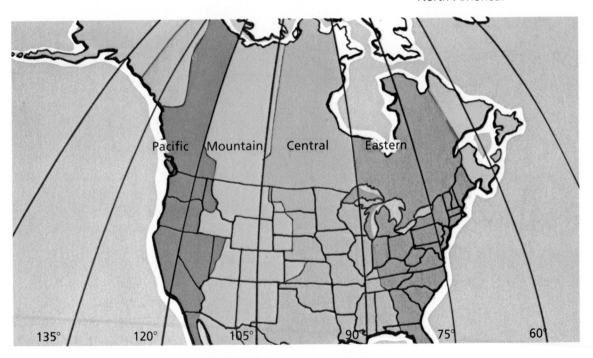

Time zones in the United States are part of the series of twenty-four International Time Zones. These twenty-four zones cover the total surface of the earth. Each zone is 15° of longitude wide. The width of a time zone is based on the speed of the earth's rotation which is 15° of longitude per hour.

Boundaries for the time zones run from the North Pole to the South Pole. These boundaries are adjusted to fit the boundaries between states and countries. If not, different parts of some states and cities would have different times. Every place within each time zone has the same time. For instance, when it is 3:00 P.M. in Washington, D.C. it is also 3:00 P.M. in Lima, Peru. Both Washington and Lima are in the same time zone.

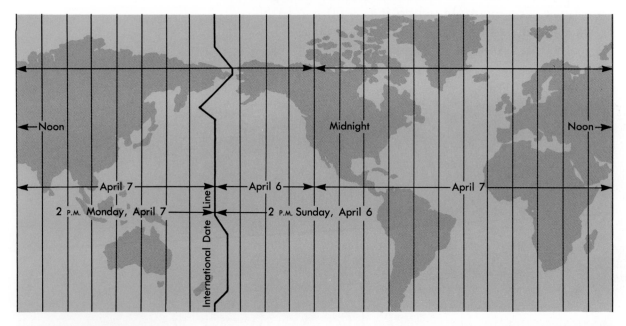

FIGURE 8–15. World time zones are determined by longitude.

Adjustments sometimes are made within a time zone. For example, daylight savings time is used to take advantage of extra daylight hours during the summer. When switching to daylight savings time, clocks are set one hour ahead. If the sun sets at 8:00 P.M. standard time, it would set at 9:00 P.M. daylight savings time. One hour of daylight is added to the evening.

Why is it necessary to have time zones? If there were no time zones, every city and town might have a different time. It would be noon in New York, five minutes before noon in Philadelphia and ten minutes before noon in Baltimore. This confusion was actually the case about 100 years ago before the time zones were established.

The **International Date Line** is on the opposite side of the earth from the prime meridian. This imaginary line follows, for the most part, the 180° line of longitude. The International Date Line has been adjusted to fit around islands and other populated land areas. The days are different on opposite sides of the date line. It is always one day later west of the date line. For instance, when it is Sunday on the east side of the line, it is Monday on the west side.

Where is the International Date Line?

8:7 The Earth as a Magnet

Have you ever used a toy magnet to pick up tacks or other metal objects? A magnet is made of iron, cobalt, or nickel. Each of these metals has magnetic properties.

The earth is a giant magnet. One way to detect the earth's magnetism is with a compass. A compass consists of a small magnet. Its needle points north and south towards the earth's magnetic poles. The **magnetic north pole** is about 1670 km from the geographic north pole near Bathurst Island in northern Canada. The **magnetic south pole** is near the coast of Antarctica about 2670 km from the geographic south pole.

How are the magnetic poles of the earth different from the geographic poles?

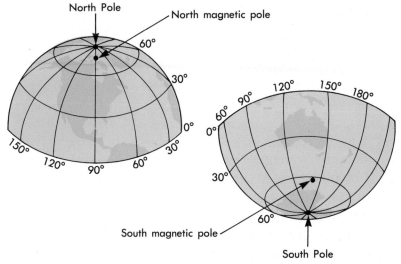

FIGURE 8–16. The north and south magnetic poles.

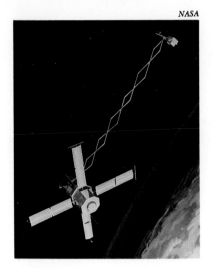

FIGURE 8–17. Mapping of the earth's magnetic field may be done through the use of satellites.

What is magnetic declination and how is it used to find directions?

Earth's magnetism is also detected with a magnetometer (mag nuh TAHM ut ur). A magnetometer measures the strength of Earth's magnetic field. Measurements made with this instrument show the earth's magnetic field varies slightly from place to place. This variation is caused by the rock structures below the earth's surface. An airplane trailing a magnetometer is often used for mapping the earth's magnetism since the airplane can cover a wide area in a short time.

From some places, a compass points directly to the geographic north pole. In most places, however, a compass points to the magnetic north pole forming an angle with the geographic north pole. This angle is called magnetic **declination** (dek luh NAY shun) or variation. Magnetic declination is different at different points on the earth. When using a compass, you must add or subtract this angle to get true directions. The magnetic declination is shown by a symbol on a topographic map.

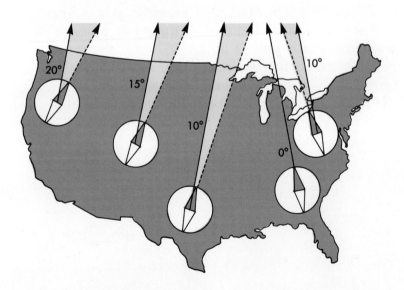

FIGURE 8–18. A compass points to the magnetic north pole which, for most locations, is a different direction than the geographic north pole.

The earth's magnetic field is constantly shifting. This change causes the positions of the north and south magnetic poles to change. Therefore, persons using magnetic compasses use up-to-date charts that show the angle of magnetic declination for an area.

What causes the earth's magnetism? As yet there are no satisfactory explanations. One theory is that the earth's magnetism is caused by the slow movements of molten iron and nickel in the earth's core.

Every magnet has a magnetic field around it which contains lines of magnetic force. These lines of force cause the magnet to attract iron and certain other metals. Also, the lines of force in the magnetic field cause the ends of two magnets to attract or repel each other. Lines of force in the earth's magnetic field pass outward from the poles into space. The earth's magnetism extends far out beyond the atmosphere to somewhere between 64 000 km to 130 000 km above the surface.

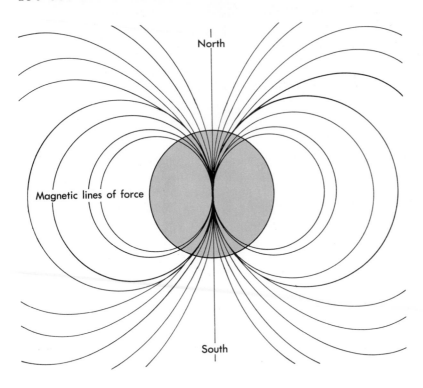

FIGURE 8–19. Earth's magnetic field.

MAKING SURE

3. How would a compass be used in making a map?

4. Why is the angle of magnetic declination at your school different from the magnetic declination 200 km west of the school?

Perspectives

skills

Reading Maps

Maps are scale drawings of the whole earth or part of it. They show many kinds of information, but no one map shows everything. Most maps are made to show specific information. For instance, you might draw a map showing a classmate how to get from school to your home. On such a map, you would likely show streets, traffic lights, and any important landmarks which would help to show were your home is. Of course, if you were asked by your teacher to draw a map of the United States, you would not include streets and landmarks. Rather, you would probably show the states, the principal cities, and main geographical features such as rivers and mountains. Let us look at some of the maps in Chapter 8 and see the kinds of information we can get from them.

Use Figure 8–9 to answer the following questions.

1. By noting many of the larger cities in the United States, locate approximately where you live.

2. Estimate the latitude and longitude of where you live.

3. Where is north on the map? Would Helena be north or south of Boston? Do you live north or south of San Francisco?

4. Using the scale 1 cm = 450 km, determine the distance between Dallas and St. Paul. What would be the distance between where you live and the nearest city shown on the map?

5. What ocean borders the western coast of the United States?

6. Does the United States occupy an entire continent or only part of one? What is the name of the continent?

Use Figure 8–13 to answer the following questions.

1. How can you tell the difference between a stream and a contour line on the map?

2. The vertical distance between contour lines is called the contour interval. What is the contour interval on the map?

3. Does any part of the land surface appear to be at sea level? How would sea level be indicated?

Use Figures 8–14 and 8–15 to answer the following questions.

1. How many time zones are found in the United States? If it is 9:00 A.M. in New York, what will be the time in San Francisco?

2. Knowing that 180° is one half of a circle, the International Date Line is opposite from what well known meridian?

3. How many time zones would you cross traveling from London, England to Phoenix, Arizona? What time would you land in Phoenix if your airplane took off at 1:00 A.M. and the flight lasted eight hours?

Use Figures 8–16 and 8–18 to answer the following questions.

1. What two hemispheres are shown in Figure 8–16? How are these maps like a globe?

2. What would you estimate the magnetic declination of your home to be?

3. Do the dashed arrows in Figure 8–18 show the direction of geographic north pole or magnetic north pole?

In chapter 8, there are maps to show four kinds of information. Maps can show many other types of information as well. Look through other chapters in this book and in your social studies book and see what other information can be shown on maps.

main ideas

1. The earth is slightly fatter at the equator.   8:1
2. Earth rotates on its axis and revolves in its orbit around the
   sun.   8:2
3. Lines of latitude and longitude are used to locate positions
   on the earth's surface.   8:4
4. Topographic maps show many landscape features.   8:5
5. The earth is divided into 24 time zones, each 15° of
   longitude in width. Time differs by one hour between each
   zone.   8:6
6. Earth is a natural magnet having a magnetic field that
   extends from the poles into space.   8:7

vocabulary

Define each of the following words or terms.

contour line   magnetic field   revolution
declination   magnetic north pole   rotation
International Date Line   magnetic south pole   standard time zone
latitude   meridian   topographic map
longitude   prime meridian

study questions

DO NOT WRITE IN THIS BOOK.

A. True or False

Determine whether each of the following sentences is true or false. If the sentence is false, rewrite it to make it true.

1. There are 24 different time zones.
2. It is possible to measure the mass of the earth by indirect methods.
3. A Foucault pendulum demonstrates the earth's rotation.
4. One rotation of the earth takes about a year.
5. Sunlight strikes the earth most directly at the North and South Poles.
6. Night and day are caused by the rotation of the earth.
7. The seasons are caused by the tilt of the earth's axis and the earth's revolution.

8. In the United States, the degrees of latitude are east of the prime meridian.
9. The equator is 0° longitude.
10. The geographic north pole is 90° north latitude.

B. Multiple Choice
Choose the word or phrase that completes correctly each of the following sentences.
1. Lines of longitude are measured in *(kilometers, meters, degrees).*
2. The prime meridian is *(0°, 90°, 180°)* longitude.
3. A scale of *(1 cm = 1 m, 1 cm = 500 m, 1 cm = 100 km)* could be used to make a map of a large city.
4. On a topographic map, a steep mountain is indicated when the contour lines are spaced *(close together, evenly, far apart).*
5. A contour line runs through all points having *(different, the same, the highest, the lowest)* elevation(s).
6. Information from *(contour, longitude, latitude)* lines indicates the shape of the landscape.
7. Pacific, mountain, central, eastern are the names of *(meridians, boundaries, time zones).*
8. The hands of a clock are moved *(forward, backward, not at all)* when switching from daylight savings time to standard time.
9. Chicago is located *(north, south, east, west)* of the prime meridian.
10. The difference in time when crossing the International Date Line is *(1 hour, 12 hours, 1 day).*

C. Completion
Complete each of the following sentences with a word or phrase that will make the sentence correct.
1. The _____ is on the opposite side of the world from the prime meridian.
2. A compass needle points towards the _____ north and south poles.
3. The strength of the earth's magnetic field can be measured with a _____.

4. The angle of _____ is the angle between the magnetic north pole and the geographic north pole.
5. A _____ will not be cast by a stick if sunlight strikes from directly above it.
6. The _____ of the earth is about 40 074 km.
7. If the earth had a larger _____ its gravity would be greater.
8. As time passes, the path of the Foucault pendulum _____.
9. The sun rises in the _____ and sets in the _____.
10. Every day the sun sets in San Francisco _____ hours later than in New York City.

D. How and Why
1. How can a Foucault pendulum be used to show the earth moves?
2. What causes the four seasons of the year?
3. Why are time zones needed and why are they 15° in width?
4. How are a distance scale and a compass used in making a map?
5. When does a compass point to the geographic north pole?

investigations

1. Obtain a book about sundials. Make a sundial and use it to tell the time of day.
2. Do library research on different timepieces that have been used through history. For example, compare an hour glass to a pendulum or grandfather clock. Prepare a report that includes drawings of the timepieces.
3. Obtain a topographic map for your area from the U.S. Geological Survey, state geology department, or nearby college geology department. Display the map in your classroom and locate major features of the local landscape.

interesting reading

Brunsden, Denys and John C. Doorkamp, *The Unquiet Landscape*. Bloomington, IN: University Press, 1975.
Jesperson, James and Jane Fritz-Randolph, *Time and Clocks for The Space Age*. New York, NY: Atheneum, 1979.

Rocks and rock formations are sources of geologic information. Many of the features in the photograph were formed by wind erosion. Wind erosion is one of several processes by which the landscape is changed. How are rocks formed? From what materials are rocks made? What geologic forces are at work within the earth?

David M. Dennis

Geology

9:1 Structure of the Earth

Geology is the science that studies the earth. Scientists in this field are called geologists. One question they ask is what is the structure of the earth? Geologists believe that the inside of the earth can be divided into three sections—core, mantle, and crust.

The **core** is the center section of the earth and consists of an inner and an outer region. The inner core begins at the center of the earth, 6400 km below Earth's surface. It has a radius of about 1300 km. Geologists believe that the inner core is mainly solid iron and nickel. This solid metal exists under great pressures and very high temperatures. The temperature may be as high as 4300°C.

The outer core surrounds the inner core and has a thickness of about 2250 km. Scientists think that the outer core is made of liquid iron and nickel. The outer core is slightly cooler than the inner core. In its upper part, it is about 3700°C.

GOAL: You will gain knowledge about the properties of rocks and minerals and the changes that occur in the earth's surface.

Name the three sections of the earth.

Describe the main features of each section of the earth.

169

The **mantle** surrounds the outer core and has a thickness of 2900 km. It is thicker and has more matter in it than any other part of the earth. The mantle is made of silicon, oxygen, aluminum, iron, and magnesium. Although most of the mantle consists of solid rock, high temperature and pressure cause certain parts of it to be somewhat fluid and to "flow" very slowly. Temperatures in the mantle vary from about 3700°C at its deepest part to about 870°C at the outer edge.

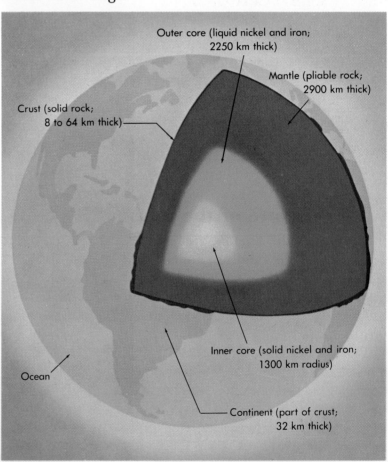

Outer core (liquid nickel and iron; 2250 km thick)

Mantle (pliable rock; 2900 km thick)

Crust (solid rock; 8 to 64 km thick)

Inner core (solid nickel and iron; 1300 km radius)

Ocean

Continent (part of crust; 32 km thick)

FIGURE 9–1. The earth consists of three major sections.

Above the mantle is the crust. The **crust** is like a thin rocky skin around the mantle. Its thickness varies from 8 to 64 km. The crust consists of all the continents and ocean floors of the earth's surface. Temperatures within the deepest parts of the crust may be hot enough to melt rock.

Near the surface of the earth, the crust is solid rock. Usually the rock is covered with a layer of soil. The layer of soil is often a meter or more deep.

MAKING SURE

1. Why would it be impossible to send a person to explore earth's mantle and core?

9:2 Plate Tectonics

Plate tectonics (tek TAHN ihks) is a theory that explains major features of the earth such as earthquakes, volcanoes, and mountains. According to this theory, the earth's surface is divided into six major plates. There are also several minor plates. A **plate** is a large section of the earth's crust that is slowly moving. For instance, North and South America are part of the American plate that is drifting westward. Most geologists believe plate movement is caused by flowing currents of hot rock within the mantle.

Explain the theory of plate tectonics.

FIGURE 9–2. According to theory, the earth's surface is divided into six major plates and several smaller ones.

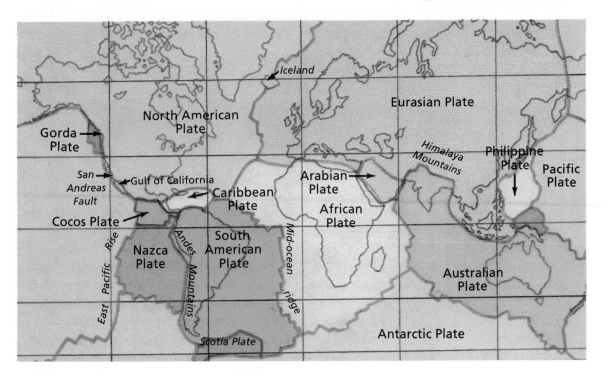

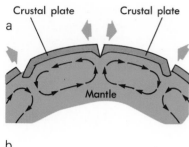

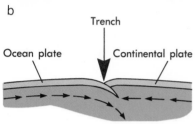

FIGURE 9–3. The movement of crustal plates is thought to be a result of convective currents of hot rock in the mantle (a). A trench forms when two plates collide, with one plate moving beneath the other (b).

What changes may occur when two plates meet?

FIGURE 9–4. The Pacific plate and the American plate slide past each other along the San Andreas fault in California.

Movement of the crustal plates creates stress and strain within the earth. When two adjoining plates are moving toward each other, one plate may pass under the edge of the other plate. The bottom plate bends downward to enter the mantle. This bending causes trenches to form. A trench is a deep, long valley in the ocean floor. The rubbing of two plates against each other produces tremendous heat and friction.

The Pacific and American plates meet along the western coast of North America. Instead of one plate passing under the other, the two plates slide past each other. The Pacific plate moves about 5 cm per year in a northwest direction. The American plate moves in a southeast direction. Movement of the two plates does not occur smoothly. The rocks tend to stick and then slip. When the rocks slip suddenly, shock waves are sent out through the surrounding area. The shock waves often go unnoticed by most people. But when they are strong enough to be felt, the event is called an earthquake.

Aerial photo by Collier/Condit

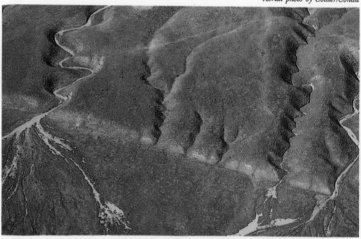

While some plates are moving together, others are moving apart. Magma flowing up from the mantle pushes the plates apart at the surface. The Eurasian (Europe and Asia) and American plates provide an example of plates moving apart. Under the Atlantic Ocean, between these two plates, a giant ridge of mountains has formed. The mountains extend north to south along the center of the Atlantic Ocean floor. They are called the Mid-Atlantic Ridge. Iceland is a part of this ridge that has been pushed up through the ocean's surface.

According to geologists, all of the earth's continents were locked together about 200 million years ago (Figure 9-5). One by one the continents drifted away from each other. The Atlantic Ocean was formed when North America moved west away from Europe. India was a plate next to Africa that moved northward to the continent of Asia. As it moved away from Africa, the Indian Ocean was formed. The collision of India with Asia formed the Himalaya mountains. The Alps mountains were born in the collision of the plate that is now Italy with the southern edge of Europe.

FIGURE 9-5. Millions of years ago, the continents were joined as one supercontinent (a). They gradually split up and moved apart to their present positions (b).

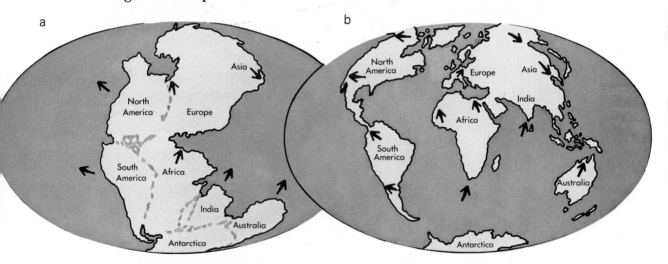

a

b

activity COMPARING THE SHAPES OF CONTINENTS

Obtain two pieces of cardboard or heavy construction paper. On one, draw an outline of North and South America. On the other, draw an outline of Europe and Africa. Cut the paper along the outline. Then try to fit the two outlines together. How do the shapes compare? How does the plate tectonics theory fit your observations?

9:3 Rocks and Minerals

How are rocks identified?

Scientists learn many things about the earth by studying rocks. There are many different kinds of rocks. Rocks can be identified by their physical properties. Color, shape, hardness, and texture are some physical properties. The region in which a rock is found is also helpful in identifying it. Hard rocks, for example, are often found in regions of tall mountains. Soft rocks are usually found in valleys.

Into what three groups are rocks divided?

Rocks may be classified into three groups—igneous (IHG nee us), sedimentary (sed uh MENT uh ree), and metamorphic (met uh MOR fihk). **Igneous rocks** are formed from hot liquid matter forced up from the mantle or lower crust. These rocks make up about 95 percent of the earth's crust. **Sedimentary rocks** result from the cementing of tiny rock particles. For example, beds of clay, sand, gravel, or limestone shells may cement together as time passes to form solid sedimentary rocks. **Metamorphic rocks** are created by changes in igneous or sedimentary rocks. These rocks may be changed to metamorphic rocks by extreme pressures and high temperatures.

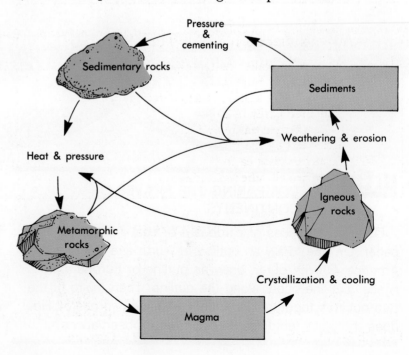

FIGURE 9–6. The rock cycle describes the processes by which rocks change from one form to another.

All rocks are made of minerals. A **mineral** is a substance which has a definite chemical composition and a crystal form. Some rocks contain only one mineral. For instance, limestone contains only calcite (calcium carbonate). Other rocks contain two or more minerals. Granite contains quartz, feldspar, and small amounts of other minerals.

More than 2000 minerals have been named. Most common minerals can be identified by properties such as luster, color, hardness, and crystal form. The hardness of minerals can be found by scratching one against another. The harder mineral will always scratch the softer one.

FIGURE 9–7.   Calcite.

FIGURE 9–8.   Fluorite.

FIGURE 9–9.   Apatite.

FIGURE 9–10.   Quartz.

FIGURE 9–11.   Topaz.

Table 9–1.
Mohs Scale of Mineral Hardness

1–Talc	6–Orthoclase
2–Gypsum	7–Quartz
3–Calcite	8–Topaz
4–Fluorite	9–Corundum
5–Apatite	10–Diamond

Table 9–2.
Approximate Scale of Mineral Hardness

1–Soft greasy flakes on fingers
2–Scratched by fingernail
3–Cut easily by knife, scratched slightly with penny
4–Scratched easily by knife
5–Not scratched easily by knife
6–Scratched by file
7–9–Scratches glass easily
10–Scratches all other materials

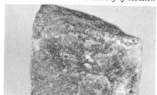
FIGURE 9–12.   Talc.

FIGURE 9–13.   Gypsum.

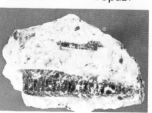
FIGURE 9–14.   Corundum.

Table 9–3.
Properties of Some Minerals

Mineral	Luster	Color	Hardness	Density (g/cm³)
Talc	Pearly to dull or greasy	Bright green to white, gray	1	2.8
Gypsum	Pearly, silky, dull, glassy	White, gray, brown	2	2.3
Calcite	Dull or pearly	White	3	2.7
Fluorite	Glassy	White, green, violet, blue, brown, yellow	4	3.1
Orthoclase	Glassy to pearly	White to gray, red, green	6	2.5
Quartz	Waxy to dull	Gray, brown, black, and so on	7	2.6
Topaz	Glassy	Yellow, white, blue, red, green	8	3.5
Corundum	Glassy to diamondlike	Gray, brown, red, yellow, blue, black, pink	9	4.0
Galena	Metallic	Dark lead gray	2.5	7.5

activity   IDENTIFYING ROCKS

Collect a dozen different small rocks. Use an egg carton as a container for the rocks (Figure 9–15). Study all of the rocks carefully and classify them. How many are light in color? How many are dark? Are some smooth and others rough? Examine the texture, or grain, of each rock. Some are coarse-grained and some are fine-grained. How many of the rocks can you identify? Compare them with the pictures on Pages 180–183. If a collection of labeled rock samples is available, it will be very helpful in identifying your rock samples.

FIGURE 9–15.

activity TESTING THE HARDNESS OF MINERALS

Obtain samples of talc, gypsum, calcite, fluorite, orthoclase, quartz, topaz, and corundum. Test the hardness of each mineral by trying to scratch it with your fingernail and with a knife blade. Try to scratch each of the minerals with a copper penny. Which of the minerals will scratch a glass plate? Compare your results with the scales of mineral hardness (Tables 9–1 and 9–2).

MAKING SURE

2. A 10-cm³ mineral sample has a mass of 23 g.
   (a) Calculate the density of the mineral.
   (b) Use Table 9–3 to identify this mineral.
3. An unknown rock sample scratches glass easily. It does not scratch other materials. What is the hardness of the sample? See Table 9–2.

9:4 Weathering and Erosion

Rocks and minerals are broken into smaller pieces by weathering. **Weathering** is the breaking down of rock by the action of water, ice, plants, animals, and chemical changes. Continued weathering of large pieces of rock produces the tiny particles that make up soil.

How does weathering produce soil?

Gene Frazier

FIGURE 9–16. Caverns and cave formations result from a type of weathering.

Weathered rock pieces are carried from one place to another by wind, moving water, and moving ice. This process by which rocks and soil are worn away is called **erosion.** Erosion in a desert may be caused by winds blowing sand that scratches exposed bedrock. Streams and rivers can carry rocks and soil for long distances. Many regions contain rocks that were carried there by glaciers a long time ago.

a

Paul Nesbit

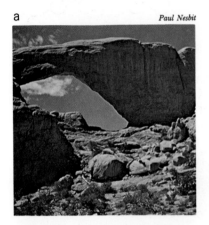

b

Steve Lissau

FIGURE 9–17. A rock bridge formed by weathering and erosion (a). Waves cutting away at a rocky cliff (b).

activity THE EFFECT OF FREEZING ON THE WEATHERING OF ROCK

Fill an empty milk carton with water and seal the top. Place it in a freezer. After one day remove the carton. What change occurred in the water? Did the shape of the container change? Why? What might have happened if the container were glass instead of cardboard? Compare your results with the effect of freezing water in the cracks of rocks.

MAKING SURE

4. How does the speed of wind and water affect the rate of erosion?
5. Suppose you found a pebble that was very smooth. Do you think it was made smooth by wind, ice, or water? Explain.

9:5 Igneous Rock

Granite, basalt, and olivine are examples of igneous rocks. Igneous rocks are formed by the cooling of molten rock material from within the earth. Molten rock material within the earth is called magma. Due to great pressure, extremely hot magma may be forced out of the lower crust and mantle. As it moves upward through the earth's crust, it cools and solidifies to form igneous rocks.

Igneous rocks may be divided into two types—extrusive (ihk STREW sihv) and intrusive (ihn TREW sihv). Extrusive igneous rocks are formed from magma that flows out over the earth's surface. The magma may flow from volcanoes or from deep cracks in the earth's crust. For instance, basalt is an extrusive igneous rock formed by the cooling of magma which flows from a volcano.

Intrusive igneous rocks are formed from magma that cools and crystallizes beneath the earth's surface. Crystallize means to form a crystal structure. Granite is an example of an intrusive igneous rock. The magma which forms intrusive igneous rock cools more slowly than magma released at the surface.

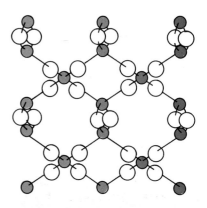

FIGURE 9–18. Quartz consists of silicon and oxygen atoms arranged in a crystal pattern. Quartz forms in granite when magma crystallizes beneath the earth's surface.

What is the difference between intrusive and extrusive igneous rocks?

a

William Huber

FIGURE 9–19. Devil's Tower (a) consists of the hard interior rock of a volcano that was exposed when the outer layers were eroded (b).

b

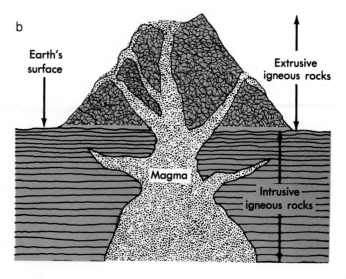

Earth's surface

Extrusive igneous rocks

Magma

Intrusive igneous rocks

Rich Brommer

Rich Brommer

FIGURE 9–20. Large grains are formed when molten rock cools slowly underground (a). Fine grains form during cooling on the surface (b).

How are sedimentary rocks formed?

The speed with which an igneous rock changes from liquid to solid affects its texture. Texture refers to the size of the crystals, or grains, of rock. Most extrusive rocks are fine-grained because they cool quickly. Their texture may be so fine that the separate rock crystals can only be seen with a microscope. Intrusive rocks are coarse-grained and hard because they cool very slowly beneath the earth's crust. Their crystals are usually large, measuring from 0.4 to 1.3 cm across.

activity TEXTURE OF IGNEOUS ROCKS

Examine specimens of igneous rock. Compare the size of the crystals in the rocks. Divide the rocks into two groups—intrusive and extrusive.

9:6 Sedimentary Rock

At one time, the entire crust of the earth was made of igneous rocks. Today, about one tenth of the total crust is made of sedimentary rocks. Sedimentary rocks are formed when particles of eroded rock are deposited together and then become cemented. These deposited rock particles are called sediments. The rock particles in sediments are produced by weathering and range in size from coarse gravel to fine powdered clay.

Larry Hamill

FIGURE 9–21. Power shovels are used to remove sediments that accumulate at the bottom of a river to allow for the safe passage of ships.

From the place where rock is weathered, particles are carried away by erosion. Wind, waves, rivers, and glaciers carry particles to places often far away from where they began. As particles are carried they are deposited to form sediments.

Sediment can accumulate in great deposits in oceans, rivers, streams, and lakes. How? When a river flows into an ocean or lake, it slows down in speed and drops the particles it is carrying. This process is called settling. The particles are deposited in layers on the ocean or lake floor. The largest and heaviest rock pieces are usually the first to settle. Then lighter and lighter pieces settle in layers above.

After thousands of years, sediment may become many layers thick. The particles of sediment in lower layers are under pressure from the sediment above. This pressure causes small particles to stick together. Larger rock fragments may be cemented together by dissolved minerals. When minerals like calcium carbonate or silica are deposited with fragments of sand or gravel, they cement the fragments together. Sedimentary rock is produced by both mineral cementing and by pressure from above.

As sedimentary rock forms, it makes strata, or distinct layers of rock. The strata are nearly

Keith Turpie

FIGURE 9–22. Sedimentary rocks form in distinct layers or strata.

Name three sedimentary rocks.

horizontal when first hardened. But, many of the layers are eventually tilted or folded by forces within the earth's crust.

Sandstone, shale, limestone, and dolomite are common sedimentary rocks. A conglomerate is a sedimentary rock that contains rock fragments mixed with sand or clay. The fragments may range in size from pebbles to boulders. Sandstone, as its name suggests, is formed from particles of sand. Sandstone is composed mainly of quartz. It is highly resistant to wear and decay. Because of its many attractive colors, sandstone is often used as a building stone. Shale is rock formed from layers of clay or silt. Limestone is largely calcium carbonate. Dolomite is composed of both calcium carbonate and magnesium carbonate.

FIGURE 9–23. Conglomerate (a), shale (b), and sandstone (c) are common sedimentary rocks.

a

Russ Lappa

b

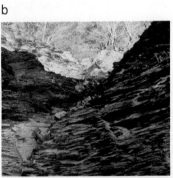

James Westwater

c

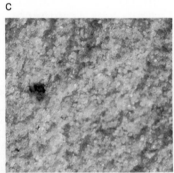

Carolina Biological Supply Co.

activity ROCKS THAT FIZZ

Place a drop of dilute hydrochloric acid on a few rocks. **CAUTION:** Use care when working with acid. Wear eye and clothing protection. If any one of the rocks contains a carbonate, the rock will fizz. The fizzing is produced by the release of bubbles of carbon dioxide gas produced in a chemical reaction between the acid and the rock. The word equation for the reaction is

Calcium carbonate + hydrochloric acid ⟶
carbon dioxide + water + calcium chloride

activity
FINDING THE COMPOSITION OF A SEDIMENT

Spread 1 mL of coarse sand on millimeter-lined graph paper. Using the millimeter squares as a scale, measure the diameters of the sand particles. Classify the sand particles by sizes. View the minerals through a hand lens. How many can you identify? What fraction of the sample is quartz?

MAKING SURE

6. How do sedimentary rocks form?
7. How is sandstone different from shale?
8. Why is sandstone sometimes used for building?

How are metamorphic rocks formed?

9:7 Metamorphic Rock

Metamorphic rocks are formed from sedimentary or igneous rocks. Metamorphic rocks are produced by extreme pressures or high temperatures below the earth's surface. Metamorphic rocks are generally the hardest and densest rocks.

A type of metamorphic rock is derived from each sedimentary and each igneous rock. Slate is a metamorphic rock derived from shale. Because slate splits lengthwise to form sheets, it is sometimes used for roofing and walkways. Quartzite is formed from sandstone. It is the hardest and most resistant common rock. Marble is a metamorphic rock formed from limestone and dolomite. It can be easily crushed into small pieces.

MAKING SURE

9. Explain why a drop of lemon juice fizzes when placed on marble.
10. How can you distinguish sandstone from quartzite?

University of Houston

a

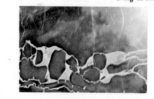

Craig Kramer

b

Jim Elliot

c

FIGURE 9–24. High pressure and temperature formed slate (a), marble (b), and quartzite (c).

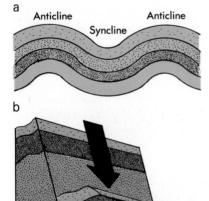

a

Anticline   Anticline

Syncline

b

FIGURE 9–25. Forces within the earth's crust cause rock layers to fold, producing anticlines and synclines (a). A vertical fault forms when the crust breaks and part of the crust slips upward or downward (b).

What is a fault in the earth's crust?

9:8 Rock Formations

The earth's crust is always changing. In some places, the crust is being slowly pushed upward due to forces below the surface. In other places, hills and mountains are being worn down by weathering and erosion. Volcanoes and earthquakes are also changing the earth's surface. These changes within the earth produce mountains, valleys, caves, cliffs, and river deltas. They also produce special rock formations. A rock formation is a group of rocks arranged in a certain way.

Changes in the crust occur when pressure causes rock layers to bend or fold. Folded rocks may sometimes be seen along the sides of roads or streams. The folds in the rocks can be gentle or quite steep. When the rock layers are folded upward like an arch, the formation is called an **anticline** (ANT ih kline). A downward fold or trough is called a **syncline** (SIHN kline). The Appalachian Mountains are made of many anticlines and synclines. The folds were caused by forces that resulted when the Eurasian plate collided with the North American plate.

If pressure on rock layers becomes too great, they may break. A break in the crust along which movement occurs is called a **fault.** In some cases, the crust slips upward or downward along the break. The Grand Teton Mountains in Wyoming were formed by this type of faulting.

FIGURE 9–26. These rock layers were once horizontal. Intense pressure from above pushed the layers downward.

James Westwater

Sometimes, parts of the earth's crust slides past each other. This type of movement occurs along the San Andreas fault in California. The San Andreas fault is the zone where the Pacific and North American plates meet.

Roger K. Burnard

FIGURE 9–27. The Grand Teton Mountains in Wyoming were formed by faulting.

activity ANTICLINES AND SYNCLINES

(1) Obtain four large pieces of modeling clay in different colors. Press each piece into a rectangle about 2 cm thick. (2) Lay the pieces of clay on top of each other so they are like rock layers. Fold the combined layers into the shape of an anticline. (3) Cut off the tip of the rounded part of the fold so you can see the rock layers (4) Make a drawing of the layers as they appear from above. Which layer (color) of clay represents the oldest rock layer in an anticline? Youngest rock layer? Label these layers on your drawing. (5) Place four layers of clay together as you did in Steps 1 and 2. (6) Fold them into the shape of a syncline. Which layer (color) of clay represents the oldest rock layer in a syncline? Youngest rock layer? (7) Make a diagram of the layers when viewed from above. Label the oldest and youngest layers.

MAKING SURE
11. How do eroded rock layers show the location of anticlines and synclines?

9:9 Earthquakes

What causes an earthquake?

An **earthquake** is caused by a sudden slippage of rock along a fault. Movement of the rocks can be vertical or horizontal. If you take hold of a stick and snap it quickly you can feel the force used in breaking it. Breaking the stick is similar to the slippage of rocks that causes an earthquake. The sudden release of energy sends out shock waves. A shock wave is a vibration which travels through the earth's interior.

FIGURE 9–28. Destruction of a highway after an earthquake in Montana.

Table 9–4.
Scale of Earthquake Intensity

1 Recorded by instruments.

2 Noticed only by few persons at rest.

3 Vibrations felt like passing truck; felt by people at rest, especially on upper floors.

4 Felt by people while walking; rocking of loose objects.

5 Felt by nearly everyone; most sleepers are awakened; bells ring.

6 Trees sway; suspended objects swing; damage by overturning and falling of loose objects.

7 Walls crack; plaster falls.

8 Difficult to drive cars; chimneys fall; poorly constructed buildings are damaged.

9 Some houses collapse where ground begins to crack; pipes break open.

10 Ground cracks badly; many buildings destroyed; railway lines bent; landslides on steep slopes.

11 Few buildings remain standing; bridges destroyed; great landslides and floods.

12 Total destruction; objects thrown into the air; ground rises and falls in waves.

A **seismograph** (SIZE muh graf) is used to record the shock waves sent out by earthquakes. Seismographs can record shocks that occur thousands of kilometers away. A seismograph contains a rotating recording drum on a base that is attached securely to the earth. A heavy weight supported by a long thin wire contains a pen that inks a line on the recording drum. What happens to the weight when the earth around it shakes? The weight remains motionless. Its inertia causes it to stand still. The recording drum vibrates however, with each earth movement. This causes the needle to ink a line of waves on the recording drum.

A recording made by a seismograph needle is shown in Figure 9–30. The recording is called a seismogram. Up and down strokes of the pen are caused by vibrations produced by an earthquake. The more severe the vibrations, the higher the up and down strokes.

The seismograph described here is too simple to work well. Modern seismographs use magnetic and electronic devices to pick up and record earth vibrations.

The first indication of an earthquake on a seismogram is a series of primary waves (P-waves). As these waves start to fade, they are followed by a burst of secondary waves (S-waves). P-waves travel 1.7 times faster than S-waves. Following these two waves, surface waves are recorded. Surface waves travel parallel to the earth's surface and are the most destructive. They are the last waves to reach the seismograph.

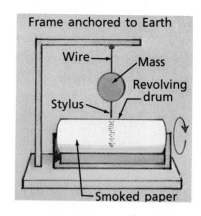

FIGURE 9–29. An earthquake is recorded when shock waves cause the drum of a seismograph to move.

Name the three kinds of waves produced by an earthquake.

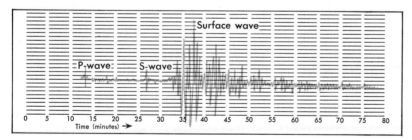

FIGURE 9–30. This seismogram is a record of both the time and intensity of an earthquake's shock waves.

Suppose an earthquake occurred 9700 km from a seismological station. It would take about 13 minutes for P-waves to reach the station. S-waves would arrive about 10 minutes after the P-waves. The time between the arrival of the P-waves and arrival of the S-waves depends on the distance between the recording station and the center of the earthquake. The greater the distance, the longer the time.

Finding the exact center of an earthquake requires reports from three or more recording stations. After the distance of each station from the earthquake center is found, a circle is drawn around each station. The radius of the circle gives the earthquake's distance. The point where the three circles meet gives the exact location of the earthquake center. This center is called the focus. The point directly above the focus on the earth's surface is called the earthquake's **epicenter.**

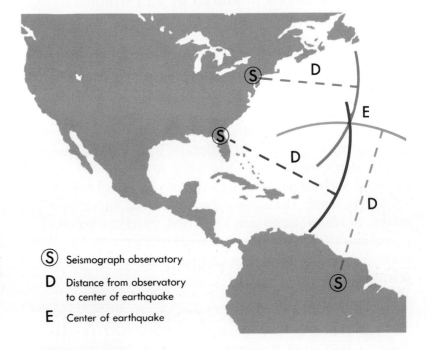

FIGURE 9–31. Exact location of an earthquake is determined by drawing circles around three or more earthquake stations. The radius of each circle is the distance of the earthquake from the station.

(S) Seismograph observatory

D Distance from observatory to center of earthquake

E Center of earthquake

MAKING SURE

12. Refer to the seismogram in Figure 9–30 to answer the following questions.
    (a) At what time was the first earthquake shock recorded?
    (b) Name the three kinds of waves produced by an earthquake.
    (c) Which waves are more severe?
    (d) What was the time interval between the initial shock and the arrival of the P-waves?
    (e) What was the time interval between the arrival of the first P-wave and the first S-wave?

9:10 Volcanoes

Volcanoes form when magma is squeezed from the earth's interior to the surface. Volcanoes form on continents as well as on the ocean floor. Most volcanic activity occurs where plates collide or move apart. Volcanism refers to the process by which magma is produced and moved to the surface. Magma that reaches the surface is called lava. Volcanism also produces and expels hot gases and solid debris from openings in the crust.

Where do volcanoes form?

What is lava?

Simon/Tom Stack & Assoc.

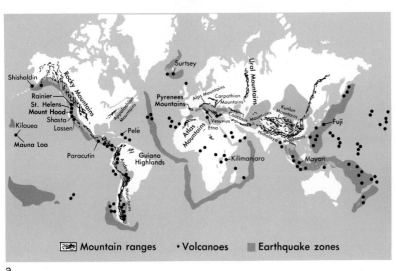

a

b

FIGURE 9–32. Locations of the world's mountain ranges, volcanoes, and earthquake zones are related to the movements of Earth's crustal plates (a). This volcano in Iceland erupted along the Mid-Atlantic Ridge where two crustal plates are moving apart (b).

Not all volcanoes erupt violently. Sometimes lava pours from great cracks in the earth's surface. The flowing lava does not build a volcano. Instead, the lava floods a large area and forms a high plateau. Parts of North America were formed in this manner.

David Spier /Tom Stack & Assoc.

FIGURE 9–33. The Columbia Plateau in northwestern United States formed when basalt lava erupted from large cracks in the earth's surface.

When magma rises to the surface through a vent or pipe, a volcano forms. See Figure 9–34. Some volcanoes have magma that flows quietly onto the surface. Other volcanoes explode violently. During the explosion, rock fragments and lava are thrown high into the air. Also, a hill or cone builds around the vent. Some volcanoes form from quiet lava flows and explosions. Mt. St. Helens, built up over many years, is an example of this type of volcano.

FIGURE 9–34. Some volcanoes may contain layers of ash and lava.

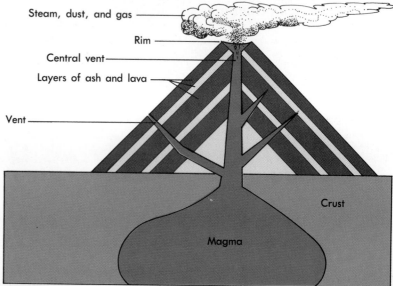

Steam, dust, and gas

Rim

Central vent

Layers of ash and lava

Vent

Crust

Magma

FIGURE 9–35. Obsidian is an igneous rock that forms when lava cools rapidly near or on the surface.

Eric Hoffhines/Courtesy of Carlton Davis

When first expelled, lava is red or white-hot. It quickly cools from a temperature of about 1000°C. Sometimes it cools to form a volcanic glass called obsidian. Obsidian cools so quickly that it has no crystals.

Lava foams when it contains gases under high pressure. The resulting material looks somewhat like shaving cream. As the foam lava hardens, it produces a rock called scoria. Scoria is filled with tiny bubbles. Pumice is a fine-grained, light-colored scoria rock.

MAKING SURE
13. Compare the locations of major volcanoes with the earth's earthquake belts. How do they compare?

main ideas

vocabulary

Define each of the following words or terms.

anticline	geology	plate
core	igneous rock	plate tectonics
crust	lava	sedimentary rock
erosion	magma	seismograph
earthquake	metamorphic rock	syncline
epicenter	mantle	volcano
fault	mineral	weathering

study questions

DO NOT WRITE IN THIS BOOK.

A. True or False

Determine whether each of the following sentences is true or false. If the sentence is false, rewrite it to make it true.

1. The crust of the earth consists entirely of liquid rock.
2. The thickness of the mantle varies from 8 to 64 km.
3. All rocks have a course-grained texture.
4. A mineral is an inorganic substance which has a definite chemical composition and a crystal form.
5. The hardness of minerals can be determined by scratching them.

6. Rocks are made of minerals.

7. Igneous rocks are always formed beneath the earth's crust.

8. Coarse-grained intrusive rocks result from the slow cooling of magma.

9. Trenches are sometimes formed when two adjoining plates move toward each other.

10. Shock waves are produced by earthquakes.

B. Multiple Choice

Choose the word or phrase that completes correctly each of the following sentences.

1. Sedimentary rock is formed from *(loose rock particles, liquid rock, soil)*.

2. Continued weathering of rock will eventually produce *(marble, sandstone, soil, shale)*.

3. *(Shale, Sandstone, Limestone, Quartz)* will react with acid to produce carbon dioxide gas.

4. *(Soil, Slate, Sandstone, Granite)* is a metamorphic rock.

5. Marble is a metamorphic rock formed from *(shale, sandstone, limestone, quartz)*.

6. Geologists believe the earth's *(inner core, outer core, mantle)* consists of solid nickel and iron.

7. As a mountain is weathered and eroded, its size *(increases, decreases, remains the same)*.

8. Anticlines and synclines are produced by the *(folding, faulting, splitting, melting)* of bedrock.

9. According to plate tectonics, Iceland was formed by the *(sinking, rising, faulting)* of the Mid-Atlantic Ridge.

10. A *(syncline, cone, fault, plate)* is a break in the earth's crust along which movement can occur.

C. Completion

Complete each of the following sentences with a word or phrase that will make the sentence correct.

1. The _____ theory states that the earth's crust is divided into six major plates.

2. Liquid rock material within the earth is called _____.

3. The shock waves of an earthquake may be recorded by a(n) _____.

4. _____, _____, and _____ are three kinds of earthquake waves.
5. Most earthquakes are located on the _____ of the plates.
6. Quartz is a _____ found in rocks.
7. _____ is molten rock that flows from a volcano and turns into solid rock when it cools.
8. Bedrock is usually covered with a layer of _____.
9. A _____ is a break in the rocks, within the earth's crust.
10. _____ is the breaking down of the earth's crust by wind, water, ice, plants, animals, and chemical changes.

D. How and Why
1. How could you identify a rock or mineral?
2. How is sedimentary rock formed?
3. Why is the earth's crust constantly changing?
4. Why is it not possible to locate the center of an earthquake with a single seismograph?
5. How were the Alps and Himalaya mountains formed?

investigations

1. Have you ever thought about becoming a rock hound? Obtain a book about rock and mineral collecting. Make a collection of different rocks and minerals. Find out about chemical tests for identifying minerals.
2. Obtain information about research that scientists are doing to predict the occurrence of earthquakes. Prepare a report for your class.
3. Obtain a book from the library on crystal growing. Learn how to grow the crystals of several kinds of minerals. Prepare an exhibit of the crystals along with a description of the process you used to grow them.

interesting reading

Deeker, Robert and Barbara, *Volcanoes.* San Francisco, CA: Freeman, 1980.
Dietrich, R. V., *Stones: Their Collection, Identification, and Uses.* San Francisco, CA: Freeman, 1980.

Scientists are working carefully to remove a fossil from the digging site. Fossils and rock layers are clues to events that took place millions of years ago. How can the ages of rocks and fossils be determined? How can geological information be used to predict events in the future?

Earthwatch

Earth History

10:1 The Grand Canyon

How would you find the date of the first expedition to the South Pole? How would you find the date the steam engine was invented? These dates were recorded by people when the events took place. They may be found in a history book.

Geologists search for clues to geologic history "written" in the earth's rocks. Geologic history is an account of Earth's past recorded in rocks. The Grand Canyon in northern Arizona is a good place to study geologic history. The Grand Canyon is located on a plateau 2300 to 2800 m above sea level. A plateau is a level land area raised above the land around it. The canyon is 349 km long, 6 to 30 km wide, and more than 1.5 km deep. The Colorado River flows in a winding path through the canyon bottom. The Grand Canyon walls are made of sedimentary rocks—sandstone, limestone, and shale. Layer upon layer of rocks lie in an almost horizontal position above folded metamorphic rocks.

How did the Grand Canyon form? How old are the rocks that make up its walls? Are all the rock layers of the same age? What do the rocks reveal about events of the past? These are a few of the questions that interest geologists.

GOAL: You will learn how the earth and its life has changed during geologic time.

FIGURE 10–1. Many sedimentary rock layers are visible in this view of the Grand Canyon.

How was the Grand Canyon formed?

What factors determine the rate of rock weathering and erosion?

The Grand Canyon was cut out of the Colorado Plateau by the Colorado River a long time ago. During that time, the plateau was slowly being uplifted. Year after year, the force of the speeding river waters eroded the rock to cut the canyon. The forces that formed the Grand Canyon continue today. As the plateau is uplifted, erosion cuts it deeper and deeper.

The rate at which rock is worn away is based on two factors—the speed of the running water and the hardness of the rock. As the speed with which water

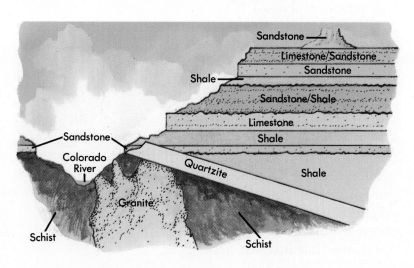

FIGURE 10–2. The sedimentary rock layers of the Grand Canyon lie above granite intrusions and tilted or folded metamorphic rocks.

runs across a rock increases, its wearing action also increases. Thus the faster the water flows, the more rapidly the rock is broken down. Soft rock is worn away faster than hard rock. The average rate of wear is about 1 m of rock for every 15 000 years.

Many fossils have been found in the rocks of the Grand Canyon. These fossils indicate that the land once lay under a shallow sea. It was at this time that the layers of sedimentary rock were formed. Later, over long periods of time, the land was uplifted from the sea. Desert conditions were present and land animals roamed the area. Fossils of animals, including reptiles, are preserved in sand sediments formed by the blowing desert winds.

The rock history of the Grand Canyon is not complete. There are some time periods from which no rocks remain. A time period for which no rock is left is called an **unconformity**. The absence of rock layers is the result of erosion. Erosion took place when a layer of rock was uplifted from beneath the sea and exposed to rain and wind. Sometimes a whole layer of rock was eroded away (Figure 10–3).

According to the **law of uniform change**, *past changes in the earth were caused by forces that still exist today.* For example, the forces of weathering and erosion account for many of the earth's features.

Define uncomformity.

Explain the law of uniform change.

FIGURE 10–3. Sedimentary deposits beneath the ocean formed sedimentary rocks. Magma cut through the rock layers and formed a granite intrusion (a). When the rock layers were uplifted, erosion removed the upper layers. As ocean waters covered the rocks again, new sedimentary rock layers were deposited (b).

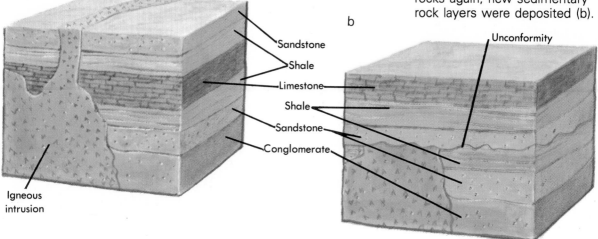

a

b

Sandstone
Shale
Limestone
Shale
Sandstone
Conglomerate

Igneous intrusion

Unconformity

These same forces are still at work changing the earth's surface. Most geologic forces do not appear to alter the landscape much during a person's life span. Yet they produce great changes over many centuries.

The forces that carve and mold the earth's surface have not always operated at their present rate. Sometimes their intensity has been greater, and sometimes less. For example, volcanoes once existed in many places where they are no longer found. The rate of weathering, erosion, and sedimentary rock formation has varied. Also, at times the climates of the world were much colder than they are today. During these periods, glaciers caused widespread erosion.

Edward Shay

a

FIGURE 10–4. Spider Rock was formed after many years of water and wind erosion (a). Ocean waves gradually erode a rocky coastline (b).

Sidney White Collection

b

MAKING SURE

1. By using a rate of erosion of 1 m/15 000 yr and a depth of 2000 m, find the approximate age of the Grand Canyon.

10:2   Age of Rocks

Layers of rocks are often arranged in order of age. In a series of level rock beds, the lowest layer is the oldest. Each higher layer is younger. The youngest rocks in the Grand Canyon are those near the surface. Deeper into the canyon, you see older and older layers of rock.

How is the age of a rock determined?

It is not possible to tell the age of a rock bed from its position alone. One method for finding the age of an igneous rock is **radioactive dating**. Radioactive dating is based on the rate of decay of certain radioactive elements. A radioactive element is one that gives off nuclear radiation. In releasing the radiation the element decays, which means it breaks down into lighter elements. Each radioactive element has a definite, fixed rate at which it decays. For instance, the rate at which radioactive uranium atoms break down into atoms of other elements is constant. Hence, uranium atoms act as a geologic clock that keeps track of the passing years.

What is a radioactive "clock?"

As time passes, the amount of uranium in a given mass of igneous rock decreases. The products of the radioactive decay, helium and lead, increase. One gram of uranium produces 1/7 600 000 000 g of lead each year. Such small amounts of lead can be detected with modern equipment.

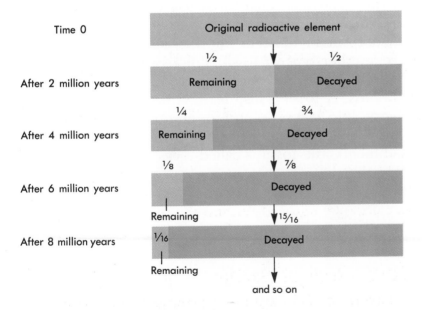

FIGURE 10–5. The fixed rate at which a radioactive element decays is called half-life. An element with a half-life of 2 million years means that one-half of the radioactive element decays after each 2-million-year period.

To discover the "birthdate" of a uranium-bearing igneous rock, the amount of lead present is compared to the amount of uranium present. Using this ratio, the rock's age may be computed. Rocks have been dated as old as 4.45 billion years.

10:3 Fossils

Fossils are preserved remains or traces of plants and animals which lived long ago. A **fossil** is any evidence of past life. The study of prehistoric living things through fossils is called **paleontology** (pay lee ahn TAHL uh jee).

Define fossil and paleontology.

Why are animal fossils more plentiful than plant fossils?

Most fossils consist of the hard parts of animals such as bones, teeth, and shells, which are preserved in rocks. When an organism dies, the soft fleshy parts usually decay. Plant fossils are scarce because plants contain few hard parts. Rarely does a whole animal or plant become a fossil. Exceptions to this are insects trapped in hardened plant sap, woolly mammoths buried and frozen in ice, and saber-toothed tigers trapped in tar pits.

Sometimes plant or animal tissue decays and is replaced with minerals. As a result the whole organism is cast in rock. Petrified wood has been formed in this way. As time passed, organic matter in the wood was replaced by silica and other minerals.

Footprints and other imprints left by organisms are another type of fossil. Tracks and footprints may be left in soft mud and preserved as the mud hardens. A fossil is also formed when an organism decays and leaves behind an empty space. If this empty space becomes filled with minerals or sediments, the fossil is called a cast.

FIGURE 10–6. Fossils of animals are preserved in areas where water holes (a) or tar pits (b) existed.

a

Sidney White Collection

b

Field Museum of Natural History, Chicago

a

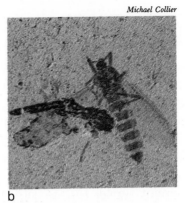

b

c

FIGURE 10–7. Petrified wood (a), an imprint of an insect (b), and a dinosaur footprint (c) are fossils.

Why is there little chance of an animal becoming a fossil when it dies?

Only a small fraction of all past living things have been preserved as fossils. Most are not preserved because they are attacked by bacteria and eaten by scavengers. But living things that die in places where sediments are collecting may be preserved. Very few fossils, if any, form where erosion takes place. The remains of living things are most often preserved in ocean sediments or in lake deposits, where quick burial occurs. You are most likely to find fossils of clams that lived along muddy coastlines than fossils of flying insects. The leaves of a tree on a lakeshore are more likely to be preserved than leaves of a tree growing on a mountainside. Most of the known fossils have been found in sedimentary rocks.

Fossils are often found in unexpected places. For instance, fossil shark teeth have been found in the rocks of mountains located far from the ocean. These fossils were formed in rock at the bottom of a sea. But, through movements of the earth plates over millions of years, the rock was uplifted to form mountains.

activity PETRIFIED WOOD AND OAK

Place a piece of oak and a piece of petrified wood, both about the same size, on opposite ends of a balance. Which has the most mass? Why? Calculate the density of petrified wood. Use the procedure described in the Activity on Page 28.

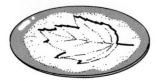

FIGURE 10–8.

Why have many species
become extinct?

activity CASTING A LEAF

(1) Mix some plaster of paris with water in an empty flat can, plastic dish, or saucer. Add just enough water to make a thick paste. The mixture should be about 3 cm deep. The top should be flat and smooth. **(2)** Lay a leaf on the surface of the mixture. Press down all over the leaf to leave an imprint. **(3)** Remove the leaf carefully and set the plaster in a safe place until it hardens. How is the leaf imprint similar to a fossil? Is the hardened plaster of paris most like igneous, metamorphic, or sedimentary rock?

activity PREDICTING FOSSIL FORMATIONS

Obtain a map of the United States. Estimate in square kilometers the area of the seafloor where fossils may now be forming off the coasts of the United States. Use 48 km for the width of shallow seas along the Atlantic and Gulf Coasts. Use 16 km for those along the Pacific Coast. List five animals that might be preserved in each region.

10:4 Fossil Records

Fossils reveal much about the past. Very old fossils are less complex than fossils of plants and animals that lived more recently. Less complex means they do not have as many different kinds of body parts. For example, shellfish are less complex than dinosaurs. A fern is less complex than a tree.

The fossil record also shows that many species of the past have become extinct. Extinct means that they no longer exist on the earth. Major changes in climate can cause a species to become extinct. Many findings indicate that climates and landforms have changed. For instance, dinosaur tracks found in hardened mud in New Jersey hint that this area was

Michael Collier

FIGURE 10–9. Crinoids (sea lilies) were abundant in shallow waters about 500 million years ago. They still live today, but only in water greater than 200 m in depth.

swampy at one time. Woolly mammoths, suited for life in a bitterly cold climate, have left their fossils in New York State. Fossils of tropical plants have been discovered close to the Artic Circle. Fossils of corals, tropical marine animals, occur in almost all regions of the world.

Fossils are used to determine the age of sedimentary rocks. Some fossil species are only present in rocks of a certain age. Thus, the presence of a single species can be used to identify rocks of the same age throughout the world. The trilobite (TRI luh bite), an ancient marine animal, is one of these fossils. Trilobites were most plentiful 500 to 600 million years ago. Thus, any rock layers rich in fossils of certain trilobite species are likely to be between 500 and 600 million years old.

A fossil used to identify specific rock layers is called a guide fossil or **index fossil**. To be an index fossil, an organism must have lived during a brief period of geologic time. It must have traits that make it distinct from other species so it can be easily identified. Also, it must be found in rocks in different parts of the earth.

Index fossils help scientists discover how rocks of different regions are related. For instance, there are trilobite-bearing rocks in the Grand Canyon. These rocks are like trilobite-bearing rocks found in New York State. Although they are more than 3200 km apart, the rocks are of the same age.

Why is a trilobite a guide fossil?

FIGURE 10–10. Trilobite fossils are index fossils because the trilobite lived for only a certain period of time in geologic history.

Roger K. Burnard

10:5 Geologic Time

The history of the earth has been classified into four major divisions called **eras.** These are known as Precambrian (pree KAM bree un) Era, Paleozoic (pay lee uh ZOH ihk) Era, Mesozoic (mez uh ZOH ihk) Era, and Cenozoic (sen uh ZOH ihk) Era (Table 10–1). Each of the eras is further divided into time sections called **periods.**

What are the four major geologic eras?

Table 10–1.
Geologic History and Characteristic Life

Era	Period	Major Life Forms	Age Estimate—Absolute (years before present)
Cenozoic	Quaternary	Modern mammals	
	Tertiary	Mammals dominant Birds	65 million years (to present)
Mesozoic	Cretaceous	Massive extinction of reptiles	135–65 million years
	Jurassic	Reptiles dominant Conifers and cycads	193–135 million years
	Triassic	First mammals	225–193 million years
Paleozoic	Permian	Great extinction of marine invertebrates	280–225 million years
	Carboniferous	First reptiles Lycopod trees Amphibians dominant	345–280 million years
	Devonian	First amphibians Age of fish	395–345 million years
	Silurian	First land plants Age of corals	435–395 million years
	Ordovician	First vertebrates	500–435 million years
	Cambrian	Invertebrates dominant (trilobites, brachiopods)	570–500 million years
Precambrian	(Not divisible into eras or periods)	Primitive plants Sponge spicules Bacterialike microscopic forms and algae	4.5 billion or more years to 570 million years

---

How do geologists divide time into eras and periods? The rocks of each era have been found to contain certain kinds of plant and animal fossils. These fossils are very different from those found in other eras. Every era has ended with major changes in landscape and climate throughout most of the world. Major changes in plants and animals also took place. Some species completely disappeared, while new species developed. Thus, the fossils in the rocks of each time period differ. Rocks from each time period contain fossils of organisms that were dominant at that time in the history of the earth.

How do the rocks of the various geologic periods differ?

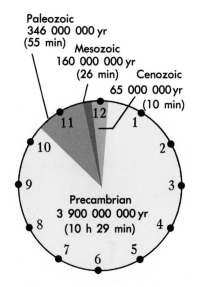

FIGURE 10–11.

MAKING SURE

2. The clock in Figure 10–11 represents 4 500 000 000 years of geologic time. Calculate the number of years that represent 1 min on the clock.

3. How are eras and periods different?

10:6 Precambrian Era

Precambrian time began when the earth was first formed over 4.5 billion years ago. It lasted for 4 billion years. This era covers about 85 percent of all geologic time. Rocks from Precambrian time are found on every continent.

When did Precambrian time begin?

Precambrian rocks contain very few fossils. No hard parts of animals or plants have been preserved in these rocks. This lack of fossils is used to tell the difference between Precambrian rocks and more recent rocks. Because details about the Precambrian Era are few, this era is not divided into periods.

Since Precambrian rocks contain very few fossils, does this mean that life was absent on earth during these early years? Probably not. Remains of algae, bacteria, sponges, and the casts of worm burrows have been found. In addition, the presence of marble and graphite serves as evidence for the existence of some living things. Marble is formed from limestone, which may be formed by the deposits of certain living things. Graphite is derived

What observations indicate that life was present on Earth during the Precambrian Era?

from either plant or animal matter. Graphite is a black, crystal form of carbon made by metamorphic forces acting on buried organic matter. Extreme pressures and high temperatures compress the organic material forcing the carbon atoms to rearrange into graphite crystals.

Large mineral deposits are found in some Precambrian rocks. Huge iron ore deposits are found in the Great Lakes region of the United States. Gold, silver, copper, and nickel ores in eastern Canada were formed during Precambrian time. The uranium ores in northwestern Canada are Precambrian deposits. Granite and marble used today in buildings were also formed during Precambrian time.

Name several important mineral deposits discovered in Precambrian rocks.

Paul W. Nesbit

FIGURE 10–12. The great iron ore deposits found in Minnesota were formed during Precambrian time.

10:7 Paleozoic Era

The Paleozoic Era began about 570 million years ago and lasted for 345 million years. At times, shallow seas invaded the land, then receded. Although climates tended to be mild, they varied at times from humid tropical in some regions to desert in others. There were large numbers of plants and animals. Therefore, the sedimentary rocks of the Paleozoic age contain many fossils.

Why do sedimentary rocks of the Paleozoic age contain many fossils?

During the closing stages of the Paleozoic Era, very high mountain ranges were formed, including the Appalachians and the Alps. Glaciers also formed in Australia, Africa, India, and South America.

The Paleozoic Era has been divided into six time periods. Each time period is marked by the appearance of new plant and animal forms.

The *Cambrian* (KAM bree un) *Period* began about 570 million years ago. During the Cambrian Period, large parts of the continents were covered by shallow seas. Great numbers of marine animals without backbones lived in these waters. Fossil traces of trilobites, jellyfish, sponges, brachiopods, snails, and cephalopods have been discovered. All of the plant fossils found in the Cambrian rocks are seaweeds.

Trilobites were the most plentiful forms of sea life. Some were only a fraction of a centimeter long and others were as long as 68 cm. Trilobites had segmented bodies with a tough outer skeleton. They were somewhat like today's lobsters and crayfish.

The *Ordovician* (ord uh VIHSH un) *Period* followed the Cambrian period. In the first part of this period, much of the land was still covered by shallow seas. There was a wider variety of marine life than existed in the Cambrian Period. The first fishlike vertebrates began to appear. Great limestone, oil, and natural gas deposits were formed.

Name a major characteristic of the Cambrian Period.

During which period did fishlike vertebrates begin to form?

FIGURE 10–13. A great number of marine animals flourished in the large shallow oceans of the Cambrian Period.

Sponge
Brachiopod
Snail
Trilobite
Jellyfish

During which period did the first land plants and the first air-breathing land animals appear?

The *Silurian* (suh LOOR ee un) *Period* had much volcanic activity. In some areas, lava and ash were deposited to depths of 1200 to 3000 m. Seas disappeared from parts of the continents. Fossils of the first land plants were found in the Silurian rocks of England and Austria. The first air-breathing land animals, the scorpions, also left fossils in Silurian rocks.

Field Museum of Natural History, Chicago

a

b

FIGURE 10–14. During the Silurian Period, the sea scorpion (a) was common and volcanic activity was widespread (b).

The *Devonian* (dih VOH nee un) *Period* had a wide variety of fish, including the first backboned fish. This period is known as the "Age of Fishes." Land plants growing as tall as 12 m were plentiful. The first amphibians appeared. At least 700 kinds of brachiopods have been found in the rocks of this period. Trilobites, once so plentiful, were slowly becoming extinct. The first fernlike seed-bearing trees appeared.

Which period is known as the "Age of Fishes?"

The *Carboniferous* (kar buh NIHF rus) *Period* followed the Devonian Period. Major coal fields date from the Carboniferous Period. The term Carboniferous refers to these coal deposits.

The coal beds in Carboniferous rocks tell much about the earth during this time. Coal was formed from the carbon in plant matter. Thus, conditions during Carboniferous time must have favored plant growth. The land was low in many parts of the world. The climate was moist and warm. These conditions were ideal for the formation of swamps filled with giant plants. Several thousand species of

What geologic period was most favorable to plant growth?

Field Museum of Natural History, Chicago

FIGURE 10–15. Some dragonflies of the Carboniferous Period had wingspans of 60 cm.

plants that lived at this time have left their fossil traces. Most of the species were ferns and cone-bearing plants.

Coal is formed in the following way. Large deposits of plant matter build up in an area. Much of the vegetation is preserved in the swampy environment. The area slowly sinks down and sea water flows in to cover it. Layers of sand and gravel are deposited at the bottom of the sea. Through millions of years, the sediment layers build upward. Intense heat and pressure change the sediments to rock and the vegetation to coal. Petroleum deposits were also formed during the Carboniferous Period. Petroleum, like coal, is a fossil fuel.

The *Permian* (PUR mee un) *Period* followed the Carboniferous Period. During this period climates became drier and colder. The land began to rise from below the sea. Because of the dry climate, the plants present during the coal ages could not survive. Flowering plants replaced the ferns that had been the main plant life for so long. All trilobites and nearly all the amphibians died out during this period.

MAKING SURE

4. How might fossils be a helpful clue in the search for petroleum?

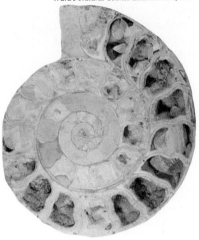

FIGURE 10–16. Ammonites have distinctive markings on their shells and are used as index fossils for the Mesozoic.

Which era is known as the "Age of Reptiles?"

FIGURE 10–17. A large variety of plants and animals existed under the seas during the Mesozoic Era (a). The *Stegosaurus* of Jurassic age was about 6 m long and had two rows of large bony plates along its backbone (b).

10:8 Mesozoic Era

The Mesozoic Era began about 225 million years ago and lasted about 160 million years. Mesozoic means middle-life. Reptiles and other dinosaurs became the main forms of animal life during this era. Thus it is known as the "Age of Reptiles." Flowering plants became the major type of plant life. Ammonites, animals that could float on the sea, were widespread. The Mesozoic era is divided into three time periods.

During the *Triassic* (tri AS ihk) *Period*, the first period of the Mesozoic Era, much of the land was above the sea. Climates were dry. Volcanic activity occurred in many places. Red sandstone and shale, like that of the Painted Desert in Arizona, were formed. Primitive mammals and many types of dinosaurs developed. Some dinosaurs lived on the open plains. Others lived in forests, while many lived in swamps. Some dinosaur species were flesh-eaters while others only ate plants. Dinosaurs varied in size. Most were small and fast and some were huge and slow. The largest was over 24 m in length and weighed over 41 metric tons.

Tropical forests were composed largely of ferns and palmlike plants. In drier, cooler regions, forests were composed of huge conifers.

a

b

The *Jurassic* (joo RAS ihk) *Period* is the middle period of the Mesozoic Era. Landforms in the Jurassic Period were like those of the Triassic. The major life form on land was the dinosaur. Brontosaurus and Stegosaurus were both planteaters.

Archaeopteryx, which was about the size of a pigeon, also lived during this time. This creature had the skin and teeth of a reptile, but the feathers and wings of a bird. Evergreens, tree ferns, and palms were the main plants in the forests.

Widespread rock folding and faulting brought the Jurassic Period to an end. The Sierra Nevada mountains and the Coast Ranges of California were pushed up at this time. Gold ore was formed in the rocks of these mountains. Millions of years later, this gold was mined by the "forty-niners" during the Gold Rush of 1849.

The *Cretaceous* (krih TAY shus) *Period* is the last period of the Mesozoic Era. During this time, the sea extended from the Gulf of Mexico to the Arctic Ocean. Fossils of marine animals are found in the Rocky Mountains. Sediments deposited in the seas were rich in limestone. The famous White Cliffs of Dover, England, were formed at this time. The snail and clam fossils of the Cretaceous Period are like the modern animals. Other rocks of this period contain fossils of trees such as fig, poplar, willow, magnolia, and maple. Grasses, grains, and fruitbearing plants were also present.

Large numbers of *Tyrannosaurus* roamed the area. *Tyrannosaurus* was the largest of all flesheating dinosaurs. This giant beast had a skull over 1 m long and a body over 6 m high. But, like all dinosaurs, its body was too large for its brain. The brain of *Tyrannosaurus* was about the size of a chicken egg. Dinosaurs became extinct during the last 10 to 15 million years of the Cretaceous Period.

MAKING SURE

5. How was the *Archaeopteryx* similar to both birds and reptiles?

FIGURE 10–18. *Archaeopteryx*, the earliest known bird resembled early reptiles.

What three periods make up the Mesozoic Era?

FIGURE 10–19. *Tyrannosaurus*, the largest land-living, flesh-eating dinosaur, lived at the end of the Cretaceous Period.

10:9 Cenozoic Era

The Cenozoic Era is the most recent in time, it began about 65 million years ago and extends into the present time. During the Cenozoic Era, mammals and birds became plentiful. The dinosaurs and ammonites had disappeared.

The *Tertiary* (TUR shee er ee) *Period* found the continents rising. Inland shallow seas did not exist. Fossils show that mammals were the main class of animal life.

Flowering plants, rodents, and the first hoofed animals have left fossil remains in Tertiary rocks. *Eohippus*, an early ancestor of the modern horse, appeared at this time. *Eohippus* was about the size of a small dog. Members of the camel family roamed North America. Mastodons and mammoths, which were similar to the modern elephant, were also present at the end of the Tertiary Period.

How was the major animal life of the Cenozoic Era different from that of the Mesozoic Era?

What two periods make up the Cenozoic Era?

Field Museum of Natural History, Chicago

FIGURE 10–20. *Eohippus,* the four-toed horse, was the size of a collie dog.

The rock movements that began during the Tertiary Period are still occurring. They are responsible for the Coast Range mountains and frequent earthquakes in California. Why are these rock movements occurring?

The *Quaternary* (KWAHT ur ner ee) *Period* includes the present time. It is only a tiny fraction of the earth's history. Suppose all of the geologic history of

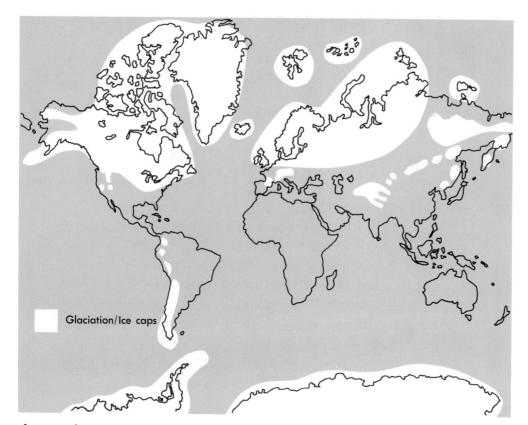

the earth were represented by 1000 days. Quaternary time would cover only about six hours out of the 1000 days.

In the early part of the Quaternary Period, mastodons and woolly mammoths roamed in herds. Flesh-eating mammals such as the saber-toothed tiger were alive. Each of these species became extinct during the ice ages.

Ice ages have occurred several times during the Quaternary Period. Huge glaciers flowed south from the Arctic. The glaciers covered the northern portions of Europe, Asia, and North America. Some sections were over 1.5 km thick. The glaciers scratched and grooved the rock surfaces. They changed valleys and river courses. In many places, large deposits of sand and gravel were left when the glaciers receded. The last glacial ice age was about 10 000 years ago.

FIGURE 10–21. This map shows the maximum extent of glaciation during the Cenozoic.

What effect did glaciers have on the land?

FIGURE 10–22. Receding glaciers left grooves and scratches in rocks.

Sidney White Collection

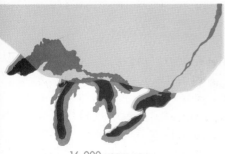
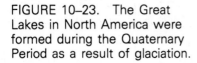
16,000 years ago

14,000 years ago

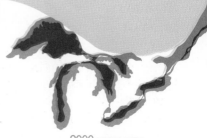
9000 years ago

FIGURE 10–23. The Great Lakes in North America were formed during the Quaternary Period as a result of glaciation.

MAKING SURE

6. What evidence suggests that the Cenozoic Era continues today?
7. Suggest a reason the saber-toothed tiger became extinct during the ice ages.
8. How did the *Eohippus*, the horse's early ancestor, differ from the modern horse?
9. How does the length of Quaternary time compare with the total time of Earth's history?

10:10 Earth's Future

What will the earth be like in the future? Scientists predict future events based upon the earth's history over 4.5 billion years. During these years of geologic time huge mountains were pushed up and worn down many times. Huge rock beds were bent, folded, and crushed. Seacoasts rose and fell as shallow seas invaded the continents. Volcanic explosions and earthquakes occurred in all parts of the world. Glaciers moved down from the north and froze areas that had been warm. The glaciers extended south far enough to cover parts of what are now the states of Missouri, Illinois, Indiana, Ohio, and Pennsylvania. Times, when much of the earth was covered with ice, are called the ice ages.

Today's world differs from past geologic ages. In the future the earth's surface may be very different than it is today. Most scientists believe the ice ages of the past will return again, but they disagree on when. Perhaps the next ice age will be here in a few thousand years or in a few hundred years. There is no certain answer.

If history repeats on schedule a new ice age should now be approaching. Yet, the impact of people on the earth's climates must be considered. Great amounts of fossil fuels are being burned, which warm our planet. Carbon dioxide produced by burning goes into the atmosphere and acts as a blanket that prevents heat loss. Another view is that the earth may actually be warming. If so, and the warming continues, the ice caps will start melting and raise sea levels around the world. Many seacoast cities and towns will be flooded.

How may the earth be different in the future?

Tides on the earth produced by the sun and moon are causing the earth to spin more slowly. It is predicted that in five million years from now, a day will be 36 hours long. Daytime hours may be much hotter and nighttime hours may be much cooler.

Will the earth last forever? Certainly not in its present form. The sun, around which the earth moves, is a star just like most other stars in the universe. Observations of stars similar to our sun reveal that stars burn out when they get old. Before the end, our sun will become many times larger than it is now. Temperatures on the earth will be hot enough to boil away the oceans as steam. Eventually, the sun will cool and shrink down to a size smaller than the earth. Do not worry! This event is predicted to take place in about 5 billion years.

MAKING SURE

10. Give three examples that show the earth is still changing.
11. How can the burning of fossil fuels cause changes on the earth?
12. List five cities that would be affected if the ice caps melted.
13. How does the sun and moon affect the earth's time of rotation?

Perspectives
frontiers

The Search for a New Beginning

A star explodes! The explosion is part of a theory about the origin of the earth. What does Earth's origin have in common with an exploding star? To find out, we have to know the age of the earth. Finding the age of the earth requires radioactive dating.

To make the measurements for radioactive dating, a mass spectrometer is used. This device identifies isotopes by their mass. By comparing the amount of different isotopes in a rock, its age can be found. Most mass spectrometers cannot give an exact number of atoms in a sample. Using them, only a general age of Earth rocks can be found.

The Earth's surface is constantly changing. Water may dissolve and separate the isotopes. New rock may bury old rock. Because of the changes, scientists have found it difficult to determine a definite age. They needed a surface that did not weather and change as the earth does. The moon has such a surface and may be the same age as Earth.

In 1969, Apollo 11 returned to Earth with moon rocks. To date the rocks, scientists at the California Institute of Technology had designed a new mass spectrometer. Using it, the moon rocks were found to be 4.45 billion years old.

In 1974, the method used to date moon rocks was used to date the earth. A large rock from Greenland was dated. From the rock, scientists found that the earth is the same age as the moon—4.45 billion years old.

Now the scientists are dating meteorites and dust from space. A meteorite is a piece of rock that crashes into Earth from space. Some of the meteorites are 4.6 billion years old. Scientists think this information will provide clues to the origin of Earth.

Using the information found with the mass spectrometer, some scientists have suggested the following theory. About 4.6 billion years ago a large star exploded. Forces from the explosion pushed the dust and gas in space together. Within a few million years, the planets and sun formed from the dust and gas. As the material came together, its temperature rose. Earth itself was liquid. The crust formed as the earth cooled. Earth solidified about 4.45 billion years ago.

Scientists do not always agree. As a result, the exploding star is not the only theory of Earth's origin. However, it is one possible explanation.

main ideas

1. Geologic forces of today are believed to be the same as those of the past.   10:1
2. Geologic forces that shape the earth have not always operated at the same rate.   10:1
3. A lower bed in a series of horizontal rock layers is older than a higher bed.   10:2
4. The age of some rocks may be found by radioactive dating.   10:2
5. Fossils reveal that many living creatures of the past are no longer alive today.   10:4
6. The geologic history of the earth has been classified into four major divisions called eras. Eras are subdivided into periods.   10:5
7. Geologic revolutions which separate eras are marked by widespread changes in plants, animals, landscape, and climate.   10:6, 10:7, 10:8, 10:9
8. Today's earth is different from what it was in the past. Based on its geologic history the earth will continue to change in the future.   10:10

vocabulary

Define each of the following words or terms.

era   law of uniform change   radioactive dating
fossil   paleontology   trilobite
index fossil   period   unconformity

study questions

DO NOT WRITE IN THIS BOOK.

A. True or False

Determine whether each of the following sentences is true or false. If the sentence is false, rewrite it to make it true.

1. The Grand Canyon is formed mostly from sedimentary rocks.
2. The lowest bed in an undisturbed series of rock layers is the oldest.
3. The speed of running water affects the rate at which it wears away rock.

4. The Grand Canyon is being uplifted.
5. Geologic forces of the past were different from those of today.
6. Radioactive dating is based on the use of radio waves.
7. Mammals appeared on the earth less than 1 million years ago.
8. Fossils of sea-living animals have been discovered in rocks hundreds of kilometers from the sea.
9. Petrified wood is a fossil.
10. Trilobites are plentiful and widespread today.

B. Multiple Choice

Choose the word or phrase that completes correctly each of the following sentences.

1. *(Petrified, Index, Old, Radioactive)* fossils are used to identify the geologic period of a rock layer.
2. Rocks of different time periods contain *(the same, different, closely related)* fossils.
3. A fossil is most likely to be formed in a *(desert, field, glacier, shallow sea)*.
4. The geologic history of the earth is classified into *(2, 3, 4, 5)* major divisions called eras.
5. The era in which we now live is *(Precambrian, Paleozoic, Cenozoic)*.
6. The geologic time scale covers about *(1, 2.5, 3.4, 4.5)* billion years.
7. Precambrian rocks contain *(many, few, reptile, mammal)* fossils.
8. Paleozoic rocks contain *(many, few, reptile, mammal)* fossils.
9. Backboned animal fossils first appeared in the *(Cambrian, Ordovician, Silurian, Devonian)* Period.
10. The *(Cambrian, Ordovician, Silurian, Devonian)* Period is known as the "Age of Fishes."

C. Completion

Complete each of the following sentences with a word or phrase that will make the sentence correct.

1. Huge coal deposits were formed during the _____ period.
2. Coal is formed from _____.

3. The _____ Era was the age of reptiles.
4. Fossils of *Archaeopteryx* first appear in the _____ Period.
5. During the _____ Period, the Sierra Nevada Mountains of California were uplifted.
6. The last ice age was about _____ years ago.
7. During the ice ages, _____ scratched rocks and changed the courses of rivers.
8. We are living in the _____ Era.
9. If the total geologic record covered 1000 days, the Quaternary Period would cover about _____.
10. During the Tertiary Period, _____ were the main class of animal life.

D. How and Why
1. Why is the Grand Canyon a good place to study geologic history?
2. How is the age of a rock formation determined?
3. How do fossils aid in discovering events of the past?
4. How is the geologic time scale divided into eras and periods?
5. Why is little known about the events of Precambrian time?

investigations

1. Make a scale model of the Grand Canyon.
2. Make a fossil collection by searching and collecting them in your home area. Identify your fossils and use them to learn about the geologic history of your area.
3. Do library research on the geologic history of your area. Prepare a report for your class.

interesting reading

Fodor, R. V., *Frozen Earth: Explaining the Ice Ages.* Hillsdale, NJ: Enslow, 1981.
Lambert, Mark, *Fossils.* NY: Arco, 1979.
Motz, Lloyd, "Earth: Final Chapters." *Science Digest.* August 1981, pp. 76-85.

A person in this glider would observe high, towering cumulus clouds. You can also observe other parts of the atmosphere while on the ground. Weather is the result of changes in the atmosphere. How do jet streams affect weather and travel? By studying clouds, how can you predict weather?

National Center for Atmospheric Research

The Atmosphere

11:1 Air

You live at the bottom of an ocean of air that surrounds the earth. Breathing, cooking, flying, and sailing, are just a few of the activities that depend upon air. Without air it is likely there would be no life at all on Earth.

Air is a mixture of gases, fine dust particles, and water vapor. It occupies space and has mass. About 78 percent of air is nitrogen. About 21 percent is oxygen. The other 1 percent is composed of argon, carbon dioxide, and tiny amounts of other gases (Table 11-1).

Nitrogen does not combine readily with other substances. Nitrogen dilutes the oxygen in air. This fact is important because oxygen enters readily into chemical reactions such as rusting and burning. If oxygen were not diluted by nitrogen, these chemical reactions would occur at a very rapid rate. For example, a forest fire burning in pure oxygen would be difficult to put out.

GOAL: You will learn the major features of the atmosphere and how winds, clouds, and precipitation are formed.

What is the composition of air?

Table 11-1.	
Composition of Air	
Gas	**Percent by volume**
Nitrogen	78.08
Oxygen	20.95
Argon	0.93
Carbon dioxide	0.03
Water vapor	0 to 4.0
Neon	trace
Helium	trace
Methane	trace
Krypton	trace
Xenon	trace
Hydrogen	trace
Ozone	trace

11:2 Parts of the Atmosphere

What is the atmosphere?

The air that surrounds the earth is called the **atmosphere** and extends about 900 km above the earth's surface. The atmosphere can be divided into five regions or layers. The layers vary in depth and blend into each other.

You live in the **troposphere** (TROHP uh sfihr). This is the first layer and extends from the ground to an average height of 11 km above the earth. The exact

FIGURE 11-1. Data about the atmosphere such as temperature and wind may be obtained through the use of balloons.

height depends on the season of the year and the latitude. Temperatures in the troposphere drop about 6.5 C° for each kilometer of increase in altitude. Almost all weather activity occurs in this layer.

The **stratosphere** (STRAT uh sfihr) lies above the troposphere. It extends from about 11 km to 50 km above the earth. In the lower part of the stratosphere, the temperature does not change with height. But, in the upper part, the temperature increases with height. At 50 km, the temperature is about 7°C. Air in the stratosphere is dry and thin, and there are very few clouds.

Radiation from the sun changes oxygen into ozone. Ozone absorbs harmful ultraviolet rays. When absorbed by ozone, ultraviolet radiation changes to heat and warms the upper stratosphere.

The **mesosphere** (MEZ uh sfir) is above the stratosphere. It extends from about 50 km to 80 km. Here the temperature decreases with height. At the top of the mesosphere, the temperature falls to about −100°C. This region is the coldest part of the atmosphere.

The **thermosphere** (THUR muh sfir) extends from 80 km to about 600 km above the earth. In the thermosphere, temperature increases rapidly with height and may reach 700°C.

The **exosphere** (EK so sfihr) is the layer of the atmosphere farthest from the earth. It begins at an altitude of about 600 km and extends outward. No precise boundary marks the outer edge of the exosphere. It gradually blends into space.

The thermosphere and parts of the mesosphere and exosphere form a region called the ionosphere. This region absorbs a large amount of solar radiation. This radiation can change air particles to ions. These ions in the ionosphere aid radio communication. Some radio waves that enter the ionosphere are reflected back to earth. Reflection of radio waves from the ionosphere enables them to travel great distances across the earth.

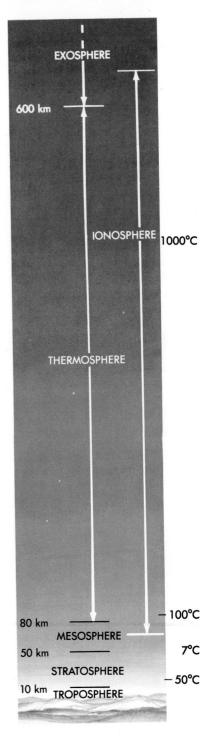

FIGURE 11–2. Each layer of the atmosphere has distinctive properties.

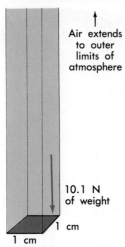

FIGURE 11–3. A force is exerted by the atmosphere on everything within and beneath it.

Air extends to outer limits of atmosphere

10.1 N of weight

1 cm

1 cm

Why is air less dense at higher altitudes?

FIGURE 11–4. The column of mercury is maintained in the glass tube by the force of air exerted on the mercury in the dish.

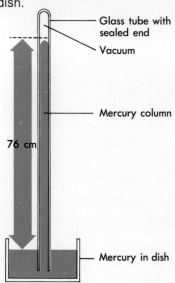

Glass tube with sealed end

Vacuum

Mercury column

76 cm

Mercury in dish

MAKING SURE

1. What temperature would you expect at 9000 m above the earth when ground temperature is 15°C?

11:3 Air Pressure

Air is most dense near the surface of the earth. It becomes less dense at higher altitudes. Why? Gravity is the force that keeps the atmosphere from drifting into space. Gravity is strongest near the earth's surface. Three fourths of the atmosphere is held within 11 km of the earth.

Air exerts pressure in every part of the atmosphere. The average air pressure at sea level is 10.1 N/cm² or 101 kPa. You can understand how this pressure exists if you think of a square centimeter of the earth's surface. Above this surface, a column of air extends from the ground up to the outer limits of the atmosphere. Air in the column exerts a force of 10.1 N on the square centimeter of surface.

The amount of air pressure depends on the altitude. Air pressure is less at high altitudes than at sea level. As altitude increases, the density of air decreases. With decreasing density, air pressure decreases.

Air pressure never stays the same for very long. It may change from hour to hour or day to day. Air pressure is measured with an instrument called a **barometer** (buh RAHM ut ur). There are two types of barometers—mercury and aneroid (AN uh royd). A mercury barometer is a glass tube containing liquid mercury (Figure 11–4). One end of the tube is sealed, and the other is placed in a dish of mercury. The space above the column of mercury is a vacuum.

The height of the mercury in a barometer depends on the force of the air on the mercury in the dish. As the air pressure increases, the mercury rises. As the air pressure decreases, the mercury falls. Average sea level pressure is about 76 cm of mercury.

An aneroid barometer contains a sealed can from which air has been removed. The can contracts or expands with changes in air pressure (Figure 11–5). An increase in air pressure pushes the sides of the can inward. When air pressure decreases, a spring inside the can pushes the sides out. The amount the can contracts or expands is proportional to the air pressure. The can is connected to a needle which travels along a dial and records the movements of the can. From the scale on the dial, the air pressure can be read.

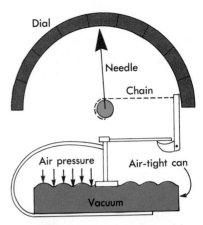

FIGURE 11–5. In an aneroid barometer, the movement of the needle depends on the force of air exerted on the air-tight can.

activity EFFECTS OF AIR PRESSURE

(1) Do this activity next to a sink. Fill an empty plastic milk container to the brim with water. (2) Obtain a 1-hole stopper to fit the opening in the container and a small piece of glass tubing to fit the stopper. You will also need a piece of rubber tubing 1 m in length. (3) Insert the glass tubing in the stopper. **CAUTION:** Moisten the end of the glass tubing with a lubricant such as glycerol. Hold the tubing with a rag or towel as you slide it into the stopper. (4) Attach the rubber tubing to the glass tubing. (5) Fill the rubber tubing with water. Hold a finger over each end so the water does not run out. (6) Insert the rubber stopper tightly into the container keeping the end of the hose high so the water does not leak out. (7) Set the container on a stack of books and lower the hose into the sink. What do you observe? What causes the change in the container? Is the container still full of water after its shape changes?

FIGURE 11–6. Aneroid and mercury barometers.

activity USING A BAROMETER

Record the air pressure reading on a barometer at the same time each day for five days. Also record the general nature of the weather for each day. Note any change in the barometer if a storm approaches. If no stormy weather occurs during the five-day period, note if there is much change in the barometer reading.

2. What keeps the atmosphere from floating off into space?

3. How does the density of air affect air pressure?

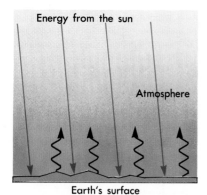

FIGURE 11–7. Energy from the sun is absorbed by the earth's surface. Reradiated energy from the surface is absorbed by the atmosphere, thereby warming the atmosphere.

11:4 Heating the Atmosphere

The sun gives off large amounts of energy each day. This energy from the sun is called radiation. Some of the radiation that travels to the earth is absorbed and scattered by the atmosphere. Most of the radiation, however, is absorbed by the earth's surface. Solar energy that reaches the surface is radiated back into the atmosphere. Carbon dioxide and water vapor in the air absorb the energy thereby warming the atmosphere.

Heating of the atmosphere is not uniform. Solar radiation that strikes the earth directly has a greater warming effect than radiation that strikes at an angle. For example, solar radiation strikes the equator at an angle close to 0°. The earth is warmed the most in this region. At the poles the angle is almost 90° and the warming effect is the lowest. Also, some of the sun's energy is reflected by the snow and ice, further reducing the warming effect at the poles.

When clouds are present during the day, much of the sun's energy does not reach the surface. Clouds block and reflect the energy. Cloud cover during the day reduces the sun's heating effect. On the other hand, clouds at night act as a blanket. Heat from the surface is prevented from escaping into outer space.

What are convection currents?

FIGURE 11–8. Convective currents in the atmosphere are caused by density differences of the air.

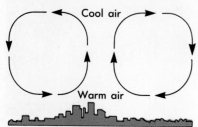

The temperature of the air affects its density. When air is heated, its density decreases. For example, air near the equator is less dense than air at the poles. Warm air rises due to its lower density. Cool air sinks because its density is greater. Upward and downward movements of air are called **convection currents.** Convection currents help to move heat quickly throughout the atmosphere. The difference in density between warm and cool air causes convection currents to form.

activity

MOVEMENT OF WARM AIR

Place a thermometer in an open cardboard box. Set the box in the sun for ten minutes. Record the temperature. Cover the box with clear plastic and repeat the procedure. Compare the two temperatures you recorded. If you remove the plastic at the end of ten minutes, does air move in or out of the box? Explain your observations.

What produces wind?

Define trade winds, westerlies, and polar easterlies.

FIGURE 11–9. The major wind systems of the earth. The curved flow of wind is due to Earth's rotation.

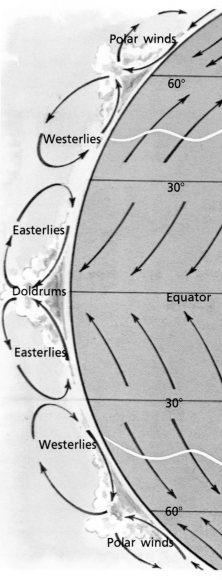

11:5 Winds

Warm air at the equator rises and moves out toward the poles. Cooler surface air flows towards the equator from both north and south to replace the rising air. The air coming from the equator gradually cools and sinks to the earth at the poles. The air then flows back to the equator again. The movement of air is called **wind.**

Rotation of the earth causes the winds blowing between the poles and the equator to break into large circular wind systems. One wind system forms between 30° latitude and the equator. The winds in this system are deflected towards the west because of Earth's rotation. These winds are called the trade winds. Winds flowing towards the poles from about 30° latitude curve to the east. These winds are known as the westerlies because they come from the west. Winds flowing from the poles are deflected to the west. They are called the polar easterlies. If the earth did not rotate, winds would flow north and south. Since the earth is rotating, however, the major wind systems flow from the east or west.

Swift, forceful winds blow from west to east in the upper troposphere. These strong winds are called **jet streams.** Jet stream winds are strong enough to reduce an airplane's speed by 100 km/h or more. Airplanes headed east at high altitudes may be speeded in their flight by jet streams.

Winds within the jet streams vary widely in speed. Some winds travel at about 80 km/h. Others speed

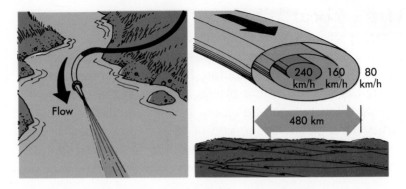

FIGURE 11–10. The jet stream winds are similar to the flow of water from a hose nozzle.

FIGURE 11–10. The jet stream winds are similar to the flow of water from a hose nozzle.

How fast do winds travel in the jet stream?

along at as much as 600 km/h. The swiftest parts of the jet streams are the fastest winds on earth.

During the summer months a jet stream is located 10 to 12 km above the earth. In the winter months, it is about 6 to 9 km above the earth. The latitude of the jet stream also changes during the year. In summer, it is as far north as southern Canada. At other times, it is as far south as the Gulf of Mexico. The weather in North America is often associated with movement of the jet streams.

activity PATH OF A WATER DROP ON A SPINNING GLOBE

Cover the upper half of a globe with a layer of chalk dust. Spin the globe west to east, the way the earth rotates. While it is spinning, use a medicine dropper to place a drop of water near the North Pole. Wait a few seconds, then stop the globe and observe the path made by the water drop. Does the water follow a straight path or an arc? Which way does it curve?

MAKING SURE

4. How might the trade winds affect sailboats headed toward or away from the equator?
5. How does the earth's rotation affect the winds blowing between the equator and the poles?
6. How does the position of jet streams change during the year?

11:6 Local Winds

The United States lies in the general flow of the westerlies. At times, different local winds may break this flow by changing the direction and speed of the winds in an area. Local winds exist in many areas and are created by the presence of mountains or bodies of water.

How are local winds created?

One kind of local wind, called a sea breeze, blows regularly in areas near an ocean or large lake. A sea breeze is caused by the uneven heating of water and land. When the sun shines during the day, the land heats up rapidly. Yet the temperature of the nearby body of water is changed very little. Air above the land is heated and rises. Air over the water flows in to replace the rising air, causing the sea breeze. In the evening if the land cools to a lower temperature than the water, the wind flow reverses. Now a land breeze blows out toward the water.

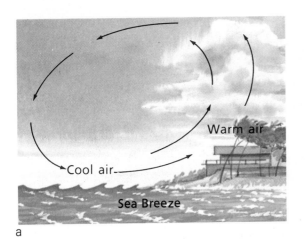

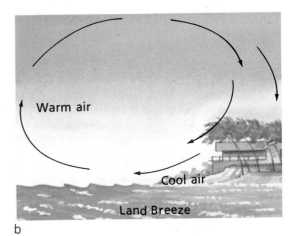

FIGURE 11–11. Sea breezes (a) and land breezes (b) occur because of different rates at which land and water surfaces absorb the sun's energy.

Many types of local winds occur in mountain regions. Valley breezes blow up the mountain slopes during sunny days. Mountain breezes blow down the slopes at night. Local winds near lakes or hilly areas make some places good for growing fruit. The steady breezes keep the air around the fruit trees moving and prevent frosts that might damage the fruit crop.

In some regions, strong downslope winds are common at certain times of the year. These downslope winds may have a warming effect. The warming by the wind is caused by the compression of air. The air is compressed because air pressure is greater at lower elevations. Compressed air increases in temperature because air molecules are forced closer together.

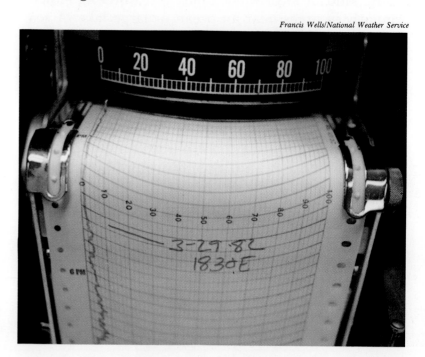

FIGURE 11–12. This equipment is used to record wind speed in knots.

activity WIND DIRECTION

Locate a wind vane near your home or school. Wind vanes are often placed on top of poles or buildings. Keep a record of the wind direction at the same time each day for five days. Does the wind blow in the same direction all the time? Which way does it blow most of the time?

MAKING SURE

7. What causes a sea breeze?
8. How can a downslope wind have a warming effect?

11:7 Moisture in Air

Water is in the atmosphere in three states—solid, liquid, and gas. Water vapor is an invisible gas. Rain, clouds, and fog are all examples of water in the liquid state. Sleet, snow, and hail are solid forms of water.

Water enters the air by evaporation from soil, lakes, oceans, streams, rivers, plants, and animals. Plants release water vapor into the air through their leaves. You breathe out water vapor every time you exhale. Evaporation of sweat from your body also adds water vapor to the air.

When water vapor in the air is cooled to the dew point, it condenses into liquid water. **Dew point** is the temperature at which water vapor first begins to condense.

Define the dew point of air.

The liquid water takes the form of small droplets. These droplets may form clouds or fog. When conditions are right, the droplets join together and fall from the clouds as rain.

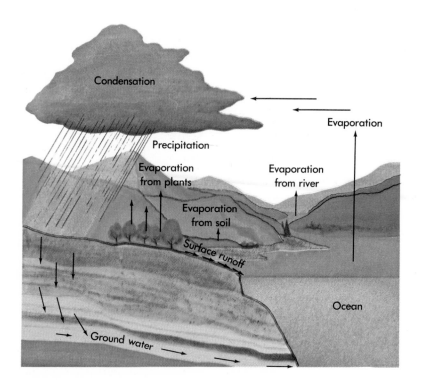

FIGURE 11–13. Evaporation, condensation, and precipitation are three parts of the water cycle.

Humidity is the amount of water vapor in air. Humidity is greatly affected by temperature. At higher temperatures, air can hold more water vapor. Air in tropical regions can hold about ten times as much water vapor as cold arctic air.

Table 11–2.
Water Vapor in Saturated Air

Temperature (°C)	Humidity (g/m³)
−20	0.892
−10	2.154
0	4.835
10	9.330
20	17.118

Define humidity, relative humidity, and hygrometer.

Relative humidity is the percent of water vapor in air based on the amount the air can hold at a given temperature. When air is absolutely dry, the relative humidity is 0 percent. When air is saturated, the relative humidity is 100 percent. Saturated air contains all the moisture it can hold.

Relative humidity is often measured with a hygrometer (hi GRAHM ut ur). One type of hygrometer contains both a dry bulb thermometer and a wet bulb thermometer. The dry bulb temperature is the actual air temperature. The wet bulb temperature depends on the relative humidity.

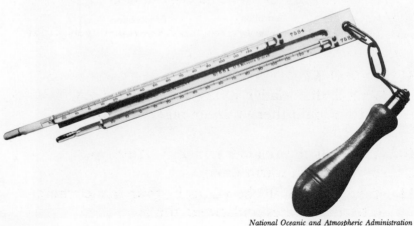

FIGURE 11–14. A sling psychrometer consists of two thermometers on a rotating frame. The difference in temperature between the wet bulb thermometer and the dry bulb thermometer indicates relative humidity.

National Oceanic and Atmospheric Administration

These two temperatures are recorded and used to find the relative humidity on a special chart.

How does a wet bulb thermometer operate? It is moistened by a wick immersed in water. As water evaporates from the wet bulb, the bulb is cooled. The rate at which the water evaporates depends on the relative humidity. The lower the relative humidity, the faster the water evaporates, and the lower the wet bulb temperature.

activity THE DEW POINT OF AIR INSIDE YOUR CLASSROOM

Fill a jar half full of water. Place a thermometer in the water and let the water stand until it reaches room temperature. Add several ice cubes and gently stir the water. Record the temperature at which water first begins to condense on the outside of the jar. This temperature is the dew point of the air in the room. Explain why dew may form on the ground on a cool humid evening.

activity USING A SLING PSYCHROMETER

Obtain a sling psychrometer. With water, saturate the cloth around the bulb of one thermometer. Swing the psychrometer around for a least 1 min. Record the temperature reading for each thermometer. Why are they different? Use Table C–1 in Appendix C to find the relative humidity.

MAKING SURE

9. What is the relative humidity when the dry bulb and wet bulb thermometer readings are the same?
10. How does the relative humidity affect your comfort on a warm day?
11. Make a list of all the places in your home where water evaporates and enters the air.

11:8 Clouds

A cloud is a collection of water droplets or ice particles in the air. It is formed when water vapor is cooled and changed into water droplets or ice crystals. There are three basic cloud forms—cirrus, cumulus, and stratus. Cirrus clouds form at high altitudes and are composed of ice crystals. The ice crystals range in size from 0.2 mm to 0.6 mm. Cirrus clouds are white in color and often have a feathery appearance. They form at altitudes above 6 km and appear during all seasons.

FIGURE 11–15. Cirrus clouds which consist of ice crystals are classified as high clouds (a). Cumulus clouds form as rising columns of air are cooled to the dew point temperature (b).

a

Wayne Scherr/Tom Stack & Assoc.

b

James Westwater

Cumulus clouds are puffy, flat-based clouds, which often look like huge wads of cotton. Cumulus clouds form at low altitudes and are composed of water droplets. The base of a cumulus cloud is found at altitudes below 2 km. The top of the cloud, however, can extend upward to great heights.

FIGURE 11–16. A stratus cloud in contact with the earth's surface is called fog (a). Stratus clouds are layered and have a uniform gray appearance (b).

a

Susan Rhoades

b

Richard Martin

Stratus clouds are flat layers of gray clouds composed of water droplets. Stratus clouds cover large portions of the sky. There are no individual cloud units. Stratus clouds are low clouds, found at altitudes below 2 km.

Certain clouds are combinations of the three basic cloud forms. For example, cirrocumulus clouds are white, puffy clouds found at high altitudes. Nimbus, the Latin word for rain, refers to a cloud associated with rain or snow. Cumulonimbus clouds are the well known "thunderheads" that produce thunderstorms.

Edward Shay

FIGURE 11–17. Thunderstorms produced by cumulonimbus clouds may only affect a small area of the earth's surface.

activity A CLOUD IN A BOTTLE

(1) Obtain one 4-L glass jar and a wooden match.
(2) Hold the jar with the neck down. (3) Light a wooden match and hold it for about 7 s close to the opening of the jar. Smoke from the match should go up into the jar. Blow out the match. (4) Now *exhale* hard into the jar several times to fill it with as much of your breath as possible.
(5) Quickly remove your mouth from the jar to release the pressure. What do you observe? How does water get into the jar? What causes the change in the air inside the jar?

MAKING SURE
12. How do cumulus clouds differ from stratus clouds?

11:9 Precipitation

List forms of precipitation.

If the water droplets in a cloud become too large, the clouds may release precipitation. **Precipitation** is moisture that falls from the atmosphere. Rain is the most common type of precipitation. Raindrops range in diameter from 0.2 mm to 5 mm.

Snow is another form of precipitation. It consists of crystals of clear ice. Snow appears to be white because light is reflected from the crystals. A snowflake often has the shape of a flat, six-sided polygon or star (Figure 11–18b). Often it has a complex and beautiful design.

National Oceanic and Atmospheric Administration

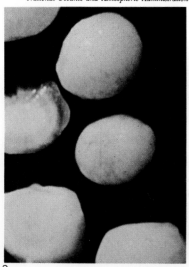

a

U.S. Dept. of Commerce, National Weather Service

b

FIGURE 11–18. Hailstones (a) are produced in cumulonimbus clouds and can be large enough to damage crops, homes, and automobiles. Snowflakes are flat six-sided crystals of ice (b).

Hail consists of hard pellets of ice that fall during a thunderstorm. It forms inside a cloud as water droplets change to ice crystals. The ice crystals grow in size by gathering added layers of ice. When they become too large to be supported by air currents within the cloud, the hail falls to the earth's surface. A lump of hail may be as large as 7.5 cm in diameter. If a hailstone is split open, it reveals a structure of alternate layers of clear and opaque white ice.

Sleet is rain that freezes as it falls through a layer of cold air near the ground. Sleet is commonly mixed with snow or rain.

main ideas

1. You live in the atmosphere, which surrounds the earth.   11:1
2. Air is a mixture of nitrogen, oxygen, carbon dioxide, argon, water vapor, and small amounts of other gases.   11:1
3. Five layers of air make up the atmosphere.   11:2
4. Barometers are used to measure air pressure. Newtons per square centimeter, kilopascals, and centimeters of mercury are units of air pressure.   11:3
5. Winds and convection currents distribute heat through the atmosphere.   11:4, 11:5
6. The winds of highest speed are found in the jet streams.   11:5
7. Local winds are caused by the presence of mountains or bodies of water.   11:6
8. Water is in the air in three forms—solid, liquid, and gas.   11:7
9. Clouds are formed from water droplets or ice crystals.   11:8
10. Clouds may release precipitation such as rain, snow, or hail, which falls to the earth's surface.   11:9

vocabulary

Define each of the following words or terms.

atmosphere   jet stream   stratosphere
barometer   mesosphere   thermosphere
convection current   ozone   troposphere
dew point   precipitation   wind
exosphere   relative humidity

study questions

DO NOT WRITE IN THIS BOOK.

A. True or False

Determine whether each of the following sentences is true or false. If the sentence is false, rewrite it to make it true.

1. Air is a compound.
2. There is a definite boundary at which the atmosphere ends.
3. The density of air decreases with increased altitude.
4. The number of air particles per liter is greater at 3000 m altitude than at sea level.

5. You live in the troposphere.
6. Temperatures within the mesosphere are fairly constant.
7. Rain and snow occur often in the stratosphere.
8. Sea level pressure is about 10 N/cm² or 100 kPa.
9. A mercury barometer measures air pressure in cm of mercury.
10. All clouds are made of water droplets.

B. Multiple Choice

Choose the word or phrase that completes correctly each of the following sentences.

1. About 78% of the air is *(nitrogen, carbon dioxide, water vapor, argon)*.
2. Changing air *(pressure, volume, temperature)* causes a change in the reading of an aneroid barometer.
3. The density of warm air is *(greater than, less than, the same as)* the density of cold air.
4. As altitude increases, the reading on a barometer will *(increase, decrease, remain the same)*.
5. A mercury barometer is used to measure *(air pressure, temperature, humidity)*.
6. *(Cirrus, Cumulus, Stratus)* clouds look like large puffy pieces of cotton.
7. The *(stratosphere, ionosphere, troposphere)* is a region of the atmosphere that contains many electrically-charged particles.
8. *(Rain, Hail, Sleet, Snow)* is a type of precipitation that occurs only during thunderstorms.
9. When air is compressed its temperature *(increases, decreases, remains the same)*.
10. *(Nitrogen, Oxygen, Carbon dioxide, Argon)* is removed from air when iron rusts.

C. Completion

Complete each of the following sentences with a word or phrase that will make the sentence correct.

1. Air travels from _____ pressure regions to _____ pressure regions.
2. A wind which blows from west to east is called a(n) _____ wind.

3. Heat is distributed through the atmosphere by _____ and _____.
4. The _____ of the earth causes winds to be deflected from a straight course.
5. As moist air cools to the dew point, water is formed by a physical change called _____.
6. Rain that freezes as it falls through a layer of cold air is called _____.
7. Relative humidity is measured with a(n) _____.
8. The lower the relative humidity, the _____ the water evaporates on a wet bulb thermometer.
9. During the night a(n) _____ cover will reduce loss of heat from the earth.
10. At the equator warm air is _____.

D. How and Why
1. Why is air pressure lower at high altitudes than at sea level?
2. Explain how winds are produced in the atmosphere.
3. Why is the relative humidity 100% when water vapor in air condenses to form dew?
4. Why does warm air rise?
5. Explain why sleet is sometimes called frozen rain.

investigations

1. Locate the Beaufort wind scale in Appendix C. Use the scale to judge the velocity of winds you observe in your neighborhood.
2. Obtain a cloud atlas from a library and learn to identify clouds in your area.

interesting reading

Comptom, Grant, *What Does a Meteorologist Do?* New York, NY: Dodd, Mead, 1981.
Witty, Margot and Ken, *A Day in the Life of a Meteorologist.* Mahwah, NJ: Troll, 1981.

12

Weather affects many aspects of your everyday life. When you awake in the morning, weather is one of the first things of which you become aware. The clothes you wear and the activities you take part in depend on the weather. What causes weather? What is climate? How are weather and climate related?

Dan McCoy/Rainbow

Weather and Climate

12:1 Observing the Weather

What is the weather outside today? It may be clear or stormy, cold or hot. Weather is the condition of the atmosphere at a certain time and a certain place. Temperature, air pressure, relative humidity, wind speed, and precipitation are some terms used to describe the weather. Another term used to describe weather is cloud cover.

Cloudiness, or cloud cover, is measured by the amount or portion of sky covered by clouds. The scale of cloud cover is divided into tenths. For example five-tenths means that half the sky is covered by clouds. The terms clear, scattered, broken, and overcast are used to describe cloud cover.

The amount of cloud cover affects how far one can see in the sky. For instance, clouds may make it very difficult for an airplane pilot to see other airplanes. If there are too many clouds, air travel may be unsafe for planes without special equipment. Radar may be needed for pilots to find their way through clouds.

The **cloud ceiling** is the altitude at which the cloud cover becomes broken or overcast. A broken sky means that 6/10 to 9/10 of the sky is covered by clouds. An overcast sky is completely covered by clouds. The clouds are scattered if they cover less than 6/10 of the sky.

GOAL: You will learn the factors that affect weather and how weather forecasts are made.

What is weather and what are some terms used to describe it?

activity

OBSERVING THE WEATHER

Objective: To observe and record the weather for one week

Materials

anemometer
barometer
empty can
hygrometer or psychrometer
ruler
thermometer
wind vane

Procedure

1. Make each of the following observations and measurements each day for a week.
2. Record the outdoor temperature in your data table at least twice a day.
3. Use the barometer to observe the air pressure at least twice a day. Record the air pressure.
4. Observe and record the relative humidity at least twice a day. If you are using a psychrometer, the relative humidity may be found in Table C–1 in Appendix C.
5. Determine the percentage of the sky that is covered. Record it in your data table. Note: If the sky is broken or overcast, there is a ceiling.
6. Determine the wind speed and direction at least twice a day. If you do not have an anemometer, a Beaufort Scale, found in Appendix C, is helpful. Record the wind data.
7. Keep a record of the type and amount of precipitation. You can determine the amount of precipitation by collecting it in a container such as an empty can.

Measure the height of water in the container with a ruler. Record the amount once each day.

Observations and Data

Date:

Time		
Temperature		
Pressure		
Relative Humidity		
Clouds		
Wind Speed		
Wind Direction		
Precipitation		

Questions and Conclusions

1. At what times did you record your highest and lowest temperatures? Why?
2. Did you notice a relationship between air pressure and cloud cover? Explain.
3. What was the total amount of precipitation you recorded for the week? How did your amount compare with amounts reported on television or in the local newspaper? Why might there be differences?
4. Did you notice any relationship between the type of precipitation and the type of clouds? Explain.

National Space Technology Laboratories, NOAA

FIGURE 12–1. Floating observing stations are used to obtain weather data over ocean surfaces.

MAKING SURE

1. A local weather station reported the following observations: air pressure—79 cm Hg; wind—from west, 16 km/h; temperature—32°C; sky—clear; relative humidity—14%; precipitation—none.
   (a) Describe the weather at the station on the day these observations were made.
   (b) During what season of the year is weather of this kind most likely to occur?

12:2 Air Masses

An **air mass** is a huge body of air covering a land or ocean area. It may extend from the earth's surface to about 6.5 km above the ground. Temperature and humidity are fairly uniform at any given height in an air mass. But these conditions may be very different in nearby air masses.

An air mass forms as air gathers in one place and develops certain properties. These properties are determined by the surface beneath the air mass and the latitude. An air mass formed over an ocean has a high moisture content. An air mass formed within the Arctic Circle is extremely cold. Temperature and humidity are two major properties of an air mass.

Name two ways in which air masses differ.

Describe the worldwide system of air mass classification.

A worldwide system to classify air masses has been devised. Within this system, air masses are classified according to where they are formed. The small letter c (continental) is used for air masses that are formed over land. The small letter m (maritime) is used for those formed over oceans. Capital letter P (polar) means an air mass is cold because it forms at higher latitudes. Capital letter T (tropical) means an air mass is warm because it forms at lower latitudes. For example, the symbol mT stands for a maritime tropical air mass. This air mass is warm and moist.

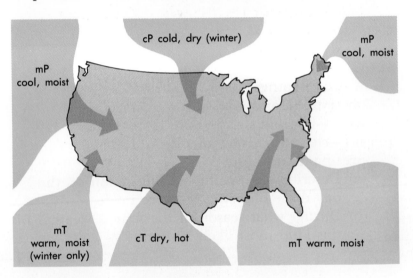

FIGURE 12–2. Air masses that affect the United States.

Air masses tend to move. When air masses move, they pass over land or ocean surfaces. These surfaces may be warm or cold and may change the air masses. A cool air mass passing over a warm land surface becomes warmer. A warm air mass passing over a cold land surface becomes colder. An air mass passing over an ocean or large lake gains moisture.

Why does the temperature of an air mass change?

MAKING SURE

2. Over what type of surface might a dry warm air mass be formed?
3. What symbol would stand for each of the following air masses: continental polar, maritime polar, continental tropical, maritime tropical? Where might each of these air masses form?

12:3 Fronts

Air masses do not mix. Like oil and water, they tend to remain separate. The region where two different air masses come together is called a **front.** A front is the boundary between two air masses. Clouds and precipitation are often associated with fronts.

Fronts move as the air masses move. One air mass usually moves into or invades a region occupied by another as the other air mass moves away. In this way, the front travels across the earth's surface.

When a warm air mass moves against a cold air mass, a **warm front** occurs. Warm air slides forward and above the cold air in a warm front. As the air rises, it cools. Cirrus clouds form about 1000 km ahead of the front. The clouds become lower and thicker as the front continues to move. A large area of snow or rain may fall from nimbostratus clouds and last for several hours. Temperatures often rise when a warm front passes.

FIGURE 12–3. Clouds and precipitation associated with a warm front.

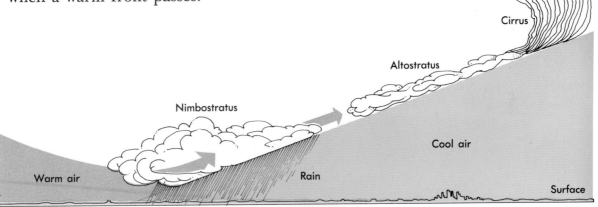

A **cold front** occurs when a cold air mass moves against a warm air mass. Cold fronts move almost twice as fast as warm fronts. As the cold air drives forward, the warm air is forced upward rapidly. Clouds that form along cold fronts are usually cumulus or cumulonimbus. Snowshowers or rainstorms may be severe, but they end quickly. When a cold front passes, temperatures drop and winds shift.

How is a cold front different from a warm front?

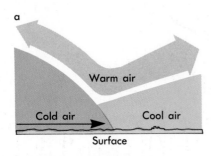

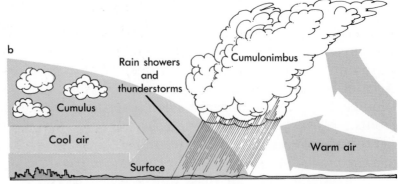

FIGURE 12–4. An occluded front has characteristics of both warm and cold fronts (a). Stormy weather may often accompany cold frontal passage (b).

How is an occluded front produced?

How do thunderstorms occur?

A cold front moves faster than a warm front. Therefore, a cold front may approach and overtake a warm front. When the two fronts meet, an **occluded front** forms. Weather in an occluded front has some of the characteristics of both warm and cold fronts. Periods of light rain or snow may be followed by heavy thunderstorms and snowshowers.

12:4 Thunderstorms

Thunderstorms may occur when warm, moist air rises rapidly through the atmosphere. For example, moist, warm air forced upward along a front or a mountain range may cause a thunderstorm. Thunderstorms also occur on hot summer afternoons. Why? Moist air is heated at the earth's surface. The warm air rises and cools. As it gains altitude, moisture in the air condenses to form cumulus clouds. Swiftly rising air currents within a cumulus cloud, called updrafts, can cause the formation of a cumulonimbus cloud. A cumulonimbus cloud is one that develops vertically into a tall, mountainlike white mass with a thick, dark base. Some cumulonimbus clouds may build as high as 18 km. The updrafts in these clouds may reach speeds of 100 km/h. Water droplets within the cloud join to become larger drops which fall as rain. Pieces of ice can also form in the cloud and fall as hail. When rain falls out of the cloud, it causes downdrafts that eventually stop the upward flow of air. As a result, the thunderstorm dies.

a

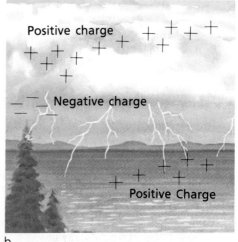

b

FIGURE 12–5. Lightning and strong winds are usually associated with thunderstorms (a). Lightning is caused by a buildup of electrical charges within a cumulonimbus cloud (b).

David M. Dennis

Electric charges build within a cumulonimbus cloud. Some parts of the cloud have a positive charge. Other parts have a negative charge. When the charges become too great, lightning flashes. Most lightning occurs within a cloud or from cloud to cloud. Occasionally, lightning strikes the ground. A bolt of lightning heats the air to high temperatures. The heated air expands rapidly and explodes. The noise from this explosion is called thunder.

What causes lightning?

MAKING SURE

4. How does a cumulonimbus cloud develop?
5. What causes a thunderstorm to "die?"

12:5 Highs and Lows

A **cyclone** is a region of low air pressure. The low pressure is caused by rising air at the center of the cyclone. In a cyclone, winds blow from the higher pressure region outside the cyclone toward the low pressure center. As they blow toward the low pressure region, the winds rotate. In the Northern Hemisphere, the winds rotate in a counterclockwise direction.

Define cyclone.

Cyclones travel. In the Northern Hemisphere they usually move from west to east at a rate of 30 to 60 km/h. Some cyclones may travel half the distance around the earth before they break up.

Cyclones may occur every few days in a certain area. However, most of them are mild and go unnoticed. Bad weather conditions caused by condensation within rising air exist in some cyclones. The weather may range from cloudy skies and drizzle to intense storms with heavy rain or snow.

A high, or **anticyclone,** is a huge area of air in which the pressure is higher than the air around it. Winds blow out from the center of the high. In the Northern Hemisphere, the winds blow in a clockwise direction. Fair weather is generally associated with a high. As with cyclones, highs move from west to east in the Northern Hemisphere.

What kind of weather exists in cyclones?

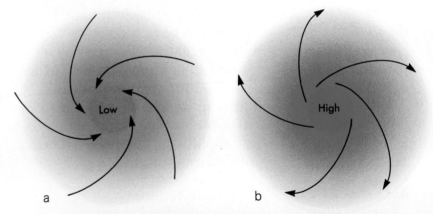

FIGURE 12–6. In the Northern Hemisphere, winds spiral counterclockwise into the center of a cyclone (a). Winds spiral in a clockwise direction as they flow from the high-pressure center of an anticyclone (b).

A **hurricane** is a stormy tropical cyclone. Hurricanes form in the trade winds, over regions of warm ocean water. In such regions a large low pressure area is created when warm, moist air rises. In the Northern Hemisphere, winds blow counterclockwise into the low pressure area. Wind speeds may be as high as 250 km/h. Huge amounts of water are released in heavy rainfall. The low-pressure center of the hurricane, called the eye, is the quiet part of the storm. Wind velocity in the eye is lower and there is much less rainfall. The sun may be shining and there may be little cloud cover in the eye.

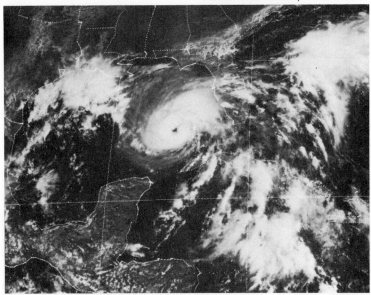

National Oceanic and Atmospheric Administration

FIGURE 12–7. A satellite photograph of hurricane Frederick in the Gulf of Mexico. Notice the absence of clouds within the eye.

A hurricane may travel hundreds of kilometers or it may remain in one area for several days. Many hurricanes form in the Gulf of Mexico and the Caribbean during the late summer and early fall. Sometimes these hurricanes travel up the east coast of the United States. A hurricane in the Pacific Ocean is called a typhoon.

A **tornado** is a special kind of cyclone. It is a whirling wind circling around a low pressure center about 60 m in diameter. A tornado is a funnel-shaped cloud and is associated with very strong thunderstorms. It extends from the base of a cumulonimbus cloud to the ground.

How do tornadoes form? This question has not yet been answered completely. One theory states that tornadoes develop from large thunderstorms that form along fast moving cold fronts. When warm and cold air meet along the front, the warm air is forced to rise rapidly in a spiral pattern. A sudden drop in pressure occurs in the center of the spiral. Violent winds begin to blow around and into the spiral producing the funnel shape of the tornado. Most tornadoes in the United States move at an average speed of 55 km/h and last 1 or 2 min. A tornado usually follows a path that is about 0.2 km wide and 1.5 km long.

Wind speeds within a tornado may reach 450 km/h. Extensive damage to houses and buildings can result when a tornado touches the ground. Strong winds can rip roofs from houses and hurl automobiles many meters into the air. It is wise to seek shelter from flying objects such as broken glass and wooden boards when a tornado is approaching. A cellar is a good place to be. If there is no cellar, you may gain protection in a closet or under a table or desk.

Joseph M. Golden

a

Gene Moore

b

FIGURE 12–8. Tornadoes over bodies of water are called waterspouts (a). Tornadoes are associated with intense thunderstorms (b).

Although tornadoes appear in many parts of the world, the greatest number occur in the United States. Tornadoes are often found in the Great Plains region and the Mississippi Valley from early spring until late summer. About 700 tornadoes are reported each year in the United States.

MAKING SURE

6. Why is a gigantic amount of energy needed to create a hurricane? What is the source of this energy?

7. For a tornado and a hurricane, compare size, movement, total energy, and force.

12:6 Weather Maps

The National Weather Service has a network of weather stations throughout the United States. At certain times every day, each station reports the local weather conditions to the National Weather Service. This information is then plotted on national weather maps. Weather maps are important in **meteorology** (meet ee uh RAHL uh jee), the scientific study of weather.

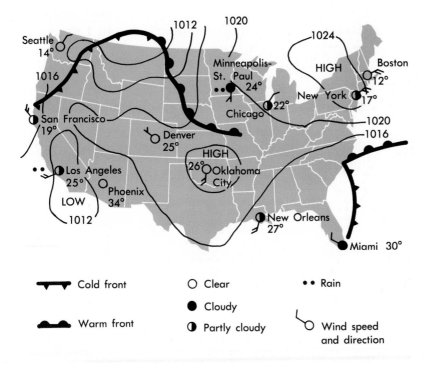

Cold front | ○ Clear | •• Rain
Warm front | ● Cloudy
| ◑ Partly cloudy | Wind speed and direction

FIGURE 12–9. Temperature, wind direction, pressure, and cloud cover are shown on a weather map.

Why is a weather map important in meteorology?

A weather map is used to organize and display weather information. These maps show temperature, dew point, and amount of precipitation. They also show the location of major fronts and regions of high and low air pressure. The locations and movements of highs and lows are used by forecasters to predict weather. Highs and lows are indicated by isobars. An **isobar** is a line on a weather map that connects points having the same air pressure. The pressure is recorded in millibars. One thousand millibars is about average sea level pressure.

LOCATING FRONTS ON A WEATHER MAP

Cut out the weather map in a newspaper and tape it to a page in your notebook. Locate the fronts shown on the map. What weather information is recorded for the largest city in your state? What is the forecast for your area?

MAKING SURE

8. Locate a front in Figure 12–9. Find two weather stations on opposite sides of the front. Compare the temperature at these stations. Are they alike or different?
9. Find a low pressure area and a high pressure area on the map in Figure 12–9. What is the weather in each of these areas?
10. Locate an isobar on the weather map and find the pressure in millibars.
11. On the weather map, what kind of front is near Miami, Florida?

12:7 Weather Forecasting

A weather forecast is a prediction of the weather for some time in the future. As you know, weather forecasts are sometimes wrong. Forecasts are based on chance or probability rather than absolute certainty. For this reason, the forecasts specify percentages, such as "there is an 80 percent chance of rain tomorrow."

How is it possible to predict the weather? It is well known that weather travels from place to place. Generally, storms, fronts, and pressure systems move from west to east across the United States. Using weather maps and photographs made with weather satellites, forecasters keep track of these movements. For example, a forecaster observes an approaching snowstorm moving to the east at a rate of 10 km/h. The forecaster can use this speed to predict the arrival of the storm.

How is the movement of a storm forecasted?

a

b

Observing changes in temperature, humidity, and air pressure is important in forecasting. Hot summer days with high humidity may indicate thunderstorms in the afternoon. A steady or sudden drop in the air pressure may indicate that a cyclone with bad weather is approaching. Also, the kinds of clouds give clues to the coming weather. Distant clouds may show an approaching front. Clouds moving out of an area at the same time the barometer is rising indicates fair weather.

FIGURE 12–10. Forecasters at many National Weather Service offices use computers to help analyze weather maps and other weather information (a). Satellites provide valuable information about locations and movements of weather systems (b).

activity   WEATHER FORECASTING

Tune in an evening television weather forecast. Write down the forecast accurately. In addition, write down the facts or reasons the weather forecaster gives for the prediction. Observe the weather the next day. Was the weather forecast correct? If it was incorrect, what factors might account for the errors?

MAKING SURE

12. What methods do forecasters use to predict the weather?

12:8 Climate

How is climate related to weather?

Weather changes day by day. **Climate** is the average weather for a region over a period of years. Average temperature per year and average precipitation per year are two important aspects of climate.

The climate of a region is determined mainly by latitude. It is also affected by height above sea level, local winds, and the location of mountains, oceans, and large lakes.

What are the three types of climate and where are they found?

Three general types of climate are temperate, tropical, and polar. Temperate climates are found between 66½° and 23½° latitude in both the Northern and Southern Hemispheres. Tropical climates are found from 23½° north latitude to 23½° south latitude. Polar climates are in the frigid zones above 66½° latitude around the poles. Within these major zones, climates may be modified by mountains or bodies of water. For example, marine climates occur along the seacoasts where moisture is high. The interior of continents have continental climates where there are hot summers and cold winters. The middle west of the United States has a continental climate.

Temperate climates are generally warmer than polar regions and cooler than tropical regions. The length of the growing season makes temperate

FIGURE 12–11. Cold temperatures in some polar climates allow snow and ice to accumulate many meters in depth.

James Westwater

a
b

regions ideal for agriculture where there is fertile soil and adequate rainfall. Rainy tropical areas are hot throughout the year with heavy rainfall. Some tropical areas have a dry season and a rainy season, when most of the rain falls. Deserts are present where little rain falls in both temperate and tropical regions.

Climates can cover vast ranges of land and water or just a small area. The climate in a valley surrounded by mountains and the climate in a city are examples of microclimates. A **microclimate** is a climate in a small area. For instance, it may be warmer and dryer in a valley than in surrounding mountains. Cities are often a few degrees warmer than nearby country areas. The blacktop streets and rooftops in a city absorb more of the sun's radiation than open fields absorb. Also, there is a warming effect caused by heated buildings. Microclimates are created inside houses by heating in winter and air conditioning in summer.

FIGURE 12–12. Rainfall in some moist tropical climates may exceed 1000 cm per year (a). Most temperate climates are characterized by a change in seasons (b).

MAKING SURE

13. Jet airliners fly at altitudes where the air is thin and very cold. What kind of microclimate is created inside the airliner?

14. What kind of microclimate is created inside a terrarium?

Perspectives

frontiers

Warning: Severe Weather

Imagine you are camping at Lake McBride in Scott County. The music on your radio is suddenly interrupted: "We interrupt this program to bring you a special weather bulletin. The National Weather Service has issued a tornado warning for Scott County until 3:00 P.M. . . . . Should threatening weather approach, seek shelter immediately."

How does the weather service know severe weather threatens an area? Weather radar is their best source of information. A signal emitted from the radar antenna strikes a storm cloud. Part of the signal reflects back to the antenna. Only those clouds that contain precipitation reflect the signal. The reflected signal, called an echo, is analyzed and displayed on a screen. Radar screens look like television screens. The display shows the position of the storm.

On the display, the echoes are color coded to show the strength of the storm. For example, a red echo might indicate a severe thunderstorm. Severe thunderstorms have winds faster than 90 km/h, large hail, and frequent lightning. Some severe storms produce tornadoes. By watching the movement of echoes, a severe storm's path may be predicted. The prediction allows a half hour warning of a severe storm's approach.

Radar, however, cannot predict which severe storms will produce tornadoes. Thus, tornado warnings cannot be issued until a tornado forms. People can be given only two or three minutes warning before a tornado strikes.

To give faster and better warnings of severe storms and tornadoes, scientists are developing a new radar system. The system is called NEXRAD. NEXRAD is a Doppler radar system.

Present weather radar shows position and strength of a storm. Doppler radar shows wind speed and direction in relation to the radar antenna. Using Doppler radar, forecasters can find the circular wind pattern within a storm cloud that indicates a forming tornado.

Echoes are also color coded in Doppler radar. An echo change from blue to red means wind speeds away from the antenna are increasing. A change from blue to yellow means wind speeds are increasing toward the antenna. An area with red and yellow next to each other means winds are rapidly rotating within a storm. Spotting a possible tornado with Doppler radar allows an average warning time of 25 minutes. Once NEXRAD is in use, the extra warning time will save more lives and reduce property damage.

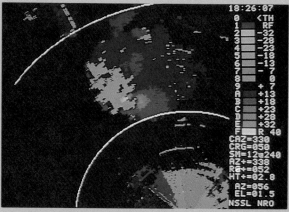

National Severe Storms Laboratory, NOAA

main ideas

1. Air pressure, temperature, relative humidity, wind direction and speed, cloud cover, and precipitation are major elements of weather.   12:1
2. An air mass is a large body of air in which temperature and humidity are fairly uniform throughout each level.   12:2
3. A front is the boundary, or meeting place, of two air masses.   12:3
4. Thunderstorms may occur when warm, moist air rises rapidly through the atmosphere.   12:4
5. A cyclone is a low pressure region around which winds rotate.   12:5
6. Hurricanes and tornadoes are examples of intense cyclones.   12:5
7. Weather maps showing the location of fronts, highs and lows, temperatures, and relative humidity are used in predicting weather.   12:6, 12:7
8. Latitude, mountains, oceans, large lakes, and winds are factors that affect climate.   12:8

vocabulary

Define each of the following words or terms.

air mass	cyclone	occluded front
anticyclone	hurricane	tornado
climate	isobar	warm front
cloud ceiling	meteorology	weather
cold front	microclimate	

study questions

DO NOT WRITE IN THIS BOOK.

A. True or False

Determine whether each of the following sentences is true or false. If the sentence is false, rewrite it to make it true.

1. Weather is the condition of the atmosphere at a particular time.
2. Weather maps are used to forecast weather.
3. Fair weather is usually found in low pressure areas.

4. A rising barometer reading often means fair weather.
5. There is little difference in the weather on opposite sides of a front.
6. Air masses travel from east to west across the United States.
7. An air mass over an ocean gains moisture.
8. Precipitation often occurs along fronts.
9. Clouds are never found along fronts.
10. An occluded front occurs when warm and cold fronts meet.

B. Multiple Choice

Choose the word or phrase that completes correctly each of the following sentences.

1. A dry, warm air mass is most likely to form over *(the Arctic, a desert, an ocean, a seacoast)*.
2. A maritime polar air mass is represented by the symbols *(cT, mT, cP, mP)*.
3. Warm fronts travel *(more rapidly than, less rapidly than, at the same speed as)* cold fronts.
4. Overcast refers to a cloud cover of *(less than 1/10, 5/10, 7/10, more than 9/10)*.
5. *(Temperate, Tropical, Polar)* climates are usually found between 23½° north latitude and 23½° south latitude.
6. A(n) *(cold, warm, occluded)* front forms when warm air moves against cold air.
7. Hurricanes are areas of *(low, high, equal)* pressure.
8. *(Hail, Rain, Lightning)* results when electric charges build inside cumulonimbus clouds.
9. A thunderstorm is associated with *(cirrus, cumulonimbus, stratus)* clouds.
10. Winds blow clockwise around a *(low, high, cold front)* in the Northern Hemisphere.

C. Completion

Complete each of the following sentences with a word or phrase that will make the sentence correct.

1. In the Northern Hemisphere, cyclones normally move in a(n) _____ direction.
2. A(n) _____ front occurs where a warm air mass moves forward to take the place of a cold air mass.

3. _____ is the noise that is produced when air heated by lightning explodes.

4. When clouds cover 8/10 of the sky, the sky is _____.

5. A tornado extends from the base of a(n) _____ cloud to the ground.

6. Changes in temperature, humidity, and air pressure are important when _____ weather.

7. _____ is the average weather for a region over many years.

8. A(n) _____ is a miniature climate.

9. Tropical climates occur between 23½° south and _____ latitude.

10. The altitude at which cloud cover becomes broken or overcast is the _____.

D. How and Why

1. How is weather different from climate?

2. What is a weather map? How is it used?

3. What weather information is collected at a weather station?

4. Using the information in this chapter, explain how you would go about forecasting tomorrow's weather.

5. Why are tornadoes associated with cold fronts?

investigations

1. You can become a weather observer. Instructions are supplied in _Weather Forecasting_ and _Instructions for Climatological Observers_, obtained at nominal cost from the Superintendent of Documents, Washington, D.C.

2. Build a weather station on your school grounds or in another suitable place.

interesting reading

Bosen, Victor, _Doing Something About the Weather._ New York, NY: Putnam's, 1975.

Brown, Billye and Walter R., _Historical Catastrophes: Hurricanes and Tornadoes._ Reading, MA: Addison-Wesley, 1972.

Moyer, Robin, "The Great Wind." _Science 80._ November 1980, pp. 60–65.

chapter

13

Many ocean studies take place below the surface. A deep-sea diver must wear a heavy diving suit in order to withstand the pressures at great depths in the ocean. While a diver is beneath the ocean's surface, there are opportunities for observation and study. What forms of life are present in the ocean? What causes currents? What resources are found within the ocean?

Steve Lissau

Oceanography

13:1 Seawater

Almost three fourths of the earth's surface is covered by seawater. The oceans are a source of both food and recreation. In the future, they may also be an important source of energy, minerals, and fresh water. Scientists have much to learn about oceans. Many of the facts in this scientific field are yet to be discovered.

Oceanography is the scientific study of the oceans. Oceanographers study the composition of seawater and trace the path of ocean currents. Also, they study marine plant and animal life. Almost everything connected with the oceans, including their history, is of interest to oceanographers.

One important property of seawater is its composition. Seawater contains dissolved compounds known as salts. It also contains organic matter and nitrogen, oxygen, and carbon dioxide gas. More than half the known chemical elements are found in seawater.

Salts are carried into the oceans by rainwater draining from the continents. When water drains from soil it dissolves sodium chloride and other salts. Weathering and erosion dissolve mineral salts present in rocks. These dissolved salts are transported to the oceans by rivers.

GOAL: You will learn the major features of the oceans, sea life, ocean currents, and tides.

Define oceanography.

How are mineral salts added to seawater?

FIGURE 13–1. Seawater at different depths is collected using sampling bottles.

What is the most plentiful element in seawater?

Seawater is rich in five salts (Table 13–1). These salts contain the following elements: sodium, magnesium, calcium, potassium, chlorine, sulfur, and oxygen. Chlorine is the most plentiful element in seawater. About 55 percent of the total mass of all matter dissolved in seawater is chlorine. Sodium accounts for about 31 percent of the dissolved matter. The proportions of the elements dissolved in seawater are fairly constant throughout the oceans.

Table 13–1.
Substances Dissolved in Seawater

Salt	Chemical formula	Average composition (g salt/1000 g water)
Sodium chloride	$NaCl$	23
Magnesium chloride	$MgCl_2$	5
Sodium sulfate	Na_2SO_4	4
Calcium chloride	$CaCl_2$	1
Potassium chloride	KCl	0.7
With other minor substances to total		34.7

The total amount of dissolved salts in a sample of seawater varies from place to place. Some parts of the oceans are saltier than others. **Salinity** (say LIHN ut ee) is a measure of this saltiness. It is the amount of dissolved salts in a given mass of water.

Define salinity.

Salinity of most ocean water ranges between 3.3 and 3.7 percent. In some regions, the salinity can be higher. In the waters of the Dead Sea, the salinity is 23 percent or more. The salinity is so high because only a small amount of fresh water flows into the Dead Sea. Also, the evaporation rate of water is very high. Thus, the amount of dissolved salts has built up. The Dead Sea has no fish and little plant life.

What is the average ocean salinity?

Brian Brake/Photo Researchers, Inc.

FIGURE 13–2. When the water of the Dead Sea evaporates, large quantities of salt are deposited.

Salinity in the deep ocean tends to be constant. It does not change much from day to day. However, the salinity of seawater near the coast may vary during the day. The mixing of fresh river water with seawater causes the salinity to change slightly. Marine animals living in the deep ocean can stand only small changes in salinity. Most sea creatures living in coastal regions can stand a wide range of salinity. Oysters living in coastal areas are one kind of marine animal exposed to daily changes in salinity.

How does salinity affect life in seawater?

Make a solution similar to the average composition of seawater by dissolving salt compounds in 1000 g (one liter) of fresh water. Measure and dissolve the given amount of each compound as listed in Table 13–1. Test the solution with litmus paper or indicator paper to discover whether it is acidic, basic, or neutral. Save the solution for the activity on Page 266.

MAKING SURE
1. Which chlorine compound is most plentiful in seawater?
2. Using Table 13–1, determine the seven most plentiful elements in seawater.
3. Which metal is most plentiful in seawater?

13:2 Temperature and Density

Average water temperatures at the surface of the ocean range from $-1.3°C$ in the Arctic Ocean to $28°C$ in the tropics. Surface water temperatures vary from season to season by as much as 8 to 10 C° within the North Atlantic and North Pacific Oceans. In waters near the equator, the temperature changes throughout the year by only about $1°C$.

Seawater temperature also varies with ocean depth. Deep ocean water is much colder than surface water. In the deepest parts of the world's oceans, water temperatures remain close to $0°C$ throughout the year. But they do not freeze because of the salt content of the water.

Why is temperature a major factor in marine life?

Temperature is a major factor in the life of marine plants and animals. Living things in warm tropical waters tend to grow faster and have shorter life spans than those living in colder waters. Tropical marine life reproduces earlier and more frequently. Certain kinds of animals can live only in cold water. Others live only in warm water.

The density of seawater depends on its temperature and its salinity. Recall that density refers to the mass per unit volume of a substance. Density is usually expressed as grams per cubic centimeter (g/cm³).

What affects seawater density?

Dissolved solids in seawater make its density slightly greater than that of pure water. Pure water has a density of 1.0 g/cm³ at 4°C. Seawater has an average density of 1.02 g/cm³ at 4°C. Water becomes more dense when its salinity increases and its temperature decreases. In general, cold water is more dense than warm water of the same salinity. Thus, the most dense seawater is found near the poles, where it is cold most of the year.

What is the average density of seawater at 4°C?

Richard Alley

FIGURE 13–3. The coldest and most dense seawater is found at the poles.

Ocean bottom water is more dense than surface water because it is colder and has more dissolved material. It does not mix easily with surface water. Seawater near the equator is not as dense as water at the poles. Why? When water is warmed by the sun it expands and becomes less dense.

FIGURE 13–4.

DENSITY OF SEAWATER

Use a laboratory balance to find the mass of 1 L of the solution prepared in the activity on Page 264. Calculate the density of the solution and record its temperature. Compare the density of the solution to the density of tap water.

Gently place an egg in tap water. Does it float? Place the egg in the salt solution. Based on your observation, do you think an egg will float in seawater?

MAKING SURE

4. Why is ocean water near the North Pole more dense than water near the equator?
5. Where does the energy come from that warms the oceans?
6. Why is deep ocean water colder than water near the surface?
7. How does salinity affect the density of ocean water?

13:3 The Seafloor

The oceans cover a vast area equal to about three fourths of the total surface of the earth. For many years, the floor of the sea was believed to be flat and smooth. But research has shown that the ocean basins contain mountains and valleys similar to those on land. For instance, the Mid-Atlantic Ridge stretches along the center of the Atlantic Ocean for a distance of more than 16 000 km.

Many deep trenches have been discovered in the seafloor. Ocean trenches commonly reach depths of 7 km. The deepest known point in the oceans is in a trench near the Mariana Islands. Here the water has been measured to a depth of nearly 11 km.

How are the seafloors mapped? Knowledge of the profile of the seafloor has come largely from soundings. A profile of the seafloor is an outline of its surface. Sounding is a method used to measure

Trace the course of the Mid-Atlantic Ridge.

Where is the deepest known ocean trench located?

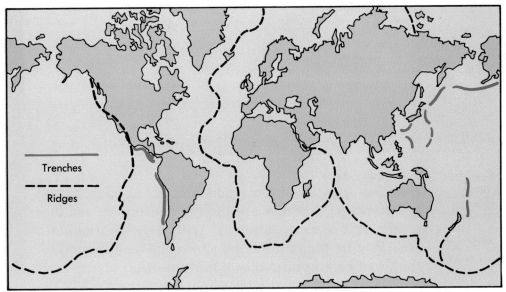

the depth of water. Soundings are made in two ways. One way involves lowering a weight on a cable until it strikes the seafloor. The measured length of the cable is the water's depth. A second way to take soundings makes use of sonic (sound) depth recorders. Ships were first equipped with sonic depth recorders in 1940. Most of the facts about the seafloor have been discovered since that time.

FIGURE 13–5. This map shows the location of the trenches and the ridges along the ocean floor.

In what two ways are seafloors mapped?

National Oceanic and Atmospheric Administration

FIGURE 13–6. Electronic instruments receive echoes from the seafloor.

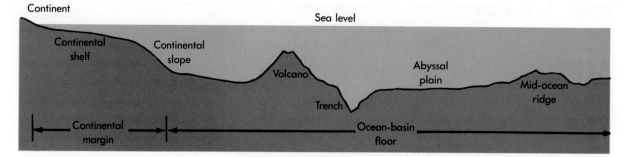

Sea level

Continent

Continental
shelf

Continental
slope

Volcano

Trench

Abyssal
plain

Mid-ocean
ridge

Continental
margin

Ocean-basin
floor

FIGURE 13–7. A profile of an ocean floor shows sloping shelves, volcanoes, trenches, and ridges.

Name the two main regions into which the seafloor may be classified.

   The seafloor may be classified into two main regions—continental margins and ocean-basin floors. **Continental margins** are the portions of the seafloor lying next to the continents. Within the continental margins lie the continental shelves. A **continental shelf** is a smooth, gently sloping portion of the ocean floor that borders the coastlines of a continent. They range in width from a few kilometers to more than 300 km. Continental shelves are less than 200 m below the ocean surface. **Ocean-basin floors** are mostly flat portions of the ocean floor. On the average, they are 4000 m beneath the ocean's surface. Mid-ocean ridges and ocean trenches are found in this region of the ocean.

Karen Lukas/Alpha

FIGURE 13–8. Most of the islands on the earth were formed as a result of volcanic activity on the seafloor.

MAKING SURE

8. What methods are used to map the ocean floor?
9. How are the features of ocean-basin floors similar to features on land?

13:4   Sea Life

The ocean is the home of many kinds of living things. Sponges, lobsters, whales, and sharks are but a few types of sea-living animals. One-celled plants called algae are the most plentiful ocean plant life. About 80 to 90 percent of food made by plants occurs in algae living in the oceans.

All animal sea life depends either directly or indirectly on plankton for food. **Plankton** are a type of tiny animal and plant life that drift about in the sea. Plankton provide food for very small fish. These small living creatures are eaten by larger fish. They in turn, are eaten by still larger fish. Plant plankton is the first link in a food chain that extends to the largest ocean animals.

What are plankton?

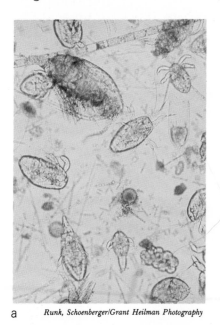

a   *Runk, Schoenberger/Grant Heilman Photography*   b   *Animals, Animals*

FIGURE 13–9. Plankton (a) and Portuguese men-of-war (b) are two links in ocean food chains.

The ocean contains a wealth of plankton. Tests made at the marine laboratory at Plymouth, England show the presence of as many as 4.5 million plankton in 1 L of seawater. The distribution of plankton in seawater varies from place to place. In the oceans, as on land, some regions are more fertile than others.

Name three physical factors that affect marine life.

Why is the ocean's food supply less at great depths than near the surface?

Plants and animals live in the parts of the ocean to which they are best suited. Sunlight, pressure, and temperature are important factors which affect marine life. Plant plankton live within the upper 60 m of seawater where light is available for photosynthesis. Deep within the ocean the absence of light prevents the growth of plant plankton. Thus, all fish that live in the ocean depths feed on organic matter that sinks from above. In general, the greater the depth, the smaller the food supply.

Most marine animals have gills which they use to obtain oxygen dissolved in seawater. Oxygen dissolves in seawater at the ocean's surface. It is also added by algae and other green plants as a product of photosynthesis. Some marine animals, such as whales, are mammals. They have lungs and obtain oxygen by coming to the surface and breathing air.

Sea life is most plentiful near coasts in tropical, subtropical, and temperate regions. Coastal waters are often shallow. Water depths are usually less than 50 m. The sunlight that penetrates these waters causes them to be rich in algae, seaweed, and other sea plants. Marine animals feed on these sea plants. Flounder, starfish, sea urchins, and crabs are a few of the animals that live within these shallow waters.

FIGURE 13–10. Coastal waters show a wide variety of life (a). Deep ocean animals must have special features to help them survive (b).

a

b

Joey Jacques

William H. Amos

13:5 Ocean Currents

Ocean currents are huge streams of water which flow within certain well-defined boundaries. The Gulf Stream, for instance, is a warm, swift current in the Atlantic Ocean. It flows out of the Gulf of Mexico between Flordia and Cuba. It sweeps northward along the east coast of the United States. Then it moves across the Atlantic Ocean to Great Britain. It is about 80 km wide and travels as fast as 6 km/h off Florida. Its speed decreases to less than 1 km/h in the North Atlantic. It is one of the strongest ocean currents and moves huge amounts of water. Warm water is carried to the British Isles by the Gulf Stream. Thus the climate of Great Britain is warmer than would be expected from its location north of the equator.

The Gulf Stream is a surface current. Surface currents are caused by wind sweeping across broad expanses of water. As a wind exerts force on the ocean's surface, the surface water is set in motion. Most surface currents follow patterns similar to those of wind systems.

What is the Gulf Stream?

FIGURE 13–11.   Cold surface currents flow from the poles toward the equator. Warm surface currents flow from the equator to the poles.

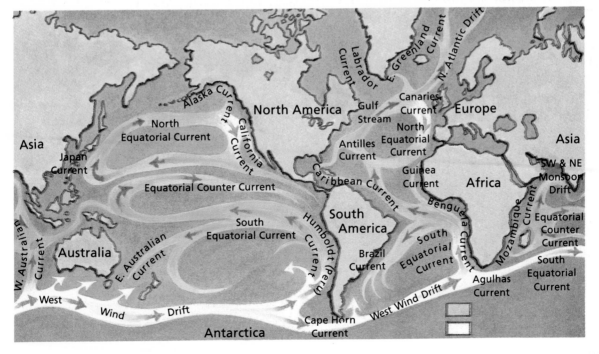

Wood's Hole Oceanographic Institution

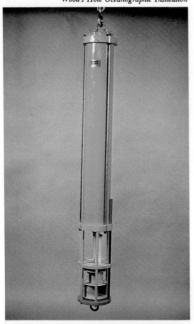

FIGURE 13–12. Oceanographers use a current meter to determine direction and speed of deep ocean currents.

What causes convection currents in the ocean?

Differences in water density result in convection currents within the ocean. A convection current in water is similar to a convection current in the atmosphere. Convection currents occur when water is cooled at the ocean's surface by loss of heat to the air. This cooled water increases in density and tends to sink because it is more dense than the warmer water beneath. At the same time, the warmer, less dense water beneath the surface water tends to rise.

Deep water currents are caused by differences in water density. Cold, dense water near the poles sinks toward the bottom of the ocean. Then this cold water flows toward the equator.

Oceanographers use sealed, floating drift bottles released at sea to check the direction of ocean currents. A drift bottle is weighted with enough sand to cause it to float nearly submerged. The bottle contains a card requesting the finder to record the date and the place in which the bottle is found. Those cards that are returned provide information about the speed and direction of ocean currents.

The speed and direction of an ocean current can also be measured with a water current meter. One of these meters is the Ekman current meter. It has a propeller and a tail fin. An Ekman current meter is suspended from a wire and lowered from a ship to the desired depth.

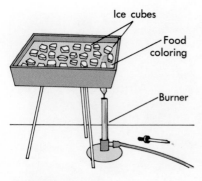

Ice cubes

Food coloring

Burner

FIGURE 13–13.

activity CONVECTION CURRENTS IN WATER

Put two dozen ice cubes in the center of a large pan and fill it three-fourths full with water. Place the pan on a tripod and heat one side with a Bunsen burner. Add a few drops of ink or food coloring to the water on the side you are heating. Draw a diagram to show the movement of the ink. What causes the movement?

MAKING SURE

10. How are convection currents in the ocean similar to convection currents in the atmosphere?

11. How is the climate of Great Britain affected by the Gulf Stream?

13:6 Waves

Where and how do ocean waves begin? Ocean waves are produced by winds. They possess kinetic energy gained from the winds. High waves are produced when winds sweep rapidly for great distances across a broad section of an ocean.

W.C. Bradley Collection

How are ocean waves produced?

FIGURE 13–14. Ocean surface waves may travel hundreds of kilometers before they reach shore.

An object floating on the ocean's surface rises and falls as a wave passes. It is not carried forward by the wave because water is not pushed forward by wave motion. The particles of water in a wave move up and down in a circular motion (Figure 13–15). Each water particle returns to the point from which it started.

Describe the motion of an object floating on the ocean as a wave passes.

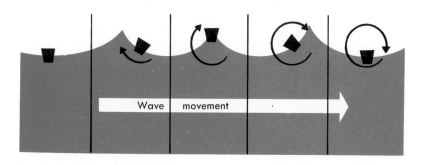

Wave movement

FIGURE 13–15. A cork rides a wave in an up and down circular motion.

Three properties that describe a wave are amplitude, wavelength, and period (Figure 13–16). The amplitude of a wave is its height. It is one-half the distance between the top of a crest and the bottom of a trough. Wavelength is the horizontal distance from one crest to another. The height and wavelength of a water wave are commonly expressed in meters.

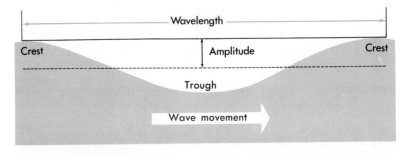

FIGURE 13–16. The crest is the highest part of a wave while the trough is the lowest.

The **period** of a wave is the time between the passage of two successive wave crests. Wave period is expressed in seconds. The shorter the period, the greater the number of waves that pass a given point during a certain amount of time. The following is the equation for finding the period of a wave.

How is the wave period determined?

$$period = \frac{time}{number\ of\ waves}$$

Example:

Ten waves pass an anchored ship in 30 s. Find the wave period.

Solution

Step 1: Write the equation for the period of a wave.

$$period = \frac{time}{number\ of\ waves}$$

Step 2: Substitute the values for time and number of waves given in the problem.

$$period = \frac{30\ s}{10\ waves}$$

Step 3: Divide to find the answer.

$$\frac{30\ s}{10\ waves} = 3\ s \qquad period = 3\ s$$

As a wave approaches the shore, it touches bottom and slows. Other waves crowd in behind it. The ocean bottom exerts friction force (drag) on the wave. This force changes the form and motion of the wave. The drag force causes the circular paths of the water particles to be squeezed together (Figure 13–17). Both wave speed and wavelength decrease as a wave approaches the shore.

Explain how a wave becomes a breaker.

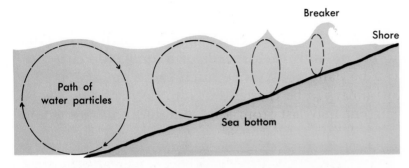

FIGURE 13–17. When water in a wave touches bottom, wavelength decreases and the wave rises.

The height of a wave increases as it approaches the shore (Figure 13–18). Its crest becomes steeper and rises to a peak. Suddenly, the whole wave breaks into a tumbling mass of foaming water. At this point, the wave becomes a breaker. After the water is carried to the shore by the breaker, it slides back into the ocean underneath the incoming waves. This flow of water back into the ocean is called an **undertow.**

What is an undertow?

Steve Lissau

FIGURE 13–18. A breaker forms when a wave topples over, spilling water onto the shore.

Waves approach a shoreline from many angles. As they reach the land, they are refracted or bent. They bend because the part of the wave entering shallow water first is slowed by the ocean bottom. The part in deeper water races ahead. Thus, waves tend to bend so that they approach the shore head-on.

Some waves do hit the shore at an angle and produce longshore currents. A **longshore current** is a flow of water along the shore.

Rip currents occur when longshore currents go back to sea. Rip currents range in length from 170 to 800 m and reach speeds of 8 km/h. Rip currents can be dangerous. They often cause unwary swimmers to be carried out into deeper water. A rip current may last from a few minutes to a few hours.

Steve Lissau

FIGURE 13–19. A rip current can carry swimmers out into deep water quickly.

activity   WAVE MOTION

Float a cork on water in a pan. Using a spoon, strike the water in the center of the container until waves are produced. Observe the motion of the cork. What do you conclude about the effect of a wave on the cork? Is the cork carried forward by the motion of the wave?

activity WAVES ALONG A SHORELINE

(1) Obtain a clear plastic container and fill it half full with water. (2) Place a thin, flat plate of metal or glass on some metal washers at one end of the container and adjust the plate so that its upper surface is about 1 mm below the water surface. This makes the water above the plate very shallow. The plate should be parallel to waves generated at the opposite end of the container.
(3) Generate waves with a wooden dowel (Figure 13–20). Observe the waves as they reach the plate. Does the wavelength increase or decrease when the waves pass into shallow water? (4) Now set the plate so that its edge is at a 45° angle to the waves. Repeat the wave generation and observe the wave path. What change occurs?

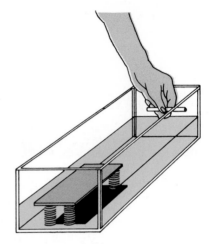

FIGURE 13–20.

MAKING SURE

12. From an ocean pier, you count 15 waves passing during 60 s. What is the wave period?

13. An average of 24 waves passes a point on a dock in 2 min. Find the wave period.

13:7 Tides

The ocean level at a seacoast is constantly changing because of tides. A **tide** is a periodic rise and fall of the ocean along a seacoast. Each day the ocean level along a coast rises to high tide, drops to low tide, rises to high tide again, and then drops to low tide. Tides are caused by gravitational forces of the sun and moon. In some areas the tides have little or no effect on the water level at the shore. In other areas, such as the Bay of Fundy near Nova Scotia, the water level changes by as much as 15 m. At low tide, the Bay of Fundy is almost completely drained of water. The height of the tides in a region is influenced by the depth and shape of the sea floor and the shape of the coast.

Define tide.

What causes tides?

Russ Kinne/Photo Researchers, Inc.

a

Russ Kinne/Photo Researchers, Inc.

b

FIGURE 13–21. High tide at the Bay of Fundy (a). Low tide at the same location leaves boats stranded (b).

Tides represent a vast source of kinetic energy. One project to harness the power of the tides has been completed in the Rance River in France. High tides cause the water in the river to reach heights of 11 to 13 m. Dams upriver trap the water at high tides. The return flow at low tide is directed through water turbines. The water turbines turn electric generators. As a result, the kinetic energy of the tides is used to produce electric energy.

activity OCEAN TIDES

Locate daily tide listings for a port city such as New York, Miami, Galveston, San Francisco, or Los Angeles. Keep a record of the time of daily tides for one week. If such listings are not readily available, use the following data:

Day	Low	High	Low	High
1	2:38 A.M.	8:56 A.M.	3:09 P.M.	10:32 P.M.
2	3:08 A.M.	9:30 A.M.	5:00 P.M.	11:34 P.M.
3	3:43 A.M.	10:11 A.M.	5:57 P.M.	12:56 A.M.

How much time is there between high tides? Compare the time from high tide to high tide for three days. Is it always the same? How does the time between high tides compare to the time between low tides?

13.8 Seismic Sea Waves and Surges

Giant ocean waves are produced by earthquakes in the sea floor. Waves produced by an earthquake are called **seismic sea waves.** Some of these waves travel at speeds of more than 600 km/h. They cross the ocean in the form of low waves. They are so low in fact that ships at sea often do not know that a seismic sea wave is passing. In deep water, some are only a meter or two high. But when they reach the shore they may exceed a height of 30 m. Although they have nothing to do with the tides, seismic sea waves are often called "tidal waves." A seismic sea wave is also referred to as a tsunami (soo NAHM eeh), a Japanese word.

Seismic sea waves can be very destructive. Some caused great disasters when they smashed against coastlines. In 1883, a seismic sea wave killed 36 380 people living on small islands in the Dutch East Indies. In April, 1946, a seismic sea wave was caused by an earthquake in the sea floor near Alaska. This wave traveled toward Hawaii at a speed of 790 km/h. Reaching Hawaii, it caused extensive damage and death to 159 people.

What kind of waves are produced by an earthquake? What are they commonly called?

a

Sidney White Collection

FIGURE 13–22. Tsunamis can do extensive damage when they strike the coastline (a). Seismic sea waves may be caused by earthquakes on the ocean floor and may rise to great height along a shore (b).

b

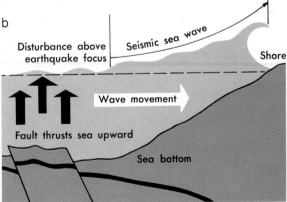

A large cyclonic storm over an ocean may produce a storm surge. A storm **surge** is a mass of water that produces an abnormal rise in sea level along a seacoast. The surge forms when water, driven by storm winds, builds up along coastlines. The hill of water produced by the swelling may raise the water level by 10 m. When the storm reaches a seacoast, the surge of water may be carried onto land. Storm surges can be destructive to low-lying coastal areas. They are extremely dangerous when they coincide with high tides, often causing property damage and loss of life.

MAKING SURE

14. How are seismic sea waves different from ordinary wind-blown waves?

13:9 Ocean Resources

Natural resources are abundant in the oceans. For example, the fishing industry harvests millions of tons of fish each year. Deep sea drilling rigs sink wells thousands of meters into the ocean floor. These wells pump out oil and natural gas that are used for fuel. Elements used in industry, such as sodium and chlorine, are obtained from the salt in seawater. In some places, seawater is even a source of fresh drinking water. The salt is removed from the water in a distillation plant.

More than 800 000 dry metric tons of seaweed are harvested from the oceans each year. The harvested seaweed plants are species of red and brown algae. They include kelp that grows to a length of 70 m. Among the many products obtained from seaweed is a substance called carrageenan (ker uh GEE nun). This material is used to thicken milkshakes, smooth skin cream, and to weave surgical thread. Agar, a gelatin substance used to grow bacteria in laboratory tests, comes from seaweed. Algin, another substance obtained from seaweed, is used to make paints, dyes, and paper. Experiments are being done to produce natural gas by decomposing seaweed. The natural gas could be used for heating homes.

FIGURE 13–23. Many products are derived from seaweed.

In the future, it is likely that valuable minerals will be mined from the oceans. Round-shaped mineral pieces, called nodules, have been discovered on the deep ocean floors. These nodules are rich in manganese and iron. Manganese is mixed with iron to make steel hard. Other important minerals present in the nodules, in lesser amounts, are copper, cobalt, and nickel.

The oceans have a tremendous amount of energy that may someday be put to use on a large scale. Have you ever watched huge waves pounding on a beach? If so, you know the vast amount of power in waves and the work they can do. The rising and falling of the tides may someday become an important source of energy. Experiments are being done to use the kinetic energy of ocean waves and tides to generate electricity. The oceans are very large and are heated by the sun every day. Therefore they contain a tremendous amount of heat. Experiments are being done to use this heat to produce convection currents in the ocean water. The flow of water in the currents would be used to generate electric power.

How can the ocean be used as a source of energy?

MAKING SURE

15. In what ways can the ocean provide sources of energy?
16. How would drilling for oil in the ocean be more difficult than drilling for oil on land?

Perspectives

frontiers

Sea Treasure

There are mysterious black lumps in the depths of the Pacific Ocean. These lumps or nodules contain valuable minerals such as manganese, copper, nickel, and cobalt. The lumps lie on the Pacific Ocean floor, about 4600 m below the surface. The nodules were first discovered by the crew of the *HMS Challenger* in 1872. Some were taken to the British Museum and put on display.

The minerals found in the nodules are valuable because of their industrial uses. For example, the United States imports about 2 billion dollars worth of these minerals each year. If an economical way of mining the nodules is found, the imports could be reduced. The largest group of nodules is in a strip about 3200 km long and 800 km wide. This strip lies west of Mexico and south of Hawaii.

Every cubic kilometer of ocean water contains approximately 150 million metric tons of dissolved minerals. Thus, the oceans could be a tremendous source of mineral wealth. In fact, it is estimated that 15 million metric tons of nodules form each year.

How are the mysterious nodules formed? Have they been thrown onto the ocean floor by volcanic activity? Are they carried to the ocean with sediment from rivers? Do they, like rock candy, crystallize from a saturated solution? These are some of the accepted ideas about nodule formation. How they form remains a mystery.

Several ideas are being tested for mining the nodules. One group suggests using many buckets connected to a 15 000 m cable. The cable would hang in a giant loop under a ship. As the ship moves forward the buckets scrape up nodules. Sediment is washed away as the buckets rise to the surface. However, buckets disturb the bottom sediment, and the looped

Christopher Springmann

cable may tangle or catch on an object. In spite of these problems, this design may be the least expensive.

Another group suggests a fleet of remote control shuttles. They descend in a continuous line and bring nodules back to a floating platform. This system eliminates handling kilometers of cable or pipe. Its major drawback is possible breakdowns with expensive and time consuming repairs.

Other groups are working on a giant "soda straw." Using pumps, a vacuum is created within a pipe. The vacuum forces the material containing the nodules upward, much like a soda straw.

Which method will be used to mine valuable deep-sea metals? Only time and technology will tell.

Originally appeared in the April, 1981 issue of *Smithsonian* © by Janet L. Hopson.

main ideas

1. Seawater is a brine solution containing at least one half of the known chemical elements.   13:1

2. Differences in seawater density are caused by differences in temperature and differences in salinity.   13:2

3. Ocean temperature varies with distance from the equator and with ocean depth.   13:2

4. Sea life is most plentiful in the shallow coastal waters of temperate, subtropical, and tropical regions.   13:4

5. Ocean currents are produced by winds and by variations in the density of seawater.   13:5

6. Ocean waves are produced by wind. They have three major properties—amplitude, wavelength, and period.   13:6

7. The heights of ocean tides are influenced by the depth and shape of the seafloor and the shape of the coast.   13:7

8. A seismic sea wave is a giant wave produced by an earthquake or a volcano.   13:8

vocabulary

Define each of the following words or terms.

continental margin	ocean current	salinity	tide
continental shelf	oceanography	seismic sea	undertow
longshore current	plankton	wave	wave period
ocean-basin floor	rip current	surge	

study questions

DO NOT WRITE IN THIS BOOK.

A. True or False

Determine whether each of the following sentences is true or false. If the sentence is false, rewrite it to make it true.

1. Seawater contains sodium, magnesium, and chlorine.
2. About 55 percent of the dissolved matter in seawater is chlorine.
3. Less than one half of the earth is covered by water.
4. The salinity of most ocean water is over 4 percent.
5. When seawater is cooled, its density decreases.

6. The density of seawater is slightly greater than the density of pure water.

7. Water within the Arctic Circle is less dense than surface water in the tropics.

8. One high tide and one low tide occur each day.

9. Water near the ocean surface is much colder than deep ocean water.

10. The Gulf Stream in the Atlantic Ocean is one of the strongest ocean currents.

B. Multiple Choice

Choose the word or phrase that completes correctly each of the following sentences.

1. The ocean-basin floor is about *(1000, 4000, 8000, 10 000)* m below the ocean surface.

2. The deepest known point in the ocean lies off *(the Aleutians, Japan, Java, the Mariana Islands)*.

3. Soundings of the ocean floor are made with *(radar, light, heat, sound)*.

4. Continental shelves occur within the *(continental margins, ocean-basin floors, mid-ocean ridges)*.

5. The water depth over a continental shelf is less than *(100, 200, 300, 500)* m.

6. *(Rip currents, Undertows, Convection currents, Breakers)* occur when longshore currents go back to sea.

7. Plankton are microscopic *(plants, animals, plants and animals)* that float in water.

8. A flow of water back into the ocean underneath incoming waves is called a(n) *(rip current, breaker, undertow, current)*.

9. A(n) *(rip current, undertow, surge, breaker)* is a wind driven mass of water produced by a storm.

10. Most marine animals obtain oxygen through *(lungs, gills, plankton, sunlight)*.

C. Completion

Complete each of the following sentences with a word or phrase that will make the sentence correct.

1. As waves reach the shore, their wavelength _____.

2. _____ and iron are two metals found in nodules present on deep ocean floors.

3. A seismic sea wave is produced by a(n) _____.
4. The density of pure water is _____ than the density of seawater.
5. _____ are the first links in marine food chains.
6. Plankton are most plentiful in the upper 60 m of seawater because _____ is available.
7. The number of plankton in a liter of seawater is likely to be greater in the _____ than near the poles.
8. Periodic changes in the ocean level along a coast are called _____.
9. Currents deep in the ocean are caused by differences in seawater _____.
10. Ocean _____ and tides have kinetic energy that can be used to generate electricity.

D. How and Why
1. How is the density of seawater affected by temperature?
2. Why do ocean currents travel in a direction different from the wind that causes them?
3. Describe what happens to a wave as it comes to the shore.
4. Why is sea life more plentiful in some parts of the ocean than in others?
5. Why is Great Britain warmer than is expected from its location north of the equator?

investigations
1. Construct a profile model of the Atlantic Ocean or Pacific Ocean seafloor with plaster of paris.
2. Build and maintain a saltwater aquarium.

interesting reading

Cook, Jan Leslie, *The Mysterious Undersea World*. Washington, D.C.: National Geographic Society, 1980.

Goldin, Augusta, *Oceans of Energy: Resources of Power for the Future*. New York, NY: Harcourt, 1980.

Herrmann, Lisa, "Alien Worlds on the Ocean Floor." *Science Digest*. April 1981, pp. 52-57.

UNDERWATER PARKS

Creating underwater parks is not a new idea. For 50 years, scientists, legislators, and divers agreed that it was important to preserve the wonders of the sea. Underwater parks for public use have been developed only within the past twenty years. Along the coast of California, undersea parks have been created for recreation and education. Undersea parks are like living museums under the sea. The first park, Point Lobos, was established near Monterey in 1960.

There are three types of underwater parks in California. One type of park is called an underwater recreational area. Recreational areas are set aside for surface activities such as boating and water skiing. These areas also provide for snorkeling and diving while preserving ecological and scenic resources. The second type, called

© Daniel W. Gotshall

an underwater park consists of a large area of great scenic beauty. Such a park may also contain areas of historical and ecologial importance. The third type is called an underwater reserve. Underwater reserves are established to maintain undisturbed natural areas. The reserves also protect unique organisms and unusual geologic features. Reserves may even be used to protect old cultural relics such as sunken ships.

At Point Lobos, 300 hectares of undersea land is designated as an underwater reserve. Explorers of Point Lobos find themselves in one of the world's largest underwater canyons. Even at a depth of 30 m, visibility is good. Divers can see brilliant displays of rare red and orange sponges along with featherduster worms and sunflower stars. There is always the possibility that a diver at Point Lobos will meet a playful sea otter. The otters sometimes dive with "underwater tourists" and accept squid and sea urchins for food.

© Daniel W. Gotshall

For those who do not dive, television cameras have been installed beneath the surface. Undersea life at Point Lobos can be observed using viewing screens located on shore.

Approximately 55 km south of Point Lobos is "J.P." Burns Underwater Park. To many divers, this park is the most exciting undersea park in California. Below the surface lies a maze of canyons, arches, and caves carved out of granite. Within the canyons are many kinds of sea anemones, colorful algae, and even a shy octopus.

The Salt Point Park is located about 200 km north of San Francisco. This park is protected from the surf and is ideal for beginning divers. Salt Point Park contains a wide variety of life including large octopuses and northern palm kelp, which grows to a height of 2 m or more. Along the rocky bottom of the park lies the wreck of the freighter Norlina. The Norlina sank near Salt Point in 1926.

Plans have been made in California to set aside more coastal areas. These areas would be designated as ocean wilderness. The purpose of the wilderness areas will be to leave some sections of the coast truly wild and primitive.

A total of 43 parks are planned along California's 1770 km coastline. When completed, the chain of parks will be the largest system of undersea parks in the world. The park planners in California hope their parks will be used as examples for other coastline states in the United States as well as nations around the world.

By Larry Wood adapted from *Sea Frontiers* © 1981, International Oceanographic Foundation. All rights reserved.

287

unit
4

Living Things

All living things have cells and reproduce. Yet, they have differences, too. A hummingbird is an animal; a cactus is a plant. How are they similar? How are they different? Plants and animals can be classified according to their differences. Why is a cactus classified as a plant? Why is a hummingbird classified as an animal?

The laboratory worker is using a set of diagnostic tests for classifying bacteria. Each disc yields information that will be used in identifying the bacteria. With the vast number of living organisms, it is easier to study them if they are in groups. What features are common to all living organisms? What are the characteristics of the simplest life forms?

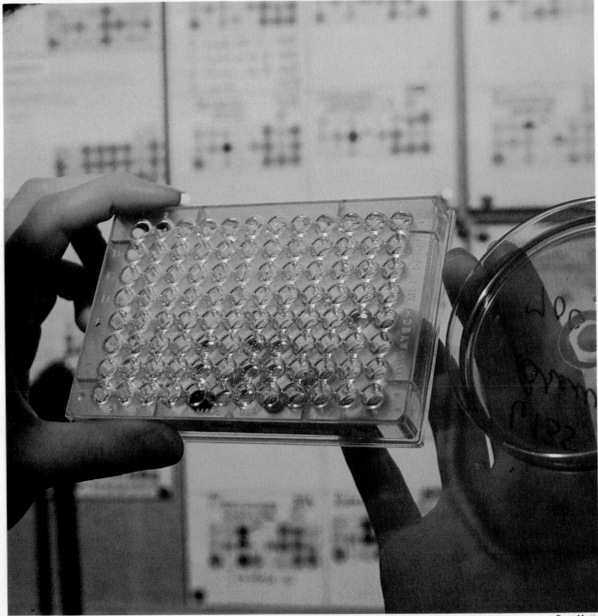

Doug Martin

Life and the Cell

14:1 Features of Living Things

Living things are found in hot climates, cold climates, oceans, mountains, and deserts. A study of life reveals that a great number of different plants and animals exist. Suppose you could find and identify all of the living things on your school grounds. You would name several hundred plants and animals. Many of them are so small you would need a microscope to see them.

Each living thing on the earth has certain features that make it different from all others. One of these features is size. An adult blue whale, the largest living animal, has a mass of 91 000 kg and is nearly 30 m long. The giant redwood trees of California grow to a height of 90 m and a diameter of 5.5 m. The smallest bacteria, however, are only 0.0001 cm long. Millions of them could swim in a spoonful of water.

How do you know if something is living or nonliving? Most living things have the following features.

(1) *Definite size and shape.* Each kind of living thing has a certain shape and grows to a particular size.

(2) *Definite life span.* A living thing begins life, grows, matures, reproduces, and dies. The time from birth to death is called the life span.

GOAL: You will learn that all living organisms are alike in certain ways. However, every kind (species) of organism is unique and different from all the other species.

What are the six special features of most living things?

291

FIGURE 14–1. The redwood is the largest kind of tree.

(3) *Reproduction.* Reproduction is necessary if a species is to survive. Reproduction is the process of producing another living thing.

(4) *Metabolism.* All living things carry on a large number of chemical processes to stay alive. The sum of all these processes is called **metabolism.** One metabolic process is digestion. Digestion is the process of breaking down food into simpler substances which can be used by a living thing. Digestion provides the materials needed for living things to grow and produce energy.

(5) *Movement.* Another feature of most living things is the ability to move. Most animals run, swim, fly, squirm, or move in other obvious ways. Plants also move, although much more slowly.

(6) *Response to the environment.* Each living thing responds in some way to its environment. Anything in the environment that causes a change in behavior is called a **stimulus.** For example, different colors in traffic lights act as stimuli (plural of stimulus) for motorists and pedestrians. The behavior caused by a stimulus is a response. The response of most people to a flashing red light is caution because of possible danger.

FIGURE 14–2. Response to the environment (a) and movement (b) are two features of living things.

a

b

activity   BURNING A CANDLE

Set a candle in a dish or pan and light it. Observe the flame. Suppose you wanted to convince a friend that the candle was alive. List on paper the reasons you would give. What reasons would you give to explain that the candle is not alive?

MAKING SURE

1. List some of the features of each of the following living things:
   - (a) human
   - (b) grasshopper
   - (c) spider
   - (d) robin
   - (e) cactus
   - (f) frog
   - (g) mushroom
   - (h) snake
   - (i) octopus
2. List three stimuli that cause responses in humans.
3. How is plant movement different from movement of animals?

14:2   The Cell

Nearly all living things are made of cells. A **cell** is a basic unit of structure and function in living things. Most cells are very small—too small to be seen with the eye alone, but they can be studied with a microscope.

A cell contains three basic parts. A thin layer called a cell membrane surrounds the cell. The cell membrane controls the movement of substances into and out of the cell. Near the center of the cell is a structure called the **nucleus** that controls the cell's life activities. The nucleus is enclosed by a membrane called the nuclear membrane. Some cells, such as human white blood cells, may contain several nuclei. Between the cell membrane and the nucleus is a jellylike substance called cytoplasm. In most cells, the nucleus is darker than the cytoplasm because it is thicker and more dense.

Define a cell and name its three basic parts.

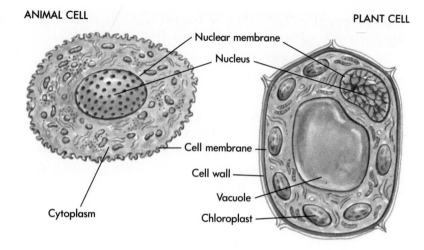

FIGURE 14–3. There are some differences between plant and animal cells.

ANIMAL CELL

PLANT CELL

Nuclear membrane

Nucleus

Cell membrane

Cell wall

Vacuole

Chloroplast

Cytoplasm

In animal cells, the cell membrane is the outer layer of the cell (Figure 14–3). Plant cells, however, have an outer layer called a cell wall which surrounds the cell membrane. The cell wall forms a stiff case around the cell. It is made mostly of a material called cellulose (SEL yuh lohs). Cellulose gives strength to the cell wall.

Protoplasm is the "living material" of the cell. Each cell is a unit or mass of protoplasm. Protoplasm is 70 percent water. Proteins, fats, carbohydrates, and minerals make the remaining 30 percent. With the exception of the cell wall in plant cells, all parts of a cell are made of protoplasm. Cytoplasm, for example, is the protoplasm that lies outside the nucleus of a cell.

How is a plant cell different from an animal cell?

What are protoplasm and cytoplasm?

Table 14–1.
Elements in Human Protoplasm

Element	Percent
Oxygen	65
Carbon	18
Hydrogen	10
Nitrogen	3
Calcium	2
Phosphorus	1
Trace elements	1

Museum of Science and Industry, Chicago

A chemical called DNA is found only in the nucleus. Another chemical called RNA is found throughout the cell. DNA and RNA molecules are some of the largest molecules in living things. Most DNA is made of thousands of smaller molecules linked to form one very large molecule. The specific order of these smaller molecules forms a "life code." This life code is used to control all activities of the cell. Every living thing has a special code of its own which makes it different from other species. Furthermore, each member of the species has a variation of the species code. Thus, all members of a species are somewhat different from each other.

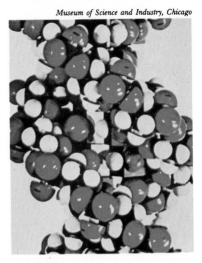

FIGURE 14–4. Model of a DNA molecule.

What is the "life code" of DNA?

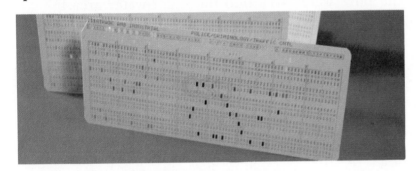

FIGURE 14–5. Like a DNA molecule, computer cards contain information in code.

14:3 Cell Activities

Recall that the cell membrane controls the movement of substances through the cell. This membrane is selective, allowing only certain substances to pass through it. The process of diffusion occurs through cell membranes. **Diffusion** is the movement of molecules from regions where they are more concentrated to regions where they are less concentrated. Dissolved substances may move from one side of the membrane to the other. A cell gets food and oxygen it needs through diffusion.

What is diffusion?

In living things, some molecules can move in a direction opposite to the expected direction of diffusion. For example, sea plants may have a higher iodine concentration than exists in the seawater around them. Iodine moves into plants in a direction opposite to diffusion.

Edward Shay

FIGURE 14–6. Molecules diffuse from where they are more concentrated to where they are less concentrated.

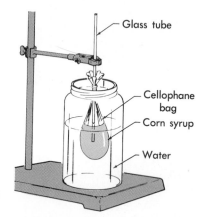

FIGURE 14–7. The solution rises in the tube as water enters the bag of corn syrup by osmosis.

- Glass tube
- Cellophane bag
- Corn syrup
- Water

Define osmosis.

How does a cell get the food and oxygen it needs for life?

Diffusion of water through a membrane is called **osmosis** (ahs MOH sus). Suppose some pure water is separated from a sugar solution by a membrane as shown in Figure 14–7. Water molecules move from the pure water area into the sugar-water area by osmosis. Sugar molecules move into the pure water by diffusion. Water and sugar in this example diffuse in opposite directions.

Cells need energy for movement, growth, and other cell activities. Cells derive their energy from a metabolic process called respiration. **Respiration** is the release of energy from the breakdown of food within the cell.

Food enters the cell by diffusion and is digested within the cytoplasm. For respiration to occur, however, most cells require oxygen. Oxygen passes into the cell by diffusion. Digested food is then combined with the oxygen. During respiration, food and oxygen are chemically changed to produce energy.

The process of respiration also produces carbon dioxide and other waste materials. These waste products are not needed by the cell. Carbon dioxide along with materials not used by the cell are expelled from the cell by diffusion.

FIGURE 14–8. Through respiration, a cell obtains energy by combining food with oxygen. Waste products of respiration include carbon dioxide and water.

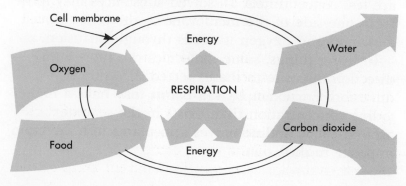

Cell membrane
Oxygen
Food
Energy
RESPIRATION
Energy
Water
Carbon dioxide

activity OSMOSIS IN CARROT CELLS

Hollow out a carrot and fill it with corn syrup. Corn syrup contains dissolved sugars. Set a one-hole stopper containing a glass tube into the top of the carrot. **CAUTION:** Before inserting the glass tube into the stopper moisten the end of the glass tube with a lubricant such as glycerol. Hold the tube with a rag or towel as you slide it into the stopper. When placed in the carrot, the tube must extend into the syrup. Use sealing wax to seal the stopper into the carrot. Place the carrot in a beaker of tap water. After several hours observe the liquid in the glass tube. What is the liquid? How did it get there?

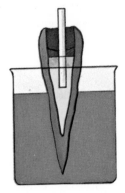

FIGURE 14–9.

MAKING SURE

4. As a solution freezes, does the rate at which substances diffuse through it increase or decrease?

5. If a cell is placed in a concentrated salt solution, water diffuses out of the cell. Why?

6. How is cell digestion different from respiration?

7. What would happen if carbon dioxide and other waste materials did not diffuse out of a cell?

14:4 Classification

Many different kinds of organisms are alive on Earth. An **organism** is a whole and complete living thing. Organisms vary in size from those that have only a single cell to those that contain billions of cells. It would take many lifetimes to study all the organisms in the world. To make the study of living organisms easier, scientists have classified them into groups.

Define organism.

The naming and classification of organisms is a major problem for scientists. Why? Many plants and animals have names by which they are known to people in one part of a country. Yet, some of these very same plants and animals have different names in other regions of the same country. For example, the mountain lion is known in different areas of the

Why are scientific names for living things used by all scientists?

United States as cougar, puma, and panther. To overcome this problem, a system has been devised by scientists to standardize the names. Each organism is given a name that is recognized and used by scientists throughout the world.

What are the five main kingdoms of living things?

Scientists classify living organisms into five main groups called **kingdoms.** The five kingdoms are monera, fungi, protist, plant, and animal. You probably know many plants and animals and their features. Protists, monerans, and fungi may be new to you. In studying these kingdoms, however, you will find familiar organisms in each group.

Organisms in each kindgom have been classified into smaller groups. Each group divides the previous group into smaller, more specific groups. There are six groups in each kingdom—phylum, class, order, family, genus, and species. Each smaller group contains organisms with similar features. At the species level there is one main type of organism.

Table 14–2.
The Five Kingdoms

Kingdom	Features	Examples
Monera	Single cell with scattered nuclear material	Bacteria
Protist	Single cell with the nucleus surrounded by a membrane	Amoeba, paramecium
Fungi	Many cells but cannot move, absorbs food from dead or living organisms	Yeasts, molds, mushrooms
Plant	Many specialized cells, uses chlorophyll to make food	Daffodils, cacti, palm trees
Animal	Many specialized cells moves, obtains food from outside sources	Whales, robins, bears

a

b

FIGURE 14–10. Tigers (a) and mountain lions (b) belong to the same genus *Felis*.

How are living things named?

Each kind of organism is given two names—one for its genus and one for its species. Genus means group. Species means kind or type. A **species** is a single, distinct group of living things. More than one million species of animals are known today. At least 250 000 species of plants have been named. You belong to the human species. Dogs, horses, and white oak trees are examples of other species.

A **genus** is a group of closely related species. A house cat, lion, tiger, and mountain lion all belong to one genus, *Felis*. Although alike in many ways, each species in the genus *Felis* has distinct features. You might befriend a house cat and take it into your home. It is unlikely that you would have a lion or tiger for a pet.

Felis leo is the scientific name for lion. *Felis* is the genus and *leo* is the species. Note that the genus name is spelled with a capital letter and the species name with a small letter. *Felis tigris* is the scientific name for tiger, with *tigris* being the species name. *Felis concolor* is the scientific name for mountain lion. What is the species name for this animal?

MAKING SURE

8. How are organisms classified?
9. List the five kingdoms in which organisms are classified. Give one example of an organism in each kingdom.

Dr. A. Ottolenghi, J. Gnau,
J. Stevens at Ohio State University

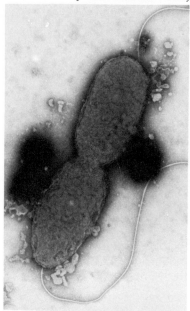

FIGURE 14–11. All bacteria contain cell walls. Some have flagella.

What are bacteria? Describe them. Where are bacteria found?

Do all bacteria need oxygen and heat to live?

FIGURE 14–12. Bacteria may be rods (a), spheres (b), and spirals (c).

14:5 Bacteria

Bacteria are classified in the kingdom, Monera. Bacteria are one-celled organisms with cell walls. They are so small that 10 000 bacteria lined up in a row equals about 1 cm. Although bacteria do not have a nucleus, they do contain DNA. A few bacteria have whiplike structures called flagella (fluh JEL uh). The beating, whipping motion of the flagella moves the bacteria through a liquid. Organisms, such as bacteria that are so tiny we use a microscope to observe them, are called microorganisms (mi kroh OR guh nihz umz).

Bacteria are found almost everywhere. They are found deep in the oceans and high in the atmosphere. They cover your skin and are present in the air you breathe. Some bacteria live on dead plants and animals. Some live on other living plants and animals. Many live harmlessly inside your body.

Most bacteria need oxygen, a warm environment, food, and water. Some species of bacteria can live at temperatures below freezing. Others grow only in the absence of oxygen. A few species contain the green pigment chlorophyll and can make their own food.

Bacteria may be further classified by their shape as spheres, rods, or spirals. From the three shapes, other forms are possible such as pairs, groups, chains, or clumps.

a

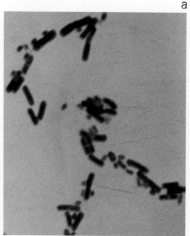

Phillip Harris Biological, Inc.

b

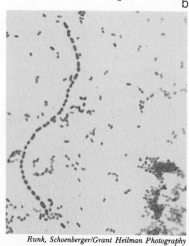

Runk, Schoenberger/Grant Heilman Photography

c

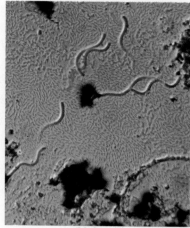

Eric Graves/Photo Researchers, Inc.

Bacteria reproduce by dividing into two parts. In this process, called fission, a cell wall forms in the middle of a bacterium cell. Two cells are produced as a result. A single bacterium cell is the parent in this kind of reproduction. When only one parent produces offspring, it is called asexual reproduction. Asexual means that male and female organisms are not part of the reproductive process.

Under ideal conditions, bacteria can divide about every 20 minutes. At this rate, one bacterium could produce about 7000 metric tons of bacteria in three days! The rapid growth of bacteria accounts for the formation of large visible colonies as shown in Figure 14–13. A single colony contains billions of bacteria. The growth of a colony is limited because the bacteria poison themselves from the wastes they produce. Some bacteria in a large colony may not be able to get food. Usually, the growth rate of a bacteria colony is greatest on the first day. By the third day, growth often stops.

Bacteria can form endospores which are structures containing a protective cell wall. Endospores can survive years of dryness, because the protective cell wall shields against harmful conditions. Some endospores survive boiling temperatures. Others are known to survive years at freezing temperatures. Many chemicals such as iodine kill bacteria, but not their endospores. When conditions improve, endospores grow into bacteria.

How do bacteria reproduce? Under what conditions do bacteria survive? What helps them survive these conditions?

FIGURE 14–13. Bacteria grow together in colonies. The colors and shape of a colony may depend on the species of bacteria.

A. Ottolenghi, Ohio State University

SEEING BACTERIA WITH A MICROSCOPE

Use a microscope to study prepared slides of different types of bacteria. The bacteria are made visible on the slide by using chemical stains which color the cells. Directions for using a microscope are given in Appendix D. First observe the slides with low power and then with high power. Draw the shape of each type and indicate the magnification used.

MAKING SURE

10. Why are the bodies of animals good places for the growth of certain kinds of bacteria?
11. How do bacteria respond to an unfavorable environment?
12. How do bacteria reproduce?
13. If bacteria reproduce so quickly, what controls the life span of a bacteria colony?
14. How are bacteria classified by shape?

14:6 Fungi

Name three kinds of fungi.

Yeasts, molds, and mushrooms are classified as fungi (FUN ji). All species of **fungi** do not contain chlorophyll and therefore cannot make their own food. Fungi obtain their food from dead organic matter or living organisms on which they live.

What causes fermentation?

Yeasts are one-celled organisms. Some yeasts obtain their food from sugar. Yeasts that live on sugar cause fermentation, a type of respiration. In fermentation, a yeast cell produces alcohol and carbon dioxide from sugar. The chemical change that occurs provides the energy the yeast needs to stay alive. Yeast is used in making raised dough products such as bread and rolls. Bubbles of carbon dioxide gas produced by the yeast cause the dough to rise. The fermentation of sugar by yeast is used in the commercial production of alcohol.

Asexual reproduction in yeast occurs through budding. In budding, a portion of the cell grows out from the rest of the cell. A new cell is formed when cell walls and cell membranes form between the cell and the "bud."

Molds grow well in warm, moist places where there is enough food. Mold can be grown on moist bread in a closed jar. Bread mold viewed with a hand lens appears as tiny threads. Under a microscope it can be seen that the bread mold threads are made of cells.

Molds reproduce by forming cells called spores. Tiny black spots visible on bread mold are spore cases. A spore case may contain millions of spores. Each spore is a single living cell. When the case matures, it opens and the spores spill out. They are often carried from place to place by wind. When a mold spore lands in a suitable place, it begins to grow. Many cell divisions result in a new growth of mold on the food.

Mushrooms are the most visible and well-known fungi. They grow in soil and decaying matter in damp areas of orchards, lawns, fields, and forests. The cap and stalk you see growing above the ground produce spores. A single mushroom may produce billions of spores. The spores are carried away by wind. If a spore lands in a suitable place, it begins forming a new mushroom.

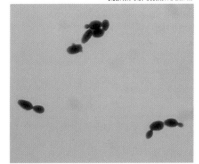

FIGURE 14–14. Yeast reproduces asexually through budding.

How does yeast reproduce?

How do molds reproduce?

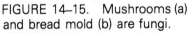

FIGURE 14–15. Mushrooms (a) and bread mold (b) are fungi.

a

b

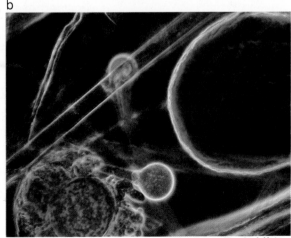

Why is it wise to avoid eating wild mushrooms?

Although some species of mushroom are good to eat, many are poisonous. There is no simple way to tell a poisonous mushroom from one that can be eaten safely. Never eat wild mushrooms. You can be poisoned.

activity   OBSERVING YEAST

(1) Obtain two packages of yeast and three identical bottles (about 250 mL each). Also obtain three identical rubber balloons and 80 g of sugar. (2) Label the bottles *A*, *B*, and *C*. (3) Fill each bottle one-half full of warm water. (4) Add 40 g of sugar to the water in bottle *A*. (5) Mix one package of yeast with the water in bottle *B*. (6) Mix one package of yeast with the water in bottle *C*. Then stir in 40 g of sugar. (7) Stretch a balloon over the top of each bottle. (8) Observe the balloons after 15 minutes. What happened to the balloon over bottle *C?* Why? (9) Remove the balloon from bottle *C*. (10) Obtain a one-hole stopper to fit bottle *C*. Insert a 10-cm glass tube into the stopper. **CAUTION:** Moisten the end of the glass tube with a lubricant such as glycerol. Hold the tube with a rag or towel as you slide it into the stopper. Connect a rubber tube to the glass tube. Place the stopper in the top of bottle *C*. (11) Place the end of the rubber tube in a beaker of limewater. As the gas from the bottle bubbles into the limewater, observe the change that takes place. Carbon dioxide gas turns limewater white. Was carbon dioxide gas formed in bottle *C?* Justify your answer. (12) Observe a drop of liquid from bottle *C* under a microscope. What shape are the yeast cells?

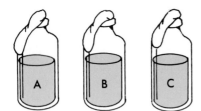

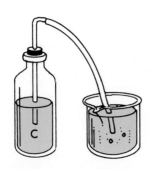

FIGURE 14–16.

MAKING SURE

15. Why are yeasts, molds, and mushrooms classified as fungi?
16. How is reproduction in yeasts different from reproduction in molds?
17. What kind of respiration takes place in yeast?
18. Why is budding considered a form of asexual reproduction?
19. How do spores move from place to place?

14:7 Amoebas and Paramecia

Amoebas (uh MEE buz) are one-celled organisms that move by changing their shape. They are members of the protist kingdom. Amoebas are found in pond water on the underside of plant leaves. They are also found in the bodies of animals and in moist soil. An amoeba moves by pushing its cytoplasm against the cell membrane to form slender, fingerlike projections. These projections stick out in the direction the amoeba is moving. The rest of the cell mass flows along behind as the amoeba moves forward.

How does an amoeba move?

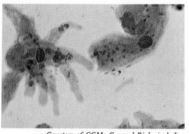
Courtesy of CCM: General Biological, Inc.

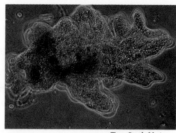
Tom Stack & Assoc.

FIGURE 14–17. Two species of Amoeba. Amoebas move by using fingerlike projections of cytoplasm.

Amoebas eat tiny protists and bits of dead matter. When an amoeba comes in contact with food, the amoeba changes shape to surround the food. The food is trapped in a bubble-like structure called a food vacuole (VAK yuh wohl). Within the vacuole, the food is digested. In digestion, food is broken down into simple substances that can be used by the amoeba. The digested food passes from the food vacuole into the cytoplasm. Here it is used in respiration to produce energy or make more protoplasm. An amoeba obtains oxygen from the water around it by diffusion.

How does an amoeba get food and oxygen?

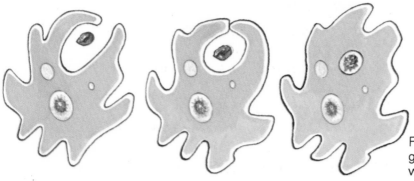

FIGURE 14–18. An amoeba gets food by surrounding it with cytoplasm.

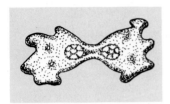

FIGURE 14–19. Amoebas reproduce asexually through fission.

What is a cyst?

How does a *Paramecium* move?

How does a *Paramecium* get food?

Waste products are expelled by the amoeba through its cell membrane. Another vacuole collects excess water from the cytoplasm. The vacuole then forces the water out through the cell membrane.

An amoeba reproduces by fission. The nucleus divides into two parts that move to opposite ends of the cell. The cell separates slowly between the two nuclei until it splits, forming two cells (Figure 14–19). During unfavorable conditions, an amoeba may form a cyst (SIHST). A cyst is a cell enclosed in a thick, protective covering. Cysts enable amoebas to survive until conditions improve.

A *Paramecium* is another kind of protist. A *Paramecium* is one-celled and shaped like a slipper (Figure 14–20). The cell membrane of a *Paramecium* is covered with short, hairlike structures called cilia (SIHL ee uh). By beating the cilia, a *Paramecium* moves through water. Paramecia live in fresh water, salt water, and in animals. Paramecia move slowly. By reversing the motion of the cilia, a *Paramecium* can move backward.

The funnel-shaped area along one side of a *Paramecium* is called an oral groove. Cilia lining the oral groove beat inward and move food particles into the cell. Here the food is collected in the food vacuole. When filled, the vacuole breaks away and moves about inside the cell. Food in the vacuole is digested and passes into the cytoplasm. Wastes are expelled by paramecia through the anal spot and other vacuoles.

FIGURE 14–20. Paramecia have many structures or features.

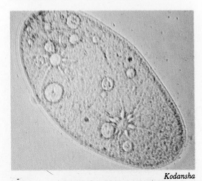

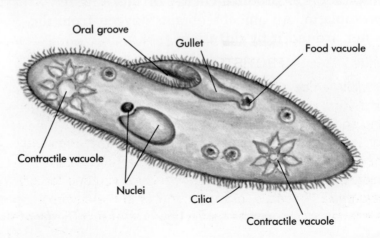

Oral groove

Gullet

Food vacuole

Contractile vacuole

Nuclei

Cilia

Contractile vacuole

Kodansha

A *Paramecium* has two nuclei. The larger nucleus controls the activities of the paramecium. The smaller nucleus functions only during reproduction. In paramecia, reproduction by fission occurs in much the same way as it does in amoebas. Under ideal conditions, paramecia divide several times a day.

When conditions are unfavorable for fission, paramecia undergo a process called conjugation (kahn juh GAY shun). In conjugation, two paramecia join at their oral grooves. The larger nuclei of both cells break and slowly disappear. Inside each cell the smaller nucleus divides. Then part of the smaller nucleus in one cell joins part of the smaller nucleus in the other cell, and vice versa (Figure 14–21). The paramecia then move apart and each organizes a new large nucleus and a new small nucleus. Since there are still only two paramecia after conjugation, there is no increase in the number of cells. However, conjugation makes the paramecia hardier and better able to continue their life.

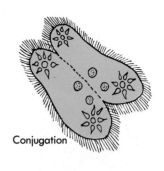
Conjugation

Fission

FIGURE 14–21. Paramecia reproduce by conjugation and by fission.

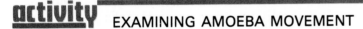

activity   EXAMINING AMOEBA MOVEMENT

Make a ring on a clean glass slide by dipping the mouth of a test tube in petroleum jelly and pressing it against the slide. Place a drop of amoeba culture inside the ring. Place a coverslip over the slide. Observe the amoebas under a microscope using low power and dim light. Why is it necessary to seal the culture with petroleum jelly?

How does a *Paramecium* reproduce?

activity   PROTISTS IN A HAY INFUSION

Make a hay infusion culture by boiling a handful of hay or dry grass in a liter of water. Place the culture in a jar and add a few grains of boiled rice. Let the mixture stand for 2 days; then add some pond water. Let the mixture stand for a few more days. Study the culture with a microscope. Describe the characteristics you see for any paramecia, amoebas, or other protists in the culture.

20. What would happen to an amoeba if it were not able to expel wastes?

21. A single amoeba was placed in a large tank. Within an hour it divided to form two amoebas. Assume that offspring continued to divide once every hour. If they all survive, how many amoebas would be in the tank after 12 hours?

22. What are the similarities in the way amoebas and paramecia obtain food? What are the differences?

23. What is the function of the smaller nucleus in the paramecium?

24. How does an amoeba respond to unfavorable conditions?

14:8   Flagellates

What is a flagellate?

A *Euglena* (yoo GLEE nuh) is an example of a flagellate, a one-celled protist with one or more flagella. Recall that a flagellum is a long, whiplike extension of a cell. By beating its flagella, a *Euglena* moves itself through water. A *Euglena* contains the green pigment chlorophyll which it uses to make food when light is present.

Some species of flagellates cause disease. African sleeping sickness is caused by a flagellate carried by the tsetse (SEET see) fly. People and animals can become infected by a bite from the tsetse fly. A person with the disease suffers from high fever, headache, and skin rash. Eventually, a person experiences mental dullness, paralysis, coma, and convulsions. If treatment with arsenic compounds is not given, death follows.

Some flagellates live together in colonies. For example, *Volvox* (VAHL vahks) is a flagellate which lives in a colony shaped like a ball about 1.5 mm in diameter. The walls of the ball contain thousands of *Volvox* cells joined by threads of cytoplasm. Flagella beat together to move the colony through the water.

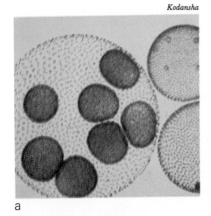

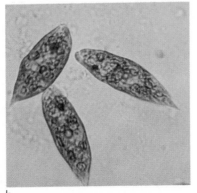

Kodansha

Carolina Biological Supply Co.

Roger K. Burnard

a   b

c

FIGURE 14–22. *Volvox* (a) is a colonial flagellate. *Euglena* (b) is a flagellate which can make its own food. A flagellate responsible for African sleeping sickness, is carried by tsetse fly (c).

MAKING SURE

25. How is the movement of paramecia, amoebas, and euglena different?

26. Why might some people classify *Euglena* in the plant kingdom?

14:9 Sporozoans

How are sporozoans harmful?

The protist kingdom also includes sporozoans (spor uh ZOH unz). Unlike amoebas and paramecia, sporozoans cannot move to obtain food. All sporozoans obtain food from the organisms in which they live. During one stage in the life cycle, sporozoans produce spores for reproduction. Sporozoans cause disease. Malaria (muh LER ee uh) and certain fevers in cattle are diseases produced by sporozoans. Sporozoans live in muscles, kidneys, and other parts of an animal.

A sporozoan goes through several different stages in its life cycle. Sometimes different parts of its life cycle occur in different animals. The life cycle of the sporozoan that causes malaria in humans involves a human and a mosquito.

MAKING SURE

27. How are sporozoans different from flagellates and other protists?

28. How are sporozoans similar to certain fungi in the method they use to obtain food?

14:10   Viruses

List the main characteristics of viruses.

Viruses are smaller than cells. They are so small that they cannot be seen with an ordinary microscope. A virus has features of both living and nonliving things. It is not classified in any of the five kingdoms. Viruses reproduce inside the living cells of organisms and can be grown on living tissue. For example, certain viruses can be grown on chick embryos. Viruses can also be changed to a crystal form that does not reproduce. In the crystal form they are like nonliving substances. A virus is made of a core of either DNA or RNA surrounded by protein. Pictures of viruses enlarged more than 100 000 times have been made with electron microscopes. These pictures show that viruses can be rodlike, or hexagonal in shape. A hexagonal-shaped virus has a tail or stalk (Figure 14-24a).

Viruses can cause disease in plants, animals, and people. The common cold, flu, smallpox, and polio are spread by air, food, water, and living organisms. When viruses infect a living organism, they invade and take over some of its cells. The virus becomes the "master" and the cell becomes a "slave." Normal activities of the cell change. It begins producing only more viruses. Eventually the cell bursts and releases new viruses. Once released, the new viruses can infect other cells.

a

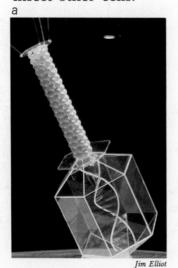

Jim Elliot

b

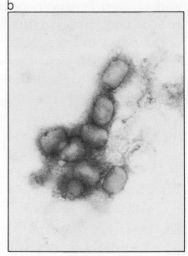

John Hanson, Ohio State University

FIGURE 14–23. A model of a virus (a). Smallpox virus magnified 47 500 times (b).

Viruses have been described as genes in search of a cell. A gene is a section of a DNA molecule which determines hereditary traits. When a virus enters a cell, the RNA or DNA of the virus controls the cell's chemical reactions.

One theory states that the first life on Earth was viruses of some kind. But this theory does not fit all the facts. Viruses can only live in the bodies of living plants and animals. Therefore, viruses as we know them could not have been the first form of life.

Another theory states that viruses are genes that got "out of hand." Viruses may be DNA or RNA molecules that escaped from cells long ago in some unexplained way. These "out of hand" DNA molecules multiplied by taking control of a cell's DNA. Today we call them viruses.

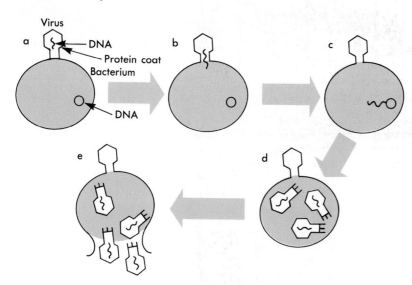

FIGURE 14-24. Some viruses attack bacteria. The virus attaches to the cell wall (a). The DNA from the virus is injected into the bacteria (b). The DNA from the virus attaches to the DNA of the bacteria (c). The DNA from the virus takes over and new viruses are formed within the bacteria (d). Within a short time bacteria burst open and the new viruses are released (e).

MAKING SURE

29. What features of a virus are similar to those of a living organism?

30. What feature of a virus makes it appear to be nonliving?

31. If we accept the theory that the first form of life on Earth were viruses why would those viruses have to have been different than present-day viruses?

Perspectives

How Words Are Formed

As new ideas and discoveries are made in science, the need for new words becomes necessary. New words come from many sources. Most often they are made from Latin and Greek words. Latin was the language of the ancient Romans. When we trace a word to its original source or language, we are studying its etymology.

Forming new words can be compared to building with blocks. We may begin with the root, the main block, and add other blocks to it to make a complete word. Blocks added before the root word are called prefixes. Blocks added after the root are called suffixes. Let us look at the word reproduction in Section 14:1 and note its parts.

Reproduction: *re* (prefix)   means again
pro (prefix)   means forward
duc (Latin root *ducere*)   means to lead
tion (suffix)   means capable of

By putting all of these meanings together, you arrive at a complete meaning: "capable of leading forward again." It refers to living organisms producing other living organisms.

When you begin to take words apart, you find that the same root may be part of many different words. This is also true of prefixes and suffixes. For example, note how many words contain the Latin root *ducere* (to lead). Some examples include conduct, produce, and reduce.

Look also at the many prefixes such as *con-*, *pro-*, and *re-* which you have seen many times in other words in our language. What other prefixes can you list?

Below is a list of the roots used by some of the words in this chapter. Can you find the word that uses each root and determine the definition of the word?

Root	Meaning	Root	Meaning
meta	to change	*kytos*	cell
protos	very first	*plassein*	to mold
spirare	to blow, breathe	*gener, genus*	birth, race, kind
chloros	greenish yellow	*phyllon*	leaf
flagellare	to whip, wave	*spore*	seed
zoion	animals	*endo*	within

This is just a beginning of the many roots used to form English words. In other chapters you will learn words that have other roots. You will also find other words which may use the same roots as those listed above. If you know the meaning of the root and the meaning of the prefixes and suffixes, you can determine the meanings of many words.

main ideas

1. The features of living things include reproduction, metabolism, movement, ability to respond to stimulus, and a definite size, shape, and lifespan.   14:1

2. Cells are the basic units of life. Most cells contain a cell membrane, nucleus, and cytoplasm.   14:2

3. Living things are classified into five kingdoms—monera, fungi, protist, plant, and animal.   14:4

4. The scientific name of an organism contains the genus and species names.   14:4

5. Fission is an asexual form of reproduction in which a cell divides to form two cells.   14:5

6. Bacteria are microscopic monerans which are shaped like spheres, rods, or spirals. All bacteria lack nuclei.   14:5

7. Yeasts, molds, and mushrooms are classified in the fungi kingdom. Fungi obtain their food from dead organic matter or other living things.   14:6

8. Amoebas and paramecia are one-celled organisms in the protist kingdom.   14:7

9. Viruses have living and nonliving features. They are made of a DNA or RNA core covered with protein.   14:10

vocabulary

Define the following words or terms.

amoeba	genus	organism	respiration
bacteria	kingdom	osmosis	species
cell	metabolism	paramecium	sporozoan
diffusion	microorganism	protist	stimulus
fission	monera	protoplasm	virus
fungi	nucleus		

study questions

DO NOT WRITE IN THIS BOOK.

A. True or False

Determine whether each of the sentences is true or false.
If the sentence is false, rewrite it to make it true.

1. People belong to the species known as *Homo sapiens*.

2. The number of plant species is greater than the number of animal species.

3. A scientific name includes the genus and species name of an organism.

4. One species name is *Canis*.

5. DNA contains a "life code."

6. Yeasts and molds contain chlorophyll.

7. Amoebas move by whipping their flagella.

8. *Euglena* contains chlorophyll.

9. One type of paramecium causes sleeping sickness.

10. Most viruses are larger than bacteria.

B. Multiple Choice

Choose the word or phrase that correctly completes each of the following sentences.

1. The *(cell membrane, nucleus, cytoplasm, vacoule)* controls the movement of material into and out of the cell.

2. The lion, house cat, leopard, and tiger belong to different *(phylum, class, genus, species)*.

3. Yeasts and molds are classified in the *(monera, fungi, plant, animal)* kingdom.

4. Diffusion of water through a membrane is called *(respiration, fermentation, osmosis, metabolism)*.

5. A *(kingdom, class, phylum, genus)* is the largest group in the classification of organisms.

6. The *(monera, plant, animal)* kingdom includes bacteria.

7. Paramecia move by the use of *(cilia, false feet, flagella, spores)*.

8. Yeast produces alcohol and carbon dioxide during *(photosynthesis, fermentation, fission, osmosis)*.

9. Malaria is caused by a species of *(mosquito, sporozoan, amoeba, bacteria)*.

10. Molds reproduce by *(osmosis, spores, fermentation)*.

C. Completion

Complete each of the following sentences with a word or phrase that will make the sentence correct.

1. In the scientific name *Felis domestica*, domestica is the _____ name.

2. Molecules diffuse from a region of _____ concentration to regions of _____ concentration.
3. A *Paramecium* has _____ nuclei.
4. A complete and entire living thing is called a(n) _____.
5. A plant cell _____ is rich in cellulose.
6. A virus can be seen with a(n) _____ microscope.
7. Every living organism is composed of one or more _____.
8. _____ form a cap and stalk above ground to produce spores.
9. _____ is a species which lives in a ball-shaped colony.
10. A common method of reproduction in single-celled protists is _____.

D. How and Why
1. How are living things different from nonliving things?
2. Draw a diagram of a cell and label the parts.
3. What advantages do scientific names have over common names for organisms?
4. Why is reproduction necessary for the survival of a species?
5. Why are bacteria able to survive in so many different environments?

investigations

1. Write a report on malaria, African sleeping sickness, or some other disease caused by a protist. Include in your report a discussion of the controls used to curb the spread of the disease and the effectiveness of the controls.
2. Obtain permission to visit a hospital or clinic laboratory to learn how bacteria are identified and cultured. Make a report to your class.

interesting reading

Simpson, Lance L. "Deadly Botulism," *Natural History*. January 1980, pp. 12–24.
Living Light: Exploring Bioluminescence. New York, NY: Messner, 1978.

A worker in a conservatory cares for a wide variety of plants. Some of the plants have flowers while other plants do not. Some plants grow in the hot, dry environment of the desert. Other plants grow in the hot, moist, environment of the tropics. How do desert plants differ from tropical plants? What processes are common to all plants?

Steve Lissau

Plants

15:1   Algae

Organisms in the plant kingdom come in a wide variety of sizes, shapes, and forms. Palm trees, seaweed, corn, grass, and dandelions all belong to the plant kingdom. Many useful products come from plants. Wood, charcoal, cotton, and paper are just a few of these products. All animals, including people, depend on plants for food.

One group of organisms that belong to the plant kingdom is algae. **Algae** are mostly one-celled plants which contain chlorophyll. **Chlorophyll** is a green substance in plant cells that is used to make food. It is chlorophyll that makes plants green.

Some species of algae are many-celled and very large. Algae are found from the poles to the equator. Certain species live in hot springs at temperatures as high as 89°C. Most algae live in fresh water or the ocean.

Protococcus is one of the many species of green algae. *Protococcus* grows on tree trunks. It forms a green coating on the bark. The cells are so small that it takes millions of them to cover a few square centimeters. *Protococcus* is a single, round or oval cell somewhat like yeast. Each cell contains a cell wall, membrane, cytoplasm, and nucleus. *Protococcus* differs from yeast in that it contains chlorophyll and can make its own food. Protococcus reproduces by fission.

GOAL: You will learn the main features of different kinds of plants and their life activities.

What are algae?

What is *Protococcus* and how does it differ from a yeast cell?

317

William Patterson/Tom Stack & Assoc.

a

Runk, Schoenberger/Grant Heilman Photography

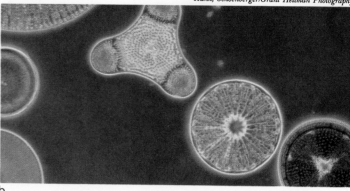

b

FIGURE 15–1. Kelp is a large brown algae (a). Diatoms are single celled algae which occur in thousands of different shapes (b).

Protococcus cells live together in colonies of two, four, or six cells. Each cell contains many green chloroplasts (KLOR uh plasts), the disc-shaped bodies that contain chlorophyll. It is in the chloroplast that food is made.

MAKING SURE

1. Why do most algae live in water environments?

2. How does *Protococcus* reproduce?

15:2   Mosses and Liverworts

Mosses and liverworts are small, many-celled plants that contain chlorophyll. They live close to the ground and rarely grow to more than a few centimeters in height. They do not have true roots, stems, and leaves. Mosses and liverworts lack the kind of transport system for moving water that is found in higher plants. Water and food move through moss and liverwort plants by diffusion.

FIGURE 15–2. *Spirogyra* (a) and *Protoccus* (b) are two species of algae.

a

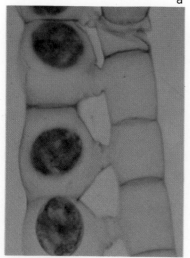

b

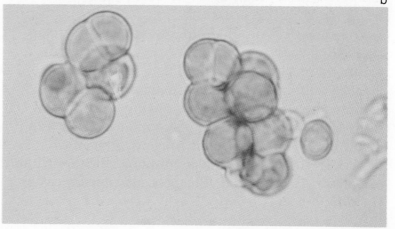

Ward's Natural Science Establishment, Inc.

Runk, Schoenberger/Grant Heilman Photography

Liverworts grow only in wet places such as the banks of a stream or spring. A liverwort looks like a leathery "leaf" lying flat against the ground. Hairlike structures called rhizoids (RI zoydz) anchor the plant and absorb water from the soil. *Marchantia*, one species of liverwort, produces umbrella-shaped reproductive structures about 2.5 cm long.

Moss grows in shaded, moist areas such as cracks in shaded sidewalks or moist soil under a tree. Moss plants appear to have "stems" with many "leaves." Rootlike rhizoids grow from the base of a moss "stem."

List the main characteristics of mosses and liverworts.

Alvin E. Staffan

a

Roger K. Burnard

b

FIGURE 15–3. *Marchantia* has umbrella-shaped reproductive structures (a). Mosses do not have true roots, stems, or leaves (b).

activity GROWING LIVERWORTS

Obtain some *Marchantia* from a field, forest, or biological supply company. Grow the *Marchantia* in a terrarium containing a layer of gravel and a layer of topsoil and humus. Cover the terrarium with a piece of glass. Observe the plants and watch for the growth of reproductive structures. Why should the relative humidity in the terrarium be kept at a high level?

MAKING SURE

3. Explain why mosses and liverworts grow close to the ground.
4. Why do mosses and liverworts grow in damp areas?
5. How are mosses and liverworts similar to algae? How are they different?

15:3 Ferns

Ferns are larger than mosses and liverworts. They have true roots, stems, and leaves, and tubelike structures to carry water and food to all parts of the plant. Ferns grow in woods, swamps, and gardens where much moisture is present. Millions of years ago large fern forests covered the earth. At that time most of the land was wet and marshy, and the climate was warm. Tree ferns 9 to 12 m high were common. Today's ferns are much smaller.

Ferns have a life cycle with two stages. In one stage, small patches of spore cases form on the underside of a fern. When ripe, the spore cases open and spores are released. In a suitable environment, a spore grows to form a small plant about 0.5 to 1mm in diameter. When an organism is produced from a spore, it is by asexual reproduction. Asexual means there is only one parent.

In the second stage of reproduction the new plant produces sex cells—eggs and sperms. A sperm swims to an egg through rainwater or dew and unites with the egg. The fused egg and sperm grow to form a new fern plant. This second stage is sexual reproduction. In sexual reproduction, two different sex cells are united to produce the offspring.

What conditions are best for ferns to grow and reproduce?

MAKING SURE

6. Explain why ferns are able to grow several meters in height while mosses rarely exceed several centimeters.

7. Why must ferns live in a moist environment in order to reproduce?

FIGURE 15–4. Ferns (a) reproduce asexually by forming spores on the underside of the leaves (b).

a

b

Roger K. Burnard

Roger K. Burnard

15:4 Seed Plants

Most of the plants you see are seed plants. There are two groups of seed plants—gymnosperms (JIHM nuh spurmz) and angiosperms (AN jee uh spurmz). **Gymnosperms** produce seeds that are not enclosed in a fruit. Pine, spruce, redwood, and fir trees are gymnosperms. Some gymnosperms, called conifers, produce seeds in cones.

Angiosperms have flowers and produce seeds inside a fruit. Maple trees, grass, corn, daisies, orchids, and tomatoes are angiosperms. More than half the known species of plants are angiosperms.

Name the two groups of seed plants.

a

Roger K. Burnard

b

Ruth Dixon

FIGURE 15–5. Spruce trees (a) and other conifers produce seeds in cones (b).

Seed plants have true roots, stems, and leaves. Each of these parts is made of cells which are grouped together to form tissues. A **tissue** is a group of cells performing the same function. For example, a stem contains tissue whose function is to carry water up the stem. An **organ** is a group of tissues working together to perform a function. Organs in a flower produce cells that form seeds allowing a seed plant to reproduce.

Define tissue and organ.

FIGURE 15–6. Cherry trees have colorful flowers (a) and produce seeds inside a fruit (b).

a

William McKinney/Alpha

b

William D. Popejoy

15:5 Roots

What are some functions of roots?

Roots anchor a plant. They also absorb, store, and transport water and dissolved substances. Have you ever tried to pull a plant out of the ground? A root system holds the plant firmly in the soil. Otherwise, wind and rain would easily uproot it. The root system of a plant spreads out from the plant. It sends many tiny roots throughout the soil in a complex pattern.

The size of a root system varies with different plants. Most land plants have as much or more growth below ground as above. The roots of some plants, such as alfalfa, are long and slender. Alfalfa roots may grow 5 m or more down into the soil.

Describe the structure and function of a root hair.

Small root hairs spread outward into the soil from the roots. Each root hair is a single cell that moves water and dissolved minerals through its cell membrane by osmosis.

Water and dissolved minerals travel through the root hairs into the xylem tissue of the root. Xylem tissue contains specialized xylem cells which transport water and dissolved minerals to all parts of the plant.

In many plants, the root is the main organ of food storage. The turnip is an example of a root that is filled with stored food. Turnips and most other roots in which food is stored are rich in starch. The stored starch allows the turnip plant to survive during the winter and to grow again in the spring.

How are some plants like turnips able to survive winter and grow again in the spring?

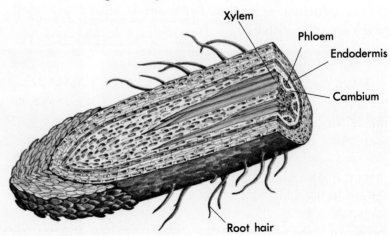

FIGURE 15–7. Tissues in a root.

The growth of roots is affected by many factors in the environment. Gravity and water are two factors which have a great effect on roots. Roots respond to gravity by growing downward. They respond to water by growing toward the water source. The response of roots to water explains why tree roots often clog sewer pipes. Water leaking from a pipe stimulates the roots to grow toward it.

What two factors affect the growth of roots?

William D. Popejoy

a

b

FIGURE 15–8. The root system of some plants consists of many roots and root hairs (a). The root system of a carrot consists of one main root (b).

activity ROOTS AND ROOT HAIRS

Soak some radish seeds in water overnight. Place them in a petri dish on a piece of a moist paper towel. Cover and allow to stand in a warm place (28°C) for several days. Keep the paper towel moist. Use a binocular microscope or hand lens to study the roots.

activity HOW DO PLANT ROOTS RESPOND TO WATER?

Make a ball of sphagnum moss and hold it together with some cord. Soak seeds, such as radish or oats, in water. Place the seeds at the top, sides, and bottom in the outer portion of the moss. Hang up the ball and keep it moist for two weeks by spraying it daily with water. Watch the seeds sprout and begin to grow. Observe how the roots grow. Is the water a greater stimulus to root growth than gravity?

8. How is the growth of roots affected by the amount of water available?

9. How does stored food aid the survival of a turnip plant?

10. Name at least five functions of roots.

15:6 Stems

What is the main function of the stem?

The transporting of water, minerals, and food is the main function of the stem. It also supports the leaves, allowing them to be exposed to sunlight. Food is made in the stems of some plants. Geranium and cactus are plants in which stem cells make food.

Name the two types of plant stems. How are they different?

There are two types of plant stems—herbaceous (hur BAY shus) and woody. Herbaceous stems are soft and green. Usually they lack woody tissue and can be bent. Tomatoes, beans, peas, and corn are plants with herbaceous stems. Most plants with herbaceous stems live only one growing season. Because they grow for only one season, the plants are called annuals. **Annual** means once a year. Thus, an annual is a plant that grows, reproduces, and dies during one growing season.

FIGURE 15–9. Annuals such as corn have herbaceous stems and must be replanted each year (a). The apple trees have woody stems and live to produce fruit for several growing seasons (b).

a

b

USDA

David M. Dennis

Plants with woody stems are called perennials. A **perennial** is a plant that lives for several growing seasons. In fact, the age of a woody-stem plant may be found by counting the annual growth rings. During the spring and summer months, a woody stem increases in length and thickness and forms branches. Its woody tissue makes it rigid and stiff. Trees and shrubs have woody stems.

Stems contain several types of tissues. These include xylem (ZI lum), phloem (FLO em), and cambium (KAM be um). The order and arrangement of xylem, phloem, and cambium tissue in herbaceous and woody plants is shown in Figure 15-11.

Xylem tissue in the stem, as in the root, transports water and dissolved minerals upward. Phloem tissue transports food substances downward. Cambium is the growth tissue of the stem. It produces new xylem and phloem cells and causes the increased thickness of a woody stem. The annual rings in a woody stem are new xylem cells produced by the cambium.

You probably think of a stem as the part of a plant that grows above the ground. Some plants, however, have underground stems. An underground stem is called a rhizome. Many grasses produce rhizomes, which spread the grass plants through the soil.

Don Parsisson

FIGURE 15–10. Plants with wood stems exhibit annual growth rings.

What is the difference between an annual and a perennial?

What three tissues are found in stems?

Define rhizome.

FIGURE 15–11. Tissues in a stem.

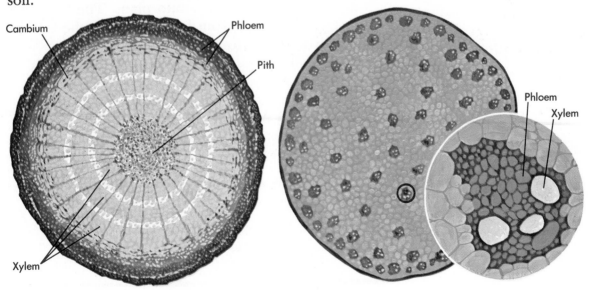

Cambium

Phloem

Pith

Xylem

Phloem

Xylem

FIGURE 15–12. Different
kinds of underground stems.

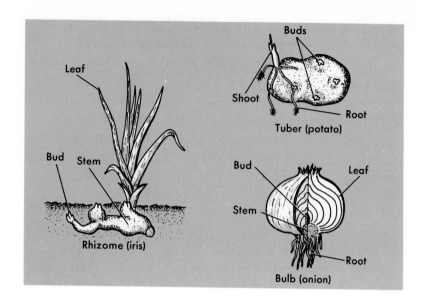

Define tuber and bulb.

White potatoes and a few other plants produce a special kind of stem called a tuber. A tuber is the tip of a rhizome that is enlarged because of the storage of food in its cells. The white potato is the tuber of the potato plant. The "eyes" of the potato are buds. These eyes or buds in the white potato tuber may be used to grow new potato plants. One potato is cut into several sections. Each section must contain at least one bud and a piece of tuber. These sections are then planted. If all conditions are favorable, each bud grows to form a new potato plant. The bud gets its energy for growth from food stored in the portion of the tuber to which it is attached.

A plant bulb is a portion of the stem that grows underground. It consists of thick leaves that grow together in compact layers around a small bud. When separated from its parent plant and planted, the bud grows to form a new plant. Can you name any plants that reproduce by bulbs?

activity TRANSPORT IN A PLANT STEM

Cut one end of a celery stalk and place it in a bottle of red ink. Observe the celery after a few hours. What happens? Explain.

activity   COUNTING THE AGE OF A TREE

Obtain a cross-section piece of a tree trunk (stem). Observe the annual rings. Determine the age of the tree by counting the rings.

activity   GROWING SWEET POTATOES

Suspend a fresh sweet potato, tapered end down, in a smallmouthed jar filled with water. You may have to insert 3 toothpicks to suspend the potato. Put the jar in a sunny window. Add water as needed to keep the water level constant. Record the number of days it takes the leaves and roots to grow. From which part of the sweet potato did new leaves and roots develop?

15:7   Leaves

In most plants, leaves are the "food factories." Leaves produce the food the plant uses to build new tissues and to carry on life activities. Leaves vary in size, shape, structure, and arrangement. The shape of a leaf can be used to identify a plant.

The outer protective layer of a leaf is the epidermis (ep uh DUR mus). A waxy cuticle covers the epidermis of some leaves. The cuticle reduces water loss from the leaves to prevent wilting and drying out during dry weather. Inside a leaf are soft, thin-walled cells arranged in two layers. Many of these cells have large amounts of chlorophyll. Veins within the leaf are part of the plant's transport system.

The epidermis of a leaf contains many small, porelike structures. These structures admit carbon dioxide and oxygen and control the release of water vapor. Each of these structures is called a stoma. A leaf may contain from 9000 to 70 000 stomata in each square centimeter of surface area. Most often, more stomata are found in the lower epidermis of a leaf than in the upper epidermis. Why?

Name the parts of a leaf.

FIGURE 15–13. A stoma on a leaf opens (a) and closes (b) to regulate the amount of gases that move into or out of a leaf.

a

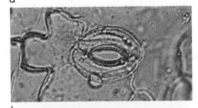

b

Kodansha

FIGURE 15–14. Structures in
a leaf.

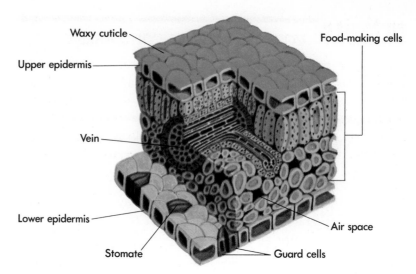

Each stoma consists of an opening or pore about 1/20 as wide as the thickness of this page. The pore opens into air spaces within the leaf. Each pore is surrounded by two guard cells. Guard cells control the opening and closing of a stoma. When the guard cells absorb water, they swell and the stoma opens. When the guard cells lose water, they relax and the stoma closes. Stomata are most often closed at night and open during the day.

Stomata admit carbon dioxide to the leaf. Carbon dioxide diffuses from the air outside the leaf through the stomata into the air spaces within the leaf. The carbon dioxide is used to make food.

Stomata regulate the loss of water through the leaves of a plant. This water loss is called **transpiration.** Much of the water absorbed by the roots leaves the plant by transpiration through open stomata. In very dry weather, stomata often remain closed all day to reduce the loss of water.

Define transpiration.

FIGURE 15–15.

activity WATER LOSS FROM PLANTS.

Obtain a geranium plant in a flowerpot. Put a small plastic bag over the pot and tie the bag tightly around the stem. Use a large plastic bag to cover the entire plant and pot. Observe any changes that occur after 24 hours. Why did the changes occur?

activity
MAKING AND OBSERVING A LEAF SKELETON

(1) Obtain a leaf that is not damaged from insect-eating, breakage, and so on. Young leaves from early spring or old leaves from late fall are best. Magnolia leaves are most effective. (2) Fill a low tray or pan with pond water containing infusoria. Place the leaf in the water. Put the pan where it is warm, but not in direct sunlight. Why? (3) After two weeks, observe the extent of decomposition of the leaf tissue. Place the leaf under a fast-flowing stream of water from a faucet. The entire mass of tissue other than the vein structure will probably wash away. If the tissue does not wash away from the veins, place the leaf in the pond water for a few more days. (4) When the tissue is removed, press the skeletonized leaf between blotters or towels. The leaf can be preserved by pressing it between two sheets of plastic. What caused the tissue of the leaf to decompose?

FIGURE 15–16. The small structures within a plant cell are chloroplasts.

15:8 Photosynthesis

If a plant is to grow, it must have light. Green plants absorb solar energy and use it in **photosynthesis** to make food. The energy stored in the food is used for the growth and repair of tissues. Plants grow most rapidly where there is plenty of light, water, and fertile soil.

Glucose, oxygen, and water are the products of photosynthesis. **Glucose,** a simple sugar, is the food used by the plant. Many glucose molecules join to make starch which is stored in the plant. Oxygen gas leaves the plant through the stomata.

The equation for photosynthesis is written as follows:

$$6CO_2 + 12H_2O \xrightarrow[\text{light}]{\text{chlorophyll}} C_6H_{12}O_6 + 6O_2 + 6H_2O$$

carbon dioxide   water   glucose   oxygen   water

Ward's Natural Science Establishment, Inc.

activity

PHOTOSYNTHESIS

Objective: To determine if sunlight and chlorophyll are needed for photosynthesis

Materials
alcohol
baby food jar
beaker
coleus leaf
construction paper, black (or aluminum foil)
electric lamp (if direct sunlight is not available)
geranium plant
hot plate or ring stand and burner
iodine solution

Procedure

1. Keep the geranium plant in darkness for a few days to "starve" it. The purpose of this procedure is to stop the production of food.

2. Remove the plant from the darkness and cover one-half the surface area of 3 separate leaves with the black construction paper, Figure 15–17.

3. Place the plant in direct sunlight or under the electric lamp for 3 days.

4. After 3 days, pluck the leaves that were partially covered with paper and remove the paper.

5. Fill a small beaker with 200 mL of water. Heat the water to boiling with a hot plate or burner.

6. Place the leaves in boiling water for about 2 min.

7. Remove the leaves from the beaker and place them in a baby food jar containing 20 mL of alcohol. Place the lid tightly on the jar.

8. Carefully shake the jar containing the leaves and alcohol for 3 or 4 min to dissolve the chlorophyll that is present.

9. Remove the leaves from the alcohol and place them on a paper towel.

10. With the iodine solution, test for food in the leaves. Pour the iodine over the surface of each of the 3 leaves. An iodine-alcohol solution, turns blue when it comes in contact with starch. Record your results.

11. Obtain a coleus leaf. A coleus leaf has chlorophyll in certain sections.

12. Test the coleus leaf for starch by repeating Steps 5–8.

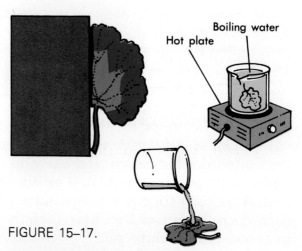

Boiling water
Hot plate

FIGURE 15–17.

Observations and Data
Record your observations.

Questions and Conclusions

1. Why was the geranium placed in the sunlight for 3 days?

2. What process must have occurred in the leaf if the iodine solution changed colors when poured on the leaf?

3. According to this activity, what was produced in the leaf.

activity
CARBON DIOXIDE AND PHOTOSYNTHESIS

Place one "starved" geranium plant on a shelf by a sunny window. Place another under an inverted bell jar, together with two small beakers one-half full of sodium hydroxide pellets. **CAUTION:** Sodium hydroxide can cause severe burns. Do not touch the chemical with your hands. Use petroleum jelly to form a seal around the base of the jar. An atmosphere with reduced carbon dioxide is within the bell jar. After three days, test a leaf from each plant for starch. Use the iodine test from the previous activity. What were the results?

NaOH   Beaker

FIGURE 15–18.

15:9   The Flower

A flower is a modified stem that contains organs for reproduction. These organs are usually surrounded by specialized leaves called petals. Often the petals of a flower, such as the rose, are brightly colored. Other plants, such as grass, have small flowers that often are not seen.

Other flower organs are sepals, stamens, and pistils. The sepals are green, leaflike structures on the underside of a flower. They enclose the parts of a flower before the flower bud opens and support it after it opens. Stamens and pistils are the reproductive parts of the flower. The stamen produces **pollen,** tiny grains which contain nuclei for reproduction. The pistil produces egg cells inside an ovule which is enclosed by an ovary (Figure 15–19).

Flowers which contain all four organs—sepals, petals, stamen, and pistil—are called complete flowers. Flowers which are missing one or more organs are incomplete flowers. In some plants, stamens and pistils are formed in different flowers. Each incomplete flower contains either stamens or pistils but not both. In the corn plant, pistil-bearing flowers form on the ear. Stamen-bearing flowers form on the tassel. In species such as the willow and meadow rue, pistil-bearing flowers grow on one

Name the parts of a flower.

Why are the some flowers incomplete?

FIGURE 15–19.   Parts of a complete flower.

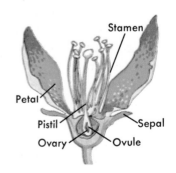

FIGURE 15–20. The reproductive structures of some flowers are easily identified.

plant, and stamen-bearing flowers grow on another plant. Both types of plants must be present for the species to reproduce. One plant produces the pollen, and the other plant produces the eggs.

Pollen produced on the stamen is carried by wind, water, or a flying insect to the pistil. The transfer of pollen from stamen to pistil is called **pollination.** The transfer may be from a stamen to a pistil within the same flower. Pollination can also occur when pollen is carried from one flower to another.

When a pollen grain lands on the pistil, it grows a tube down into an ovule. Inside the ovule is an ovary containing an egg nucleus. When the tube reaches the ovule it grows into the ovule inside the ovary. A nucleus from the pollen cell fuses with the egg nucleus. The joining of the pollen and egg nuclei is called **fertilization.** After fertilization, a small plant called an embryo begins to grow inside the ovule. Meanwhile, the walls of the ovule toughen and starch is stored inside. The fertilized ovule is now a seed. The seed has a hard coat surrounding an embryo plant and stored food.

Define pollination. In what two ways can pollination occur?

Define fertilization.

Which part of a flower becomes a seed? Which part becomes a fruit?

The ovary part of the pistil surrounds the growing seeds. The ovary enlarges and becomes a fruit. A pea pod, for example, is the ovary of a pea plant. For this reason, a pea pod is actually a fruit. Fruits such as oranges, grapes, tomatoes, blueberries, and plums are enlarged ovaries of plants. Each ovary enlarged with stored food after its ovules were fertilized.

MAKING SURE

11. Classify each of the following as a fruit or seed.
    (a) apple   (c) bean   (e) lemon
    (b) pea   (d) peach

12. Which of the above is formed from an ovary? Ovule?

15:10 Seeds

Seeds provide food for people and animals. Every seed consists of two main parts—the embryo and the seed coat. The seed coat is a protective covering for the developing embryo. It develops from the wall of the ovule. In some seeds, a material called endosperm is present. Endosperm is a tissue that contains stored food. Both the endosperm and the embryo are enclosed with the seed coats. Cotyledons (kaht ul EED unz) are the seed leaves that are attached to the plant embryo. They store food. When the seed begins to grow, the one part of the embryo becomes the root of the new plant. Another part becomes the lower stem and the rest becomes the upper stem and leaves.

Name the two main parts of a seed.

What important function do endosperm and cotyledons perform?

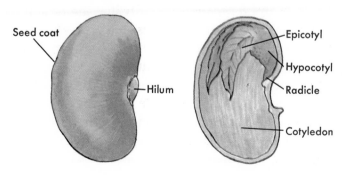

FIGURE 15–21. Parts of a bean seed.

FIGURE 15–22. New roots and stems can be observed growing from germinating seeds.

What conditions are favorable for germination? After germination, what conditions determine life?

FIGURE 15-23.

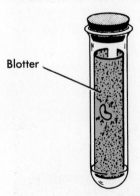

Blotter

Endosperm is found in the grains of corn, wheat, and other cereals. In many seeds, the endosperm which stores food is absorbed by the developing embryo. This food storage process is true for bean, pea, alfalfa, and clover. In the seeds of these plants, most of the stored food is in the cotyledons.

The early growth of an embryo plant is called **germination** (jur muh NAY shun). Germination will take place only if conditions are favorable. There must be a favorable temperature and enough moisture and oxygen. For some plants, certain light requirements must be met.

After germination is completed, a plant requires air, water, light, and fertile soil. The fertility of the soil is a very important factor. It may mean the difference between life and death for a plant.

activity   FACTORS AFFECTING SEED GERMINATION

(1) Soak 54 bean seeds in water overnight. This process will soften the hard coat covering each. (2) The next day, place 3 beans and a piece of blotter in each of 18 test tubes. Press the seeds between the blotter and the wall of the test tube (Figure 15–23).

(3) In 9 of the test tubes, moisten the blotters with water. Seal the test tubes with stoppers. (4) Arrange the 18 tubes into 6 groups—3 groups with wet blotters and 3 groups with dry blotters. Each group will contain 3 test tubes. (5) Place group A (3 dry tubes) and group B (3 wet tubes) under the lamp. (6) Place group C (3 dry tubes) and group D (3 wet tubes) in a refrigerator set at 10°C. Be sure the light in the refrigerator is off. (7) Place group E (3 dry tubes) and group F (3 wet tubes) in a drawer where the temperature is about 25°C. (8) Observe all 6 groups each day. Record the number of seeds in each group that germinate after 1 week. Which group or groups germinated in the least amount of time? Which group or groups took the most time to germinate? What were the best conditions for seed germination?

activity   SEED GERMINATION

Fill a small tray or wooden flat with soil. Plant 20 bean seeds (soaked overnight in water) in the soil. Water regularly. Be careful not to overwater. Dig up 2 seeds every other day. Observe changes above and below the soil. Diagram what you see.

What special seed structures adapt the seed for wide dispersal?

15:11 Seed Dispersal

Few seeds would grow into new plants if they all grew in the same place. There would be too much competition for water, minerals, and sunlight. Only a few plants would survive. As a result, many seeds have features that aid seed dispersal. Seed dispersal is the carrying away of seeds from the plant on which they grow. Wind, water, and animals are the chief agents of seed dispersal.

Fruits and seeds often have special structures that allow them to be carried by the wind. For example, the fruit of the maple, ash, and elm have wings. Cotton, milkweed, and willow have long, silky hairs. Dandelion seeds are attached to hairlike tufts that form a parachute-like structure. A gentle breeze can carry a dandelion seed far from where it began its life.

Fleshy, edible fruits aid in seed dispersal. They are eaten by animals, often at a distance from where they grew. When the fruit is eaten, the seeds are exposed and may be dropped to the ground. If conditions are favorable, the seeds may grow.

Seeds of wild barley and most grasses have bristles. The bristles cling to the hair of animals or to clothing. Some fruits, such as cocklebur, have hooks or barbs that aid in their dispersal. You may have noticed after a walk in a park, field or forest, that your clothing has picked up some wild seeds or fruits. If so, you were an agent in the dispersal of plant seeds.

FIGURE 15–24. The seeds of milkweed (a) and maple (b) are dispersed by the wind.

a   J.W. Thompson

b   General Biological Supply House

Perspectives

people

Cactus Cop

Cactus rustling! What is it? It is the illegal taking of cactus. In the 47 states where cacti grow, several of the 250 species are approaching extinction.

In the southwest deserts, cacti are important because they help protect soil from wind and rain erosion. Besides being beautiful, they provide fruit for people, birds, and insects. It takes a long time for these plants to grow. A saguaro cactus grows about 1 cm each year. During its life span of 150 years, it produces millions of seeds, but less than 10 reach maturity and grow into new cacti.

In 1929, Arizona passed a native plant law. In 1967, additional laws were passed establishing a Compliance Division or "cactus cops". Arizona's laws are tough concerning removal and destruction of protected plants.

Arizona law allows specific numbers and types of cactus to be taken from a certain area. Purchasers of cacti must keep permit tags as proof of legal sale. In 1979 more than 1.8 million dollars worth of cacti was legally dug from the wild. Approximately 0.5 million dollars worth of plants were taken illegally, however. Cactus rustling is growing.

How do cactus cops do their job? Besides catching the rustlers, a cactus cop also gives talks to garden clubs, schools, and fairs. When someone transports plants across state lines, cards are filled out and checked by cactus cops at inspection stations.

At one of these inspection stations, a cactus cop examines several plants, suspecting that they have been rustled. A large saguaro cactus shows a dark substance oozing from its chopped roots. "A tissue infection that comes from abusing the plants," comments the cactus cop. Stopping by a large ocotillo cactus, the cop points to deep gashes in its bark. "Some cactus haulers are in a hurry, so they use heavy chains wrapped around a truck bumper and the cactus to tear it out. Because cacti grow very slowly, it may take over a year for these injured plants to die." The cactus cop is gathering evidence for a trial of the cactus rustlers.

New laws are being prepared to increase the protection of cacti. Meanwhile, cactus cops work hard in many ways to protect these vanishing plants.

Vic Banks

Adapted from "Cactus Cops Wage War on Rustlers" by Timothy Branning in *National Wildlife* © 1978 and "Our Cacti Have Met the Enemies—and They Are Us," which originally appeared in the December, 1980 issue of *Smithsonian* © 1980 by Victor Banks.

main ideas

1. Algae are mostly one-celled green plants. 15:1
2. Mosses and liverworts grow close to the ground. They lack true roots, stems, and leaves. 15:2
3. Ferns are larger than mosses and liverworts. They have roots, stems, and leaves. 15:3
4. Seed plants dominate the plant life on Earth. 15:4
5. Roots provide anchorage, water and mineral absorption, and food storage for plants. 15:5
6. A plant stem conducts water and dissolved minerals upward to the leaves. It also conducts food substances downward from the leaves. 15:6
7. Leaves are the "food factories" for most plants. 15:7
8. A seed requires moisture, the proper temperature, and oxygen to germinate. 15:10
9. Seeds are dispersed by wind, water, animals, and people. 15:11

vocabulary

Define each of the following words or terms.

algae	germination	pollen
angiosperm	gymnosperm	pollination
annual	liverwort	sperm
egg	moss	spore
fern	organ	tissue
fertilization	perennial	transpiration
flower	photosynthesis	tuber

study questions

DO NOT WRITE IN THIS BOOK.

A. True or False

Determine whether each of the following sentences is true or false. If the sentence is false, rewrite it to make it true.

1. Most of the land plants are algae.
2. In most plants, food is stored in the leaves.

3. *Protococcus* is a green algae.
4. All stems grow above the ground.
5. A moss has roots, stems, and leaves.
6. Tubers and bulbs are special roots that store food.
7. A fern produces spores.
8. Transpiration occurs most rapidly when the stomata of a plant are closed.
9. Ferns reproduce through seeds.
10. Seed plants have roots, stems and leaves.

B. Multiple Choice

Choose the word or phrase that completes correctly each of the following sentences.

1. A *(stoma, pistil, root hair, stamen)* absorbs water and minerals from the soil.
2. A *(tomato, corn grain, bulb, white potato)* is a tuber.
3. Water enters a root through the process of *(pollination, osmosis, fertilization, transpiration)*.
4. *(Xylem, Cambium, Epidermis)* tissue conducts water upward in a plant stem.
5. The *(tomato, elm, maple, palm)* is an example of an herbaceous plant.
6. *(Xylem, Cambium, Phloem, Epidermis)* is the growth tissue of a stem.
7. Pollen is produced in a *(flower, leaf, stem, root)*.
8. A maple seed will most likely be dispersed by *(wind, water, animals, people)*.
9. Plants lose water from their leaves by *(transpiration, photosynthesis, osmosis)*.
10. *(Chlorophyll, Water, Glucose, Carbon dioxide)* is produced in photosynthesis.

C. Completion

Complete each of the following sentences with a word or phrase that will make the sentence correct.

1. Plants use _____ energy in photosynthesis.
2. _____ flowers do not contain all the parts found in a complete flower.

3. Leaves are called the _____ factories of plants.
4. Photosynthesis occurs primarily in the _____ of plants.
5. _____ gas is formed in photosynthesis.
6. Plants are green because they contain a green pigment called _____.
7. In a flower, the reproductive parts are usually surrounded by very colorful, modified leaves called _____.
8. The fertilized _____ of a flower becomes a seed.
9. The union of a nucleus in a pollen cell and the egg nucleus in the ovary is called _____.
10. _____, _____, and _____ are three conditions necessary for germination.

D. How and Why
1. Why do many desert plants have small leaves or no leaves at all?
2. Why is seed dispersal important to a plant species' survival?
3. Why is a bee a good agent for pollination?
4. Draw a diagram of a *Protococcus* cell and label its parts.
5. Why is photosynthesis necessary for a green plant to stay alive?

investigations

1. Make a collection of tree leaves of 15 common species. Learn to identify these trees by their leaves.
2. Green leaves use only a portion of the light spectrum in photosynthesis. Plan and carry out, under the supervision of your teacher, an experiment to discover what colors of light are used in food making.

interesting reading

Keller, Evelyn Fox, "McClintock's Maise." *Science 81*. Oct. 1981, pp. 54-59.

Selsam, Millicent and Jerome Wexler, *Eat the Fruit, Plant the Seed*. New York, NY: Morrow, 1980.

Wexler, Jerome, *Secrets of the Venus' Fly Trap*. New York, NY: Dodd, Mead, 1981.

16

When you think of an animal, you may think of a furry creature like a dog or a rabbit. However, a wide variety of living organisms without fur are animals. Many people do not consider insects like this praying mantis to be animals. What are the characteristics of animals? What are cells, tissues, and organs? What are the main animal groups?

Roger K. Burnard

Animals

16:1 Tissues, Organs, and Systems

More than one million species belong to the animal kingdom. Most animals move about, take in oxygen, and obtain food from plants or other animals. Some animals, such as sponges and jellyfish, live in water. Others, such as honeybees, can fly through air. Every animal species has special traits and structures that make it different from other species.

Animals have cells that are specialized. That is, each cell has a certain kind of job to do. For example, a red blood cell carries oxygen. A muscle cell helps to move a part of an animal's body. These specialized cells are grouped together to form tissues. Blood is a tissue containing different kinds of blood cells. Muscle tissue is made of muscle cells. Bone tissue contains bone cells.

Groups of tissues working together make organs. Examples of organs in an animal are the heart, lungs, eyes, and ears. Can you name the function of each of these organs? Organs are grouped together in **systems.** Two systems in animals are the circulatory system and the digestive system. The circulatory system moves blood through the animal.

GOAL: You will learn the characteristics of the invertebrate animal phyla and examples of each. Life activities of each will be discussed.

What are specialized cells?

How are a tissue, organ, and system different?

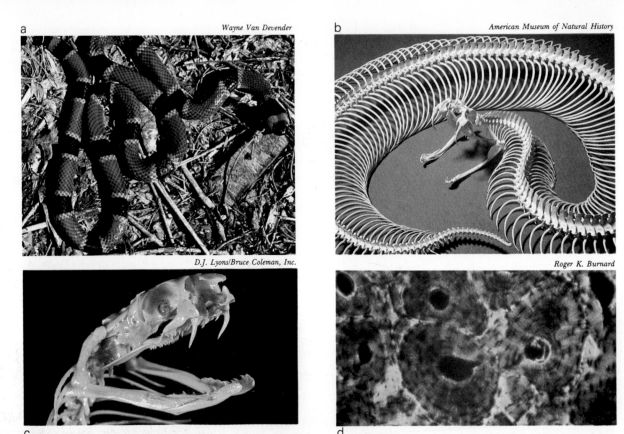

a

b

c

d

FIGURE 16–1. A snake (a) and other complex organisms are made up of systems (b), organs (c), tissues, and cells (d).

The digestive system breaks down food into simpler substances that cells can use. Systems work together in doing all the activities needed to keep an animal alive.

16:2 Sponges

One of the simplest animals is the sponge. A sponge's body is a sack of cells containing pores, canals, and chambers. Most sponges are attached to the rocks at the ocean bottom near the coast. Ocean water constantly flows through the body of the sponge. From this water, the sponge obtains food and oxygen. As it uses food and oxygen, the sponge, like every animal, produces wastes which must be expelled from its body. The flow of ocean water through a sponge removes these wastes.

There are about 5000 different species of sponges. A natural sponge used for washing or cleaning is the

How does a sponge obtain food?

mineral matter or skeleton of a sponge's body. It is the material left after the cells have died and decayed. Artificial sponges for cleaning are made from cellulose, rubber, or plastic.

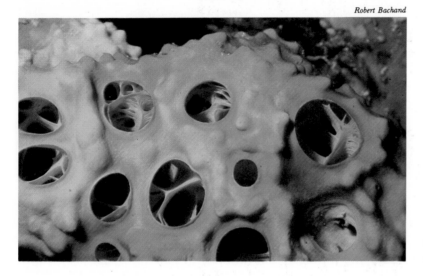

Robert Bachand

FIGURE 16–2. Adult sponges live along shallow coastlines, attached to rocks along the bottom.

16:3 Jellyfish and Their Relatives

Jellyfish also live in water but are more complex than sponges. Their relatives include sea anemones (uh NEM uh neez), corals, and hydra. These animals are alike in that they all have a cavity in the center of their bodies. Unlike a sponge, jellyfish can move slowly through water. It swims by contracting and releasing fibers in its body.

Most jellyfish have tentacles. The tentacles are ropelike organs containing special stinging structures. Each stinger contains a slender coiled thread having spines attached to it and is used to sting other animals.

How does a jellyfish catch its food? It grasps a nearby animal with its tentacles. The coiled threads shoot out from the tentacles and stick into the animal. Poison from the threads is injected into the animal. The poison paralyzes it. The tentacles then pull the paralyzed creature into the jellyfish's central body cavity. Here the animal is digested and absorbed by the body cells.

How are jellyfish, sea anemones, corals, and hydra alike?

FIGURE 16–3. A jellyfish has a soft body that contains a central body cavity.

Joey Jacques

FIGURE 16–4. Small fish are paralyzed by the poison injected from the tentacles of a jellyfish.

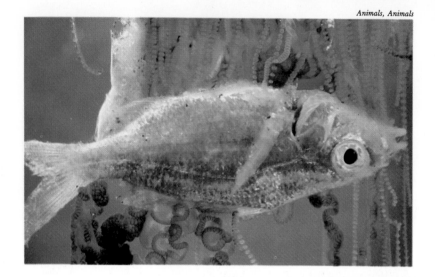

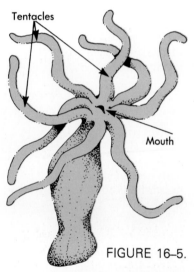

Tentacles

Mouth

FIGURE 16–5.

activity OBSERVING HYDRA

Obtain a watch glass (small jar) and add 10 mL of aquarium water. Use a dropper to pick up hydra from the surface of a hydra culture. Transfer the hydra to the water in the watch glass. Use a hand lens to observe the hydra. Draw a diagram showing the shape of a hydra's body. Where are the tentacles located? Describe any motion you observe. Touch a hydra gently with a dissecting needle. What is the animal's reaction? How do you think a hydra obtains food? After you have completed your observation, empty the liquid in the watch glass back into the culture container.

MAKING SURE
1. How is a jellyfish different from a sponge?
2. What special structures in a jellyfish enable it to catch food?

16:4 Flatworms and Roundworms

Tapeworms and flukes are two kinds of flatworms. Both of these animals are parasites. A **parasite** is an organism that lives on or in another organism called the **host**.

Define parasite.

Tapeworms may live in the bodies of animals. A tapeworm is a long flat worm with a small head at one end of its body. Hooks and suckers on the head are used by the tapeworm to attach itself to the inside of its host. The tapeworm obtains food, water, and a place to live from the host.

A planarian (pluh NER ee un) is an example of a flatworm that is not a parasite. A planarian obtains food from the water in which it lives. Different planaria species range from microscopic size to 7 or 8 cm in length. Planaria are found in streams and ponds. They live on the bottom surfaces of underwater plants, rocks, and logs. One method for collecting planaria is to place bits of meat in shallow water. The worms are drawn to the meat by juices that diffuse through the water.

As their name indicates, roundworms have rounded, tubelike bodies that taper to a point at each end. There are over 3000 species of roundworms. Hookworms, hairworms, and eelworms belong to the roundworm phylum. Many microscopic roundworms live in soil and water.

Trichina (trihk I nuh) is a parasitic roundworm that can cause a disease called trichinosis (trihk uh NOH sus). People may contract the disease if they eat pork that is not thoroughly cooked. Symptoms of the disease are severe muscle pains, fever, and weakness. The disease may even cause death. Trichinosis is prevented by freezing pork or cooking it until it is well done. Animals can become infected with trichina by eating garbage containing these roundworms. Farmers can stop the spread of the trichina worms by cooking garbage before it is fed to pigs.

Harris Biological Supplies, Ltd.

a

b

Hickson-Bender Photography

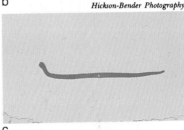

c

FIGURE 16–6. A tapeworm (a) and a planarian (b) are flatworms. A hookworm (c) is a roundworm.

Why are *Trichina* harmful?

MAKING SURE
3. How is a parasite different from a host?
4. Why is a tapeworm called a parasite?
5. How is a planarian different from a tapeworm?
6. What features of a tapeworm allow it to live inside the bodies of animals?

16:5 Earthworms and Their Relatives

Earthworms, sandworms, and leeches are members of the same phylum. Animals in this group have bodies composed of ringlike segments. Most of the members of this group live in damp soil or fresh water. Some are marine worms that live along the seashore. Some species of segmented worms are free-living and others, such as leeches, are parasites.

Earthworms burrow underground. They feed near the surface on decaying leaves and other organic matter. In areas where the soil freezes in the winter, earthworms burrow deep below the frost line. They may burrow as much as 2 m below the soil surface.

An earthworm's body is long, cylindrical, and tapered at one end. Its underside is flat and light-colored. The body of the earthworm is divided into 100 to 180 segments. Tiny bristles on each of the body segments help the earthworm pull itself along the ground or through its burrow. If you have ever tried to pull an earthworm out of the ground, you know how tightly these bristles cling to the soil.

An earthworm's body has several systems that carry on the life activities of the animal. Food is digested and absorbed in a group of organs that compose the digestive system (Figure 16–7). Leaves, grass, and other plant materials are drawn in through the mouth. Rock particles mixed with the food aid the digestive system in grinding it up. Chemicals called enzymes produced by the digestive organs dissolve the food. The digested food is then absorbed into the earthworm's blood through the walls of the intestine.

FIGURE 16–7. Digestive system of the earthworm.

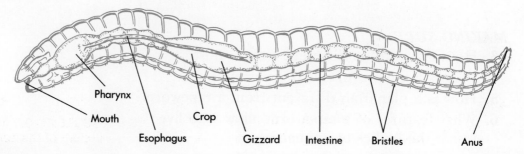

Mouth   Pharynx   Crop   Esophagus   Gizzard   Intestine   Bristles   Anus

The circulatory system of an earthworm has two blood vessels and several hearts. Blood moves digested food and oxygen to all of the cells in the earthworm's body. Oxygen absorbed through the skin is needed by the cells for respiration. Wastes produced by respiration are carried away from the cells by a special fluid. Coiled tubes filter the fluid and remove the wastes. The tubes move the wastes to the surface of the earth worm. Food wastes are excreted through the open end of the digestive tract. **Excretion** (ihk SKREE shun) is the process by which wastes are removed from an organism.

Describe the circulatory system of the earthworm.

How does an earthworm obtain oxygen?

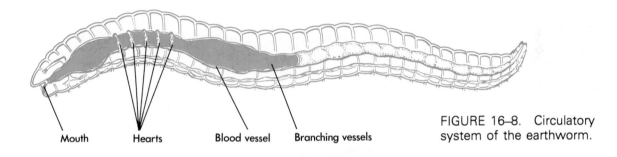

| Mouth | Hearts | Blood vessel | Branching vessels |

FIGURE 16–8. Circulatory system of the earthworm.

An earthworm has a simple nervous system. A nerve center is located just above the pharynx of the digestive system. Nerves extend from the nerve center through the length of the earthworm's body and connect to each of the body organs. These nerves control the operation of muscles and body organs.

Where is the nerve center of the earthworm located?

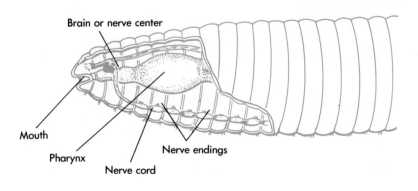

Brain or nerve center
Mouth
Pharynx
Nerve cord
Nerve endings

FIGURE 16–9. Nervous system of the earthworm.

Earthworms are neither male nor female. Each earthworm has both male and female sex organs. The male sex organs are called testes and the female sex organs are called ovaries. The testes produce the sperm cells. Sperm cells move with the aid of a long whiplike tail. Ovaries produce the ova or eggs.

Earthworms reproduce mainly during warm, moist weather. Mating occurs at night and requires two to three hours. Two worms stretch out and lie parallel to one another. Sperm cells from each worm are exchanged. Union of sperm and egg cells, called fertilization, occurs after the worms move apart. Sexual reproduction occurs when sperm cells and eggs are produced and fertilization takes place. The eggs are fertilized in a band of slime the earthworm secretes around itself. The slime band slips off, dries, and forms a cocoon around the fertilized eggs. Cocoons of the common earthworm measure about 5 mm by 7 mm. In each cocoon there are many eggs. The eggs grow by cell division and form young earthworms. The young soon break out of the cocoon and crawl away.

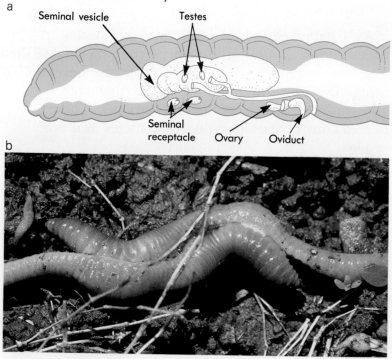

FIGURE 16–10. Reproductive system of the earthworm (a). During mating, earthworms exchange sperm through collarlike structures (b).

Rich Brommer

activity
DISSECTION OF AN EARTHWORM

Objective: To identify the major parts of an earthworm

Materials

earthworm
dissecting needle
dissecting pan or board of soft wood
scalpel or sharp knife
20 straight pins

Procedure

1. Place the worm in a dissecting pan or on a board. See Figure 16–11.

2. Observe that the worm's body is made of ringed segments. Identify the mouth, clitellum, and anus.

3. With a scalpel or knife, cut lengthwise through the body wall from the anus to the mouth. Pin back the body wall on each side to hold it down.

4. Identify the parts that make up the digestive tract (Figure 16–7).

5. Locate the large blood vessels that run along the digestive tract. Find the blood vessels (hearts) that circle around the esophagus.

6. Remove the esophagus with a dissecting needle and identify the seminal vesicles that are part of the reproductive system. They appear as three lobes on each side of the esophagus. Try to locate the small testes at segments 10 and 11.

7. In segment 13, look for a small ovary. Also, look for the yellowish seminal receptacles in segments 9 and 10.

8. Find the cerebral nerves in segment 3 and the long nerve cord to which they are attached.

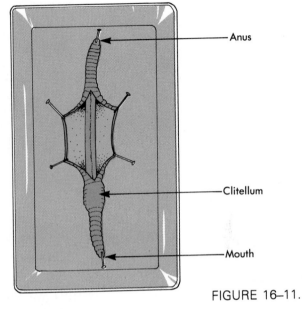

FIGURE 16–11.

Observations and Data

Draw a diagram of an earthworm and label the external parts you identified.

Questions and Conclusions

1. What are the parts of an earthworm's digestive tract?

2. How does the length of the digestive tract benefit the earthworm?

3. How are the large blood vessels along the digestive tract of benefit to the earthworm?

4. Why do you think the blood vessels around the esophagus are called hearts?

5. What are the male parts of an earthworm? Female parts?

6. What body parts carry "messages" through an earthworm?

7. How do earthworms reproduce?

8. Why is it necessary for earthworms to live in moist soil?

16:6 Spiny-Skinned Animals

Define radial symmetry.

Spiny-skinned animals belong to the phylum which includes starfish, sea urchins, and sand dollars. All of these animals live in the ocean. Their bodies have a tough outer skin covered with coarse spines. Spiny-skinned animals also have a body form and shape called radial symmetry. **Radial symmetry** means similar body parts extend out from the center. A wagon wheel with spokes extending out from a hub has radial symmetry. Most starfish have five arms which extend out from the center of their bodies in the form of a star.

Describe the systems of the starfish.

Inside a starfish's body is a network of canals through which water is pumped. A starfish has a simple digestive system with a mouth and stomach. Its circulatory system includes blood vessels surrounding the mouth. Each arm also contains a blood vessel. The nervous system has a central nerve ring with nerves that extend into each arm.

FIGURE 16–12. A sea urchin (a) and a starfish (b) are spiny-skinned animals.

a

b

Geri Murphy

MJW

A starfish uses its arms to move and cling to objects. The underside of each arm has rows of small structures which work like suction cups. To move, a starfish slowly reaches out and attaches an arm to the seafloor. Then it uses the arm to pull the rest of its body along. The arms are also used to grasp and pull open oysters and clams, which provide food for a starfish.

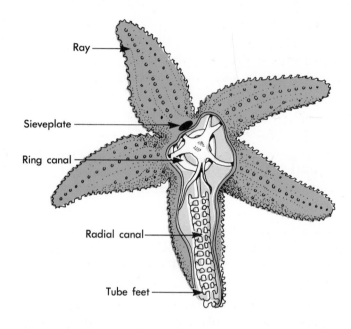

Ray

Sieveplate

Ring canal

Radial canal

Tube feet

FIGURE 16–13. Internal features of a starfish.

MAKING SURE

9. How do starfish move?
10. What feature makes spiny-skinned animals different from other animals?

16:7 Mollusks

All mollusks have soft bodies; many have hard shells or shell-like coverings. Snails, oysters, and clams are mollusks. This group also includes the octopus and squid. There are about 40 000 different species of mollusks. Most of the species live in the ocean in shallow water near the shore. Some snails live in fresh water and others live on land.

What do all mollusks have in common?

Many mollusks are used for food. Some have beautiful shells and are collected and used for decorations. Oyster shells are crushed and fed to poultry as a source of calcium in their diet. Pearls are removed from oysters and used in jewelry. A pearl is made when an oyster secretes material that surrounds a foreign object lodged inside the shell.

A common garden snail is another example of the animals in the mollusk phylum. The snail has a round, looped shell which is used to protect the snail's soft body. Attached to the body are two pairs of tentacles and a pair of eyes. The garden snail is most active at night in damp weather. It moves slowly by contracting muscles in the bottom of its foot. Garden snails eat plants. When present in large numbers, the snails may severely damage gardens and fields.

Squids and octopuses live in the ocean and have a large head, two eyes, and a mouth. Tentacles or fleshy arms attached to the body are used to obtain food. Cuplike suckers that aid in grasping and holding things are located on the tentacles. Both squids and octopuses can swim. An octopus has eight

FIGURE 16–14. A snail has a single, coiled shell that protects the snail's soft body (a). Octopuses have well developed eyesight and may grow to a length of 10 m (b).

a

David M. Dennis

b

Zig Leszczynski/Animals, Animals

arms which it uses to crawl about rocks and tidepools along seacoasts. Squids and octopuses feed on small marine animals such as fish and shrimp. Small squids are eaten by fish and other marine animals. They are used as bait for fishing and in some places are used for food by people.

16:8 Arthropods

Insects, spiders, crayfish, crabs, shrimps, and lobsters belong to the arthropod (AR thruh pahd) phylum. The members of this group have segmented bodies, jointed legs, and exoskeletons. An **exoskeleton** is a skeleton on the outside of an animal's body. It protects the soft internal body parts. There are more than 800 000 species of arthropods, making it the largest phylum in the animal kingdom.

Name the characteristics of the arthropod phylum.

a

Alvin E. Staffan

b

Ward's Natural Science Establishment, Inc.

FIGURE 16–15. A crayfish (a) and a crab (b) are examples of crustaceans.

A group within the phylum, the crustaceans (krus TAY shunz), includes fairy shrimp, water fleas, barnacles, crayfish, and crabs. Although most of these animals live in the sea, many live in inland waters. Various species of crayfish live in freshwater streams, ponds, and lakes all over the world.

Other groups of arthropods include the millipedes and centipedes. Both have wormlike bodies. Centipedes have one pair of legs for each body segment. Millipedes have two pair of legs for each segment.

Name three animals with exoskeletons.

Angabe A. Schmidecker/Alpha

Alvin E. Staffan

a

b

FIGURE 16–16. The sting of a scorpion (a) may be harmful to humans. Most spiders inject a poison to paralyze their prey (b).

Spiders and scorpions are two closely related types of arthropods. These animals live on land with more living in warm, dry regions than elsewhere. Many species of spiders and scorpions have poison glands and poison claws or "fangs." They use the poison to kill insects and other small animals for food. Some spiders catch their food, while others spin webs in which they trap their prey. A few spiders and scorpions have bites or stings that can cause people serious illness and even death. Two body segments, head and thorax, and four pair of legs are distinct features of spiders.

MAKING SURE
11. What is the purpose of an exoskeleton?
12. What features make arthropods different from other animals?

16:9 Insects

Insects are the largest group of arthropods with about 700 000 different species. Grasshoppers, flies, lice, butterflies, beetles, and bees are but a few of the many different kinds of insect. An insect's body is divided into three parts, the head, thorax, and abdomen. Insects have three pair of legs and usually two pair of wings. Insects are the most plentiful and widespread of all land animals.

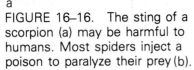

List the body parts common to all insects.

a

b

Insects go through a series of changes in their lives called **metamorphosis** (met uh MOR fuh sus). Some insects, like the grasshopper, undergo an incomplete metamorphosis in which young grasshoppers develop gradually into adults. Other insects undergo a complete metamorphosis in a series of four different stages. The stages are egg, larva, pupa, and adult. For example, a caterpillar emerges from a butterfly egg. A caterpillar is the larva stage of a butterfly. The pupa stage occurs when a caterpillar spins a cocoon around itself. The caterpillar changes in the cocoon, and an adult butterfly hatches out of the cocoon.

FIGURE 16–17. Insects such as a grasshopper (a) and a stag beetle (b) have three pairs of legs and usually two pairs of wings.

What is metamorphosis?

Name the four stages of complete metamorphosis.

a

b

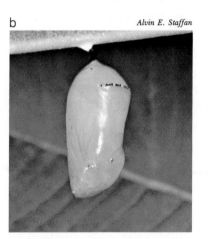

c

A grasshopper has all the body parts of a typical insect. The hind legs are unusually strong and its wings fold in a narrow line along the body. The wings unfold and spread when the grasshopper flies.

FIGURE 16–18. The larva stage (a), the pupa stage (b), and the adult stage (c) of a Monarch butterfly.

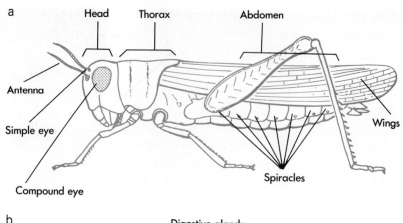

FIGURE 16–19. External body parts of a grasshopper (a). Digestive system of a grasshopper (b).

a
Head   Thorax   Abdomen
Antenna
Simple eye
Compound eye
Wings
Spiracles

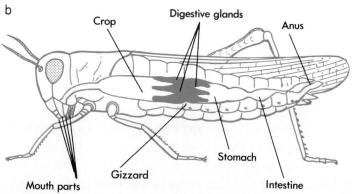

b
Crop   Digestive glands   Anus
Mouth parts
Gizzard   Stomach
Intestine

As the food a grasshopper eats passes through its digestive system, it is digested and absorbed into the blood. An insect's blood fills its entire body cavity. A long tube on top of the digestive tract acts as a heart and pumps blood. The blood is pumped forward through the tube to the head. Blood bathes all the organs and is circulated by muscular movements. It then reenters the heart through tiny openings. This cycle is repeated over and over. A grasshopper's blood does not carry oxygen. It is used solely to carry food and wastes.

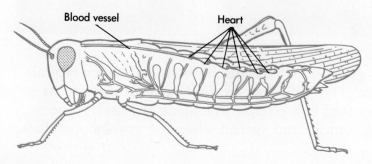

Blood vessel   Heart

FIGURE 16–20. Circulatory system of a grasshopper.

A grasshopper's respiratory system is a complex network of tubes inside the body. These tubes open to the outside through tiny openings called spiracles (SPIHR ih kulz). There are ten pair of spiracles, eight pair on the abdomen and two pair on the thorax. Air is pumped into and out of the spiracles by the movement of the abdomen and wings. The pumping allows an exchange of gases between the cells and the air in the tubes. Oxygen diffuses into the cells and carbon dioxide diffuses out.

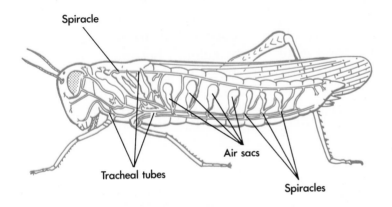

FIGURE 16–21. Respiratory system of a grasshopper.

The nervous system of the grasshopper is located in the bottom of the body cavity. The system is made of nerves and a nerve center. Antennas on the grasshopper's head provide a sense of touch. Three simple eyes are located on the front of the grasshopper's head. These eyes detect darkness and light. Two large eyes on the sides of the head detect light, color, and motion.

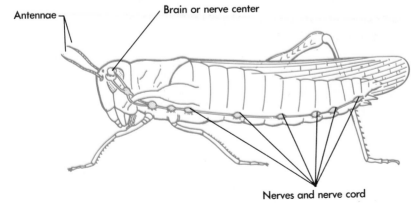

FIGURE 16–22. Nervous system of a grasshopper.

A grasshopper also has a sense of hearing. Earlike structures are located in the abdomen next to the thorax. They are large, membrane-covered cavities.

Grasshoppers have separate sexes. The male deposits sperm inside the female. Fertilization of the eggs takes place in the body of the female.

A female grasshopper lays eggs in a hole in the ground. She uses a special structure called an ovipositor (OH vuh pahz ut ur) to dig the hole. A female grasshopper may deposit 100 or more eggs during late autumn. These eggs hatch in the spring.

Young grasshoppers are called nymphs. They resemble the adult grasshopper but are wingless. The nymph grows until its exoskeleton becomes too small. Then it sheds, or molts, its exoskeleton. Molting occurs at different times until the grasshopper reaches its full size.

activity   START AN INSECT COLLECTION

Catch insects with a net or jar. To kill them, put them in a jar with a piece of cotton soaked in fingernail polish remover. Cover the jar with a lid. **CAUTION:** The fumes of fingernail polish remover are poisonous. When the insects are dead, mount them with pins on cardboard or Styrofoam. Label the insects in your collection with their scientific names.

MAKING SURE

13. How are insects different from lobsters and spiders? How are they similar?
14. Explain the four stages of metamorphosis of a Monarch butterfly.
15. Describe the external features of a grasshopper.
16. How does the circulatory system of a grasshopper differ from the circulatory system of an earthworm?
17. How do grasshoppers reproduce?

main ideas

1. The animal kingdom consists of more than one million species.

16:1

2. Animals are made of specialized cells grouped together in tissues.

16:1

3. Tissues make up organs which are part of systems that carry on life activities.

16:1

4. Examples of systems in animals are the digestive, circulatory, respiratory, excretory, and nervous systems.

16:1

5. Some animals, such as the tapeworm, are parasites.

16:4

6. Spiny-skinned animals have tough outer skins covered with coarse spines.

16:6

7. Most animals reproduce sexually through the fertilization of eggs by sperm.

16:5, 16:9

8. Mollusks have soft bodies and many have hard shells or shell-like coverings.

16:7

9. The arthropod phylum has the largest number of species of any animal phylum. Most of these species are insects.

16:8, 16:9

10. As they grow and develop, insects go through a series of changes called metamorphosis.

16:9

vocabulary

Define each of the following words or terms.

arthropod	mollusk	roundworm
excretion	metamorphosis	specialized cell
exoskeleton	parasite	spiracle
flatworm	radial symmetry	system
host		

study questions

DO NOT WRITE IN THIS BOOK.

A. True or False

Determine whether each of the following sentences is true or false. If the sentence is false, rewrite it to make it true.

1. A muscle cell is a specialized cell that carries oxygen to all parts of the body.

2. A system is made of organs.

3. One example of an arthropod is a sponge.
4. The tentacles of a jellyfish are used to obtain food.
5. An earthworm is a parasite.
6. Trichina is a parasitic roundworm.
7. Food is digested in an earthworm's circulatory system.
8. Earthworms produce offspring through sexual reproduction.
9. Every earthworm has a nervous system.
10. A starfish has radial symmetry.

B. Multiple Choice

Choose the word or phrase that completes correctly each of the following sentences.

1. A(n) (*sponge, earthworm, clam, fly*) is a mollusk.
2. An insect is a(n) (*roundworm, mollusk, arthropod*).
3. (*Flatworms, Mollusks, Arthropods*) have the greatest number of species.
4. (*Antennae, Spiracles, Eyes*) are openings through which a grasshopper takes air into its body.
5. Grasshoppers reproduce by (*sexual, asexual*) reproduction.
6. In complete metamorphosis, the adult stage comes after the (*egg, larva, pupa*) stage.
7. Jellyfish and their relatives have a(n) (*lung, cavity, heart, brain*) in the center of their bodies.
8. Animals with jointed legs and segmented bodies are (*flatworms, mollusks, arthropods*).
9. (*Blood, Water, Air*) moves food and oxygen through the body of an earthworm.
10. In (*sexual, asexual*) reproduction, there is a union of a sperm cell and an egg cell.

C. Completion

Complete each of the following sentences with a word or phrase that will make the sentence correct.

1. A group of tissues working together is called a(n) _____.
2. _____ is a disease people may contract by eating uncooked pork.
3. A crayfish is a(n) _____.

4. _____ are the largest group of animals in the arthropod phylum.
5. _____ stage of a butterfly is a caterpillar.
6. The two _____ of a grasshopper detect colors.
7. _____ have three pairs of legs and their bodies are divided into three parts.
8. A(n) _____ is an animal that contains both male and female sex organs.
9. There are over one million species in the _____ kingdom.
10. A group of _____ working together is called a system.

D. How and Why
1. What happens to parasites if they kill their host animal?
2. Name four animal body systems. What is the function of each system?
3. What are the general body features of an insect?
4. Describe the stages in the complete metamorphosis of an insect.
5. Why do you think insects are the most plentiful and widespread of all land animals?

investigations

1. Obtain a library book on entomology, the study of insects, and learn how to make an insect collection. Visit a natural history museum to see insect collections prepared by entomologists.
2. Obtain information on a career in entomology. Find out what kinds of jobs exist and how a person prepares for a career in this field.

interesting reading

Olesky, Walter, *Careers in the Animal Kingdom.* New York, NY: Messner, 1980.
Patent, Dorothy Hinshaw, *The Lives of Spiders.* New York, NY: Holiday House, 1980.

chapter

17

Animals can be divided into two major groups—those with backbones and those without backbones. Animals such as birds, reptiles, and amphibians have backbones. Why is this animal classified as a bird? What are the differences between warm-blooded and cold-blooded animals? What characteristics are unique to each of the groups of animals with backbones?

Tom Stack & Assoc.

Animals with Backbones

17:1   Backbones and Skeletons

A catfish, a toad, and a squirrel are three very different kinds of animals. Yet these animals are alike in a very important way. They all have a brain and a skeleton inside their bodies. How many animals can you name that have a brain and an internal skeleton made of bones?

Animals can be divided into two large groups called the vertebrates (VURT uh brayts) and invertebrates (ihn VURT uh brayts). A **vertebrate** is an animal that has an internal skeleton. Part of the skeleton is a case that surrounds and protects the animal's brain. Vertebrates are part of a large phylum called chordates (KOR dayts). This phylum includes fish, amphibians, reptiles, birds, and mammals. The skeleton of a vertebrate supports and protects body organs. Muscles attached to the skeleton cover and provide protection for the brain and the spinal cord. A spinal cord is a long bundle of nerves that connects the brain to other parts of the body. The backbone of an animal consists of bones or vertebrae that protect the spinal cord. In this chapter, you will study the features of vertebrate animals.

GOAL: You will learn the characteristics of the chordate animal phylum. Similarities and differences among the species are explained.

Name the animals in the chordate phylum.

363

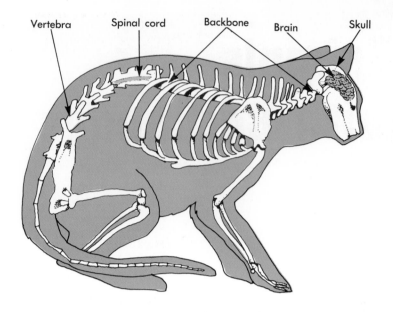

FIGURE 17–1. A vertebrate has an internal skeleton which protects the brain, spinal cord, and other internal organs.

Vertebra   Spinal cord   Backbone   Brain   Skull

In Chapter 16, you learned about the animals that are invertebrates. **Invertebrates** do not have a backbone or an internal skeleton. Many of these invertebrate animals, such as worms and jellyfish, have soft bodies. Others, such as insects, lobsters, and clams, have a hard exoskeleton that protects the soft internal body parts.

MAKING SURE
1. How do vertebrates differ from invertebrates?
2. Why are fish considered vertebrates when jellyfish are not?

17:2   Fish

What kind of animal do you think of when you see the word fish? Fish are vertebrates that live in water. They obtain oxygen from water and have fins which are used for swimming. Sharks, skates, and rays belong to one group of fish. The fish in this group have skeletons made of cartilage (KART ul ihj). **Cartilage** is a dense, strong, rubbery tissue. It is different from bone in that it lacks the minerals that make bone hard. Cartilage is present in your body in your nose, ears, and parts of your backbone.

How is cartilage different from bone?

FIGURE 17–2. A blue shark is an example of an animal with a skeleton made of cartilage.

Fish with skeletons made of bones are classified in a group called bony fish. Most of the fish you know belong to this group. Trout, bass, salmon, catfish, and goldfish are examples of bony fish. All fish are cold-blooded. Cold-blooded means an animal's body temperature changes as the temperature of its environment changes. The temperature of a fish depends on the temperature of the water in which it lives. As the water temperature changes, so does the body temperature of the fish.

Define cold-blooded.

There are many different sizes and kinds of bony fish. Some minnows are about 1 cm in length. Swordfish grow as long as 4 m. Mackerel have streamlined bodies for very fast swimming. In contrast, the seahorse has an unusual shape and swims slowly in an erect position. Flounders can change color to blend with the sea bottom. Most fish species live either in salt or in fresh water only. Sticklebacks, however, are at home in either kind of water. Salmon live in salt water but return to freshwater rivers to lay their eggs.

Give an example of a bony fish.

Joey Jacques

FIGURE 17–3. A flounder can change color to match the ocean bottom.

A yellow perch provides a good example of the structure of a bony fish. It has a large mouth and small, thin teeth. One eye is located on each side of the head. The eyes do not have eyelids. Behind each eye is a thin bony gill cover. Under each gill cover are four comblike gills. Two fins are attached to the back of the perch and there is a large tail fin. One fin is located behind each gill and two fins are located on the bottom of the perch.

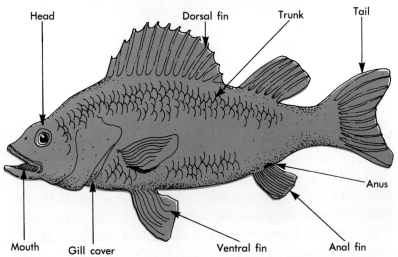

FIGURE 17–4. External body parts of a yellow perch.

The skeleton of a yellow perch contains about 40 bones. A skull and a spinal column made of bones called vertebrae are part of the skeleton. Muscles attached to the bones are used by the fish to swim and turn in the water. The digestive system includes a stomach and an intestine in which food is digested and absorbed. Bile is produced in an organ called the liver and is stored in the gall bladder. Bile, which aids in the digestion of fat, is carried through a duct, or small tube, to the intestine. Food that is not digested passes out of the fish through an opening called the anus.

Like other fish, a yellow perch has a heart with two sections or chambers. The pumping action of the chambers forces blood through the circulatory system. Blood carries food and oxygen to cells throughout the fish. The blood also has white cells and substances that fight disease. Arteries carry

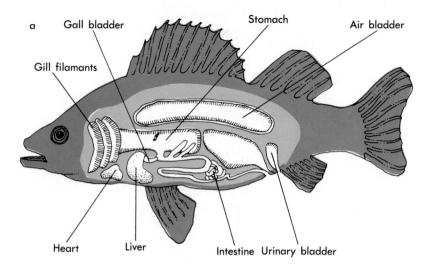

a

Gall bladder

Gill filamants

Stomach

Air bladder

Heart   Liver

Intestine Urinary bladder

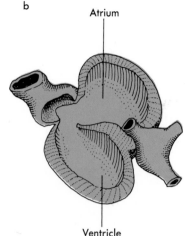

b

Atrium

Ventricle

blood away from the heart. Veins carry blood back to the heart. Tiny capillaries connect the arteries and veins. The food and oxygen from the blood passes through the capillary walls to reach the cells.

To obtain oxygen, a fish pumps water over its gills. Oxygen dissolved in the water diffuses through the thin membranes of the gills into the fish's blood. Carbon dioxide, a waste product, moves out of the blood into the water. A fish soon dies when removed from water because it cannot obtain oxygen.

FIGURE 17–5. Internal structures (a) and heart (b) of a yellow perch.

activity CIRCULATION OF BLOOD

(1) Place a goldfish in a beaker of water at room temperature. (2) Take some cotton and wet it in the water. (3) Remove the goldfish from the beaker and wrap it with the moist cotton. Leave the tail exposed. (4) Place the fish in a petri dish and lay a microscope slide over the tail. (5) Place the dish on a microscope stage. Focus on the tail so you can observe the circulation of blood. (6). Add water to the cotton with a dropper to keep it moist. (7) After you have observed the circulation quickly return the goldfish to the beaker of water. Does the blood flow in blood vessels? Does the blood always flow in the same direction?

FIGURE 17–6.

activity FEATURES OF A FISH

Observe some fish in an aquarium tank. Select one fish and carefully study its size, shape, and other features. Make a drawing of the fish that shows its shape, fins, eyes, gills, and other parts. Label all the parts you can identify. Repeat this procedure with another kind of fish in the tank. Compare your two drawings. How are the two fish similar? How are they different? How are the two fish different from the perch shown in Figure 17–4?

MAKING SURE

3. List three features common to all fish.

4. How do fish obtain the oxygen they need to live?

5. How do the cells in a fish obtain food and oxygen?

6. What structures do fish use to move through the water?

17:3 Amphibians

What is an amphibian?

Frogs, toads, and salamanders are amphibians. These animals live part of their lives in water and part on land. Amphibians are vertebrates that have moist skin and no scales. Adult amphibians have two eyes, ears, and breathe through lungs. Amphibians, like fish, are cold-blooded.

How does a frog reproduce?

Frogs live in or near bodies of fresh water while toads live on land. Some species of toads live in moist areas such as the floor of a forest and others live in desert regions. Frogs and toads are usually 5 to 12 cm long, through the head and back. They eat live insects and worms. Some species, such as the bullfrog, also feed on small fish.

FIGURE 17–7. A toad is an amphibian that lives mostly on land.

Frogs and toads reproduce during the spring. Fertilization of the eggs by the sperm takes place outside the female. After a female lays its eggs in water, the male fertilizes them with sperm. The fertilized eggs develop into tadpoles. A tadpole has gills, a tail, and lives in water. As it develops into an

Courtesy CCM: General Biological, Inc.

FIGURE 17–8. A green salamander is an amphibian.

adult, the tadpole loses its tail and gills and develops lungs and legs. Some species of toads lay their eggs in streams. Others lay their eggs in temporary pools of water formed after spring or summer rains. Tadpoles feed on algae and small plants.

In regions with severe winters, frogs burrow into the muddy bottom of a pond during the cold season. Toads burrow down into the ground below the frost line. During the cold winter months, these frogs and toads are in a winter sleep called hibernation. During hibernation an animal's body metabolism decreases and its heartbeat is very slow. The animal lives on materials stored within its body.

FIGURE 17–9. A tadpole has gills, a tail, and lives in water (a). Most frogs lay their eggs in large masses in the water (b).

a

b

In what two ways does a frog obtain oxygen?

17:4 The Frog

A frog obtains oxygen through its moist skin. It also obtains oxygen by breathing through a pair of lungs. An exchange of gases occurs in the lungs of the frogs. Oxygen diffuses from the lungs into the blood. Carbon dioxide and water vapor diffuse out of the blood into the lungs. Thus, a frog inhales air rich in oxygen. It exhales air rich in carbon dioxide and water vapor. In water, a frog must come to the surface to breathe air.

The digestive system of a frog is shown in Figure 17–11. Muscles in the walls of these organs cause them to contract and push the food through the system. It is the same kind of motion that occurs in your own digestive system.

Digestive juices containing enzymes are made in the walls of the stomach and intestines. An enzyme is a chemical that aids in the digestion of food. Two organs, the **liver** and **pancreas** (PAN kree us), also produce digestive juices. Bile from the liver aids the digestion of fat in the small intestine. The pancreas produces digestive enzymes which pass through a duct to the small intestine.

Grant Heilman Photography

FIGURE 17–10. Frogs have a long, sticky tongue for catching insects.

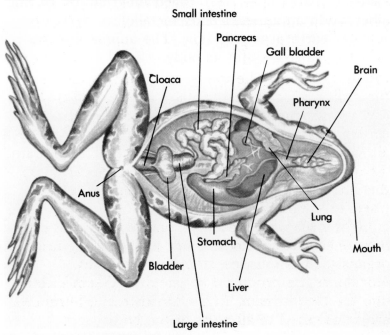

FIGURE 17–11. Internal organs of a frog.

Most of the digestion and absorption of food occurs in the **small intestine** of the frog. Waste products pass through the **large intestine** into the cloaca, a storage area. Wastes are then excreted through the anus.

A frog's circulatory system contains a heart and a network of blood vessels. The heart has three chambers. They are the right atrium, left atrium, and ventricle. Blood from the frog's body enters the right atrium. Blood returning from the lungs enters the left atrium. Both the right atrium and the left atrium contract and push blood into the ventricle. Then the ventricle contracts and pushes blood through vessels to the lungs and other body organs.

The blood is pumped through a circulatory system of arteries, veins, and capillaries. Red blood cells contain a compound called hemoglobin (HEE muh glo bun) which carries oxygen. White blood cells, which fight disease, are also present in the blood.

A frog's brain and spinal cord compose its central nervous system. Many nerves go from the brain and spinal cord to other organs in the body of the frog. Also, nerves return from these organs to the central nervous system. Through these nerves, the brain controls the life activities of the frog.

The eyes of a frog are much like your eyes. Six muscles are attached to the eyeball and rotate the eye in its socket. The eye is connected by nerves to the brain. A frog does not have an external fleshy ear. Its eardrum is on the surface of the head. The eardrum can receive sound through either water or air. Sound reaching the eardrum causes it to vibrate. These vibrations are carried to the inner ear. Here the vibrations are changed to nerve messages that travel to the brain.

All animals with backbones have compounds called hormones in their blood. They help control various organs such as muscles, stomach, and heart. Hormones are produced by glands and sent directly into the bloodstream. In the bloodstream, hormones are transported to all parts of the body.

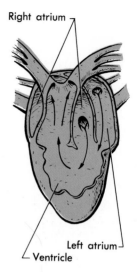

FIGURE 17–12. Circulation through the heart of a frog.

Describe the circulatory system of the frog.

What makes up the frog's nervous system?

Objective: To dissect and learn the parts of a frog

Materials

dissecting needle
dissecting pan or soft wooden board
frog, preserved
paper towel
pointed scissors, small and sharp
scalpel or small knife
6 straight pins
tweezers

Procedure

1. Lay the frog, backside up, on a paper towel in the dissecting pan.

2. Find the nostrils, mouth, tympanic membrane, forelegs, hind legs, and feet.

3. Make a cut with the scissors on both sides of the mouth so it can be opened wide. Locate the internal nostrils and teeth. Find the gullet, glottis, and tongue. Observe how the tongue is attached inside the mouth.

4. Turn the frog over on its back. Use the scalpel to cut through the abdomen in a line from the lower jaw to the anus. Make a cut across one end of the first cut at the lower jaw. Make a second cut across the body just forward of the anus. Locate the muscles in the chest inside the skin. Pull the body wall and pin it down with straight pins.

5. Use the dissecting needle to move and separate body parts as needed. Locate the heart. Observe the blood vessels leading from the heart. Find the lungs, liver, and gall bladder.

6. If your frog is female, it will have large masses of small dark eggs in the body cavity. Remove the egg masses if they are present.

7. Examine the parts of the digestive tract. Find the pancreas and spleen. The pancreas is in the first loop of the small intestine. The spleen is a round, red organ under the intestines.

8. Lift up and cut out the intestines. Locate the kidneys and bladder.

9. If you have a female frog, you removed the ovaries with the eggs. The two long, coiled white tubes are the oviducts. In a male frog, the round white organs near the kidneys are testes.

10. Remove the pins and turn the frog over. Cut through the skin, muscle, and skull to expose the brain. Do not cut too deeply. Find the cerebrum, cerebellum, medulla, and spinal cord.

Observations and Data

Draw a diagram that shows the organs inside the body cavity.

Questions and Conclusions

1. What parts of the frog protected internal body organs?

2. Name one organ you observed in each body system.

3. What organs are part of the digestive tract?

activity

OBSERVING METAMORPHOSIS IN FROGS

During the spring, some tadpoles may be obtained from a pond. Keep them in an aquarium with an air pump and filter. Maintain the water at room temperature. Feed the tadpoles every day with chopped lettuce, spinach, or cooked egg yolk. Remove any excess food so it does not decay in the water. Observe the tadpoles until they grow into mature frogs.

MAKING SURE

7. How are amphibians similar to fish?
8. Give an example of how an amphibian reproduces.
9. How do frogs respond to the change in seasons from fall to winter?
10. How is the body temperature of a cold-blooded animal affected by a change in the temperature around it?
11. What compound in a frog is used to transport oxygen through the body?

17:5 Reptiles

Reptiles are vertebrate animals that are cold-blooded, breathe air, and live mainly on land. Lizards, snakes, turtles, crocodiles, and alligators are reptiles. The outer skin of a reptile consists of dead cells that form a layer of dry scales. These dry scales resist water loss from the body and protect the animal from the rough surfaces of sand and rocks.

What is a reptile?

Name five reptiles.

FIGURE 17–13. The iguana (a), turtle (b), and alligator (c) are reptiles.

a

b

c

Carl W. Rettenmeyer/University of Connecticut Biology Dept.

Alvin E. Staffan

Warren Garst/Tom Stack & Assoc.

Except for snakes and some lizards, reptiles have four legs which are suited for running, crawling, or climbing. Most species of reptiles live in tropical or subtropical regions.

Snakes have long round bodies and no legs. The skeleton of a snake includes the skull, backbone, and ribs. Very long snakes like boas and pythons may have 200 to 400 bones in their backbones. Snakes have teeth, each slanted backwards, on the roofs of their mouths. The teeth hold food while it is swallowed. When snakes eat, they swallow their food whole without tearing or chewing it. The bones of a snake's jaw are arranged so the jaws can open very wide. This feature allows a snake to swallow prey greater than the diameter of the snake's body. Some snakes have special teeth called fangs that are used to inject venom. Venom is a poison used to paralyze and kill animals for food and as a defense against enemies. Rattlesnakes have fangs which are folded back when not in use. A snake has a ribbonlike tongue with a forked tip that provides the animal with a sense of smell.

Describe the reproduction of reptiles.

During reproduction, the fertilization of eggs in reptiles occurs inside the female's body. Most species deposit the fertilized eggs outside the body where they develop into young reptiles. Often the eggs are deposited in spaces between rocks and logs, or in

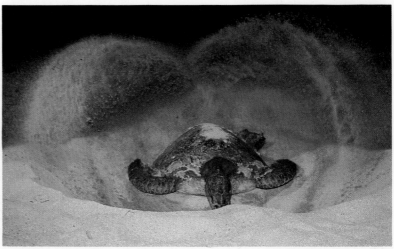

FIGURE 17–14. A female sea turtle lays eggs in a sandy beach at night.

C. Allan Morgan/Peter Arnold, Inc.

mud or sand. In some species, such as rattlesnakes and garter snakes, the eggs develop into young inside the female reptile. The eggs of many reptile species are somewhat like bird's eggs having a leathery or hard shell. Sea turtles produce about 400 eggs each year. Small snakes and lizards produce 10 to 20 eggs and the American alligator produces 30 to 60 eggs each year.

MAKING SURE

12. How is a reptile different from an amphibian?

13. Amphibians and reptiles lay many eggs each year. Why is there no large increase in the number of these animals?

14. How are many reptiles suited to life in tropical or subtropical regions?

15. How is reproduction in rattlesnakes different from reproduction in other species of snakes?

17:6 Birds

Birds are warm-blooded. Warm-blooded means an animal's body temperature is maintained at a certain level. For most birds, the daytime body temperature is 40 to 43°C. They have wings, two legs, feathers, and reproduce by laying eggs. Feathers insulate a bird's body and help regulate its body temperature. Birds are noted for their colors. Using these colors, different species can be identified. A blue jay, for example, has a distinctive blue color. One way to tell the difference in the sexes of some bird species is to notice the difference in their colors. Usually the males are more brightly colored than the females. Some birds, such as pheasants, are hunted as game, and others, such as chickens, are raised for meat and eggs.

Birds have a four-chambered heart, a delicate, strong skeleton, no teeth, and a projecting beak or bill. The bones of a bird have many hollow air spaces. Between the internal organs are air sacks.

Define warm-blooded.

What is the function of feathers?

FIGURE 17–15. A bald eagle can be easily identified because of the white feathers on its head.

Birds are noted for their loud voices and characteristic calls. They use their calls to warn of danger, attract mates, and keep other birds out of their territory.

Some birds, such as the bobwhite, live in the same area throughout the year. Other species, such as the robin, migrate to another region with the change of seasons. Most migration occurs north and south. Migratory birds go north to feed and nest in the spring and summer. They return south for the winter. Some birds migrate to the mountains for the summer and return to the lowlands in winter.

FIGURE 17–16. Cardinals live in the same area throughout the year (a). Canada geese are migratory birds (b).

a

b

Birds that migrate use the same routes every year. They arrive and depart from a region at about the same time each year. Some birds migrate at altitudes up to 1700 m. Even with stopping occasionally to feed, a bird travels an average of 50 km each day. Species migrating long distances fly at night and use the stars to find their way.

During reproduction, fertilization of the eggs takes place inside the female bird. The female then lays the fertilized eggs, which have hard shells. One or more eggs may be laid. A California quail hen will lay about 14 eggs. Either parent may sit on the eggs and keep them warm until they hatch. The length of time before the eggs hatch varies with the species. It is about 18 days for pigeons, 28 days for hawks, and 42 to 60 days for ostriches. Young birds require great care or they will die. Their parents feed and guard them and keep them warm.

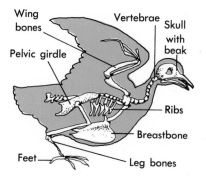

activity INTERNAL ORGANS OF A CHICKEN

Obtain the internal body parts of a chicken from a butcher shop. These are the parts that are removed when a chicken is cleaned before it is sold for food. Wash the organs with cold water, then place them in a flat pan. Use Figure 17–17 to identify the heart, liver, lungs, and kidneys. Identify each part of the digestive system shown in Figure 17–17. Make a drawing of the digestive system, labeling each of the organs. Slice the gizzard in half and examine its contents. Why is a gizzard called the "hen's teeth"?

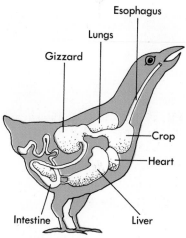

FIGURE 17–17. The internal body parts of a bird.

MAKING SURE
16. How does the sight and hearing of birds help to keep them alive?
17. Why do birds have bones with hollow spaces and air sacs between internal organs?
18. Why are female birds usually not as brightly colored as the male?
19. Why do most species of birds have their own distinct "birdcall"?

17:7 Mammals

Name some characteristics of mammals.

Whales, porpoises, bats, kangaroos, bears, and rats are all mammals. Mammals are warm-blooded vertebrates that have hair and feed their young with milk. Compared to other kinds of animals, mammals have a large brain. Many domestic animals, such as cats, dogs, cows, and horses, are also mammals. Domestic means the animals are usually tame and are raised and cared for by people.

There is a wide variety of mammal species. Shrews and mice are the smallest mammals, measuring less than 5 cm in length. Elephants are almost 4 m tall. The largest mammals are whales, which reach a length of 35 m and have a mass of about 100 metric tons. A bat is an unusual mammal because it has wings and can fly.

FIGURE 17–18. A killer whale has lungs and cannot breathe underwater (a). A shrew is the smallest mammal (b).

Marineland of the Pacific

Stouffer Enterprises/Animals, Animals

a

b

A mammal generally has a large head due to the size of its brain. Many mammal species have external ears that aid in hearing. Deer and other animals that graze on grass have long necks. Tails of some mammals, such as monkeys, are used to hold tree branches and vines.

Different species of mammals have many different sources of food. Hoofed mammals, such as cows and sheep, eat grass and other plants. Some mammals, such as the weasel and seal, eat only the flesh of other animals. Rats, bears, and pigs are examples of mammals that eat both plants and animals.

Toni Angermayer/Photo Researchers, Inc.

a

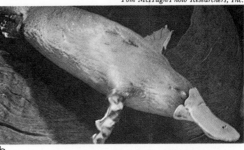
Tom McHugh/Photo Researchers, Inc.

b

FIGURE 17–19. Most bats are active only at night (a). A platypus is a mammal that has birdlike features (b).

Some mammals that eat flesh are **predators,** meaning they must kill other animals, prey, for their food. For example, cattle are eaten by tigers, deer are eaten by wolves, and mice are eaten by weasels.

Most animals hatch from eggs. However, the young of most mammals develop inside the mother's body. A kangaroo is an exception. The young kangaroo develops inside the mother for only a few days and then crawls out of the mother's body and into a pouch. Here the development of the new animal continues. Female mammals feed their young on milk produced by mammary glands in the chest or abdomen. A newborn mammal requires more care for a longer period of time than the young of other kinds of animals.

A duck-billed platypus is a very unusual mammal. This animal lives in Australia and is 45 to 50 cm long. It has a hard bill like a duck, webbed feet, a flat tail, and lives in or near water. The duck-billed platypus reproduces by building a nest in which it lays one to three small eggs. When hatched, the young are about 2.5 cm long and nurse on the mother's mammary glands.

People do not always see themselves as animals because they think, speak, read, and write. Also, people make and use all kinds of tools. People are mammals and they belong to the animal kingdom. People have hair, an internal skeleton, feed their young on milk, and are warm-blooded.

Do the young of most mammals develop inside or outside the mother's body?

MAKING SURE
20. Why are mammals considered the most advanced of all animals?

Perspectives
people

Life Among the Gentle Giants

Gerard Photography

Dianna Frisch, is the keeper in charge of the great apes at the Columbus Zoo. Included in her job are the care, cleaning, and medicating of the gorillas. "People often think of gorillas as monsters, but they are actually a shy, gentle, and intelligent animal which eats only vegetation." Dianna would be the person to know, gorillas are her specialty.

After high school, Diana trained to be veterinary technician. She worked as a technician for three years before deciding to become a veterinarian. During the summers of her veterinary training, Dianna worked as a keeper at the zoo. She did not become a veterinarian; she decided to stay with the zoo. Dianna was fascinated by the gorillas. Their great size, for males 810–1100 kg, females may weigh half as much, was matched with great strength. She found that each gorilla has a very distinct personality. "They like to play and tease."

She explained that there are two types of gorillas. The lowland gorilla is the type most often found in zoos. The second type is the rare mountain gorilla. "Only about 200 mountain gorillas exist in the wild today. They may become extinct within the next ten years. About 2000 lowland gorillas exist in the wild now, but their numbers are decreasing as civilization destroys their habitat. Once these animals are gone, they are gone forever."

When asked about qualities and personality traits that are important for a zoo keeper, Dianna answered, "Of course you need a great love for animals. You need to be a jack-of-all-trades and to be flexible. You will also need to be strong-minded and strong-willed. You will need to be tolerant of both animal behavior and people behavior."

In closing, Dianna described the ideal zoo: "A zoo should be thought of as the animal's home. If possible, there should be no bars. Very few animals in zoos, today, are taken from the wild. They are usually bought or traded from other zoos. Zoos should be places where people learn more about animals and themselves. If we can't take care of the animals, how can we expect to care for ourselves?" After the interview, Dianna moved toward the great ape house—back among her gentle giants.

main ideas

1. Animals can be divided into two groups, vertebrates and invertebrates. 17:1
2. Fish are vertebrates that live in water, obtain oxygen through gills, and are covered with scales. 17:2
3. Amphibians are vertebrates with moist skin and no scales. They live part of their lives in water and part on land. 17:3
4. A frog's body is a good illustration of the systems of organs present in vertebrate animals. 17:4
5. Fish, amphibians, and reptiles are cold-blooded animals. Birds and mammals are warm-blooded. 17:2–17:7
6. Birds are vertebrates that have wings, two legs, feathers, and reproduce by laying eggs. 17:6
7. Some birds stay in the same area all year and others migrate when the seasons change. 17:6
8. Mammals are vertebrates that have hair, are warm-blooded, and feed their young on milk. 17:7
9. Most animals reproduce by laying eggs. 17:7
10. Fertilization and development in most species of mammals occur inside the mother's body. 17:7

vocabulary

Define each of the following words or terms.

amphibian	cartilage	mammal	small intestine
atrium	invertebrate	pancreas	spinal cord
bile	large intestine	predator	ventricle
bird	liver	reptile	vertebrate

study questions

DO NOT WRITE IN THIS BOOK.

A. True or False

Determine whether each of the following sentences is true or false. If the sentence is false, rewrite it to make it true.

1. The fertilization of eggs in a reptile occurs outside the female's body.
2. Bones protect internal body organs.

3. A fish's heart has four chambers.

4. Fish obtain oxygen through gills.

5. In mammals, blood circulates through blood vessels.

6. Tadpoles have lungs.

7. Hormones help regulate the body functions of an animal.

8. Reptiles are warm-blooded animals.

9. All reptiles have four legs.

10. The bones of a bird contain space filled with air.

B. Multiple Choice

Choose the word or phrase that completes correctly each of the following sentences.

1. A(n) (*crayfish, perch, alligator, snake*) is an invertebrate animal.

2. Oxygen is taken into an adult frog through its (*gills, lungs, right atrium, ventricle*).

3. (*Arteries, Veins, Capillaries*) are tiny blood vessels.

4. A toad is a(n) (*reptile, amphibian, sponge, mammal*).

5. Food is absorbed into the blood mostly through a frog's (*mouth, stomach, intestine, pancreas*).

6. An animal with a backbone is classified in the (*arthropod, mollusk, chordate*) phylum.

7. The heart of a bird has (*one, two, three, four*) chambers.

8. (*Reptiles, Fish, Mammals, Birds*) are the most advanced of all animals.

9. (*Reptiles, Fish, Mammals, Birds*) feed their young on milk.

10. In most mammals, the young develop (*inside, outside*) the mother's body.

C. Completion

Complete each of the following sentences with a word or phrase that will make the sentence correct.

1. A spinal column of _____ surrounds and protects the spinal cord.

2. _____ and bones are used by vertebrates to move their body parts.

3. _____ are blood vessels that connect arteries and veins.

4. Birds and _____ are two groups of warm-blooded animals.

5. The central nervous system of a frog includes the _____ and spinal cord.

6. A turtle belongs to the _____ group of vertebrates.

7. _____ insulate a bird's body.

8. Many migratory birds fly at night and use the _____ to find their way.

9. A(n) _____ is an example of a domestic animal.

10. A(n) _____ is an animal that eats other animals.

D. How and Why

1. How are vertebrates different from invertebrates?

2. How are fish different from amphibians?

3. Name three systems in a frog and indicate the functions of each system.

4. What features are used to identify a species of bird?

5. Name three species of mammals. List the ways in which these three species are alike.

investigations

1. Plan a field trip to a zoo. Take along a camera and take pictures of different animals. Find out the scientific name for each animal. Mount your photos on a poster board and label each with the animal's common name and scientific name.

2. Investigate raising tropical fish as a hobby. Visit a pet shop or aquarium store to obtain information. Find out what equipment is needed and what care is needed to keep the fish alive and healthy.

interesting reading

Cole, Joanna, *A Frog's Body.* New York, NY: Morrow, 1980.

Lobb, Charlotte, *Exploring Animal Care Careers.* New York, NY: Richards Rosen Press, 1981.

Minton, Sherman and Madge, *Venomous Reptiles.* New York NY: Scribner's, 1980.

A

E.S. Ross

CAMOUFLAGE

Imagine you are walking in a woods. Suddenly a "dead leaf" scurries away on legs. An insect crawls along an orchid that suddenly comes to life. The "orchid" is a type of mantis and the insect is its dinner. See Figure A. Many insects imitate different plant parts. Some katydids resemble leaves. When they move, they sway like leaves on a branch swaying in the wind. Other bugs resemble flowers or twigs. By imitating plants, insects can hide from predators. They can also hide from their prey. The method used to hide is called camouflage. There are many types of camouflage. Let us examine some of them.

The angler fish uses several kinds of camouflage. The angler's body looks like an alga or sponge-covered rock. This kind of rock is found in the coral reefs of the fish's habitat. The angler uses another type of camouflage to "fish" for its dinner. It has a flexible spine on the tip of its nose. The "bait" is a fleshy part of the fish at the end of the spine. The bait resembles algae, worms, or even fish. The angler vibrates the bait directly in front of its mouth. If a fish takes the bait, it is snapped up by the angler as a tasty meal.

Many animals use a form of camouflage called protective coloration. By freezing in their position, they seem to disappear in the surroundings. Their coat color blends completely with their background. The tiger's stripes blend in with the tall grass of its natural habitat (Figure B). By the time the victim realizes the tiger is present, it is too late for the victim to escape. The cheetah's spotted coat blends with the spotted pattern of sunlight in the forest were the cheetah is found. The white polar bear is almost invisible against the snowy background of its natural habitat.

A wide variety of animals uses protective coloration. A chameleon is well-known for its ability to change its color to match its background. Many green frogs and snakes live in grass. Desert animals are often brown or sand colored. Certain rabbits, weasels, and birds such as the ptarmigans have seasonal color changes in their coats or feathers. In the warm season, they are earth colored. In the cold, snowy season, they are white (Figures C and D).

Fish show an excellent example of protective coloration. Often the top side of

B

Z. Leszczynski/Animals, Animals

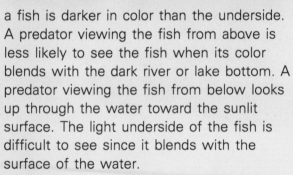

a fish is darker in color than the underside. A predator viewing the fish from above is less likely to see the fish when its color blends with the dark river or lake bottom. A predator viewing the fish from below looks up through the water toward the sunlit surface. The light underside of the fish is difficult to see since it blends with the surface of the water.

Mimicry is another form of camouflage based on color. In this type of camouflage, the coloration of a harmless animal has changed over a long period of time to resemble a poisonous animal. The harmless scarlet king snake has the same bright red, yellow, and black stripes as the poisonous coral snake. Because the king snake resembles the coral snake, predators often leave it alone. The snake resembling the poisonous snake survives to reproduce.

Thus, the coloration eventually becomes dominant in the species. Some butterflies also show this method of camouflage.

A monarch butterfly feeds on milkweed plants during the caterpillar stage. Milkweed contains a poison which can kill large animals but does not harm the caterpillar. The butterfly stage retains this poison. When a bird eats a monarch butterfly, it becomes ill. Birds learn quickly not to eat monarch butterflies. Several forms of butterflies look like the orange and black monarch butterfly. Any butterfly that resembles a monarch is avoided, too. The resemblance serves as a protection from predators.

We have looked at several methods of camouflage. Camouflage does not completely protect an organism. Even if the camouflage is effective part of the time, it helps a species to survive and reproduce.

Environment is all the surroundings of an organism. The environment includes the plants, animals, climate, and nonliving parts of an area. Only the plants and animals that are suited to a particular environment live in it. How are these big horn sheep suited to their environment? Why is a water buffalo unsuited to this environment?

18

A group of frogs make up a population. Many environmental factors determine the types and sizes of populations in an area. What are those factors? How does a population differ from a community? What cycles occur in a community? How does succession affect a community?

Gene Frazier

Populations and Communities

18:1 Communities

Living organisms are found in many different places from the equator to the poles. Some animals spend much of their lives underground while others spend their time flying through the air. Living creatures inhabit the deepest oceans and the highest mountains.

A **community** consists of all the living things in a certain area. For example, fields, forests, swamps, and lakes are communities. Each community contains populations of plants and animals that live together. A pond is an example of a community. Living in a pond are populations of fish, different species of plants, and various kinds of insects. The pond community may also include frogs and turtles. Within a community, each different species affects each other in many ways. For example, in a pond frogs eat insects and fish eat tadpoles.

GOAL: You will learn about the interrelationships among living things and their environment and the communities in which they live.

Define community. List five examples.

Roger K. Burnard

Dennis Brokaw

a

b

FIGURE 18–1.   Although a pond and a tidepool are both water communities, life in a pond (a) is quite different from the life in a tidepool (b).

Many fascinating facts can be learned about organisms by studying them in their own community. Where do they go? What do they eat? How do they move? Other living things in the community must be observed also. How do they relate to other living things? These are a few questions a scientist asks when studying a plant or animal in its community.

MAKING SURE

1. How does a pond community differ from a community in a river or stream?

18:2   Populations

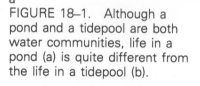

Define population. List five examples.

Organisms of the same species live together in small or large numbers. A **population** is the total number of any one species living in a community. For instance, all of the bass in a lake is a population of bass. All of the mice in a city block make up the mice population of the block. The total number of ants in an anthill or dandelions in a lawn is each a population. What are some other plant or animal populations?

To describe a community, you need to know the types and sizes of the populations present. Any one community contains hundreds of different plant and animal populations. Among these hundreds, there are often two or three **dominant** (DAHM uh nunt) **species.** Dominant, in this case, means present in the greatest numbers. Dominant plant species may make up from 30 to 90 percent of the living things in a community.

Define dominant population.

Ted Rice

FIGURE 18–2. The bloodfin tetra is the dominant population in this aquarium community.

Oak and hickory trees are dominant in some forests in the United States. They are the major plants growing in these forest communities. In the same way, a small pond may be dominated by sunfish and catfish. Although other fish species are present, the sunfish and catfish are present in greatest numbers.

Each species occupies a certain place within a community. A **habitat** (HAB uh tat) is the place where a species of plant or animal normally lives. Where would you look for birds in a forest? Many birds live in trees and bushes. This is their habitat. Where would you expect to find deer or earthworms? Deer spend their lives among trees and bushes. Earthworms live in the topsoil. All of these animals have their own unique habitats. However, they may be part of the same community.

Define habitat. Describe the habitat of a deer and an earthworm.

Margot Conte/Animals, Animals

FIGURE 18–3. The black buck, threatened by hunting and destruction of its habitat in India, now lives only on game ranches in Texas.

If you were to fish for catfish, you would plan to catch them in their habitat. Catfish are usually found near the bottom of a freshwater pond or stream. To catch them, baited hooks are tied at the end of a weighted line. These hooks then sink to the bottom of the pond, the catfish's habitat.

Every population and every living organism in a population has an environment. The **environment** is the surroundings of an organism or population. Environment includes all other living and nonliving things. For example, the environment of a rabbit includes grass, trees, and other animals. It also includes enemies, such as foxes. The rabbit breathes air. It also drinks water. Air and water are also part of its environment.

FIGURE 18–4. Some of the factors in a rabbit's environment.

Heat and light

Shelter

Other animals

Food and water

activity
POPULATIONS IN A COMMUNITY

Objective: To study the life in a community

Materials

hand lens
meter stick
plastic dishpan
shovel
string
4 wooden stakes

Procedure

1. Obtain permission to remove a 900-cm² sample of soil from an area in your yard, an empty lot, or woods.

2. Measure a square area, 30 cm by 30 cm, to study. Mark the area using stakes at the four corners of the square.

3. Count and record the number of plants and the number of animals in the square. List the names of the plants and animals you can identify.

4. Dig up some soil within your square and fill the dishpan one-third full.

5. Gently break up the soil and look for organisms. Use the hand lens to observe any organisms you find.

6. Make a sketch of one organism you find.

7. Return the soil to its original place when you finish your observations.

FIGURE 18–5.

Questions and Conclusions

1. What type of biological community did you observe—yard, forest, or empty lot?

2. Which type of living organisms—plants or animals—were present in greater number? Why?

3. What living organisms present in your soil sample were not observed? Why?

4. How do organisms living in soil aid in the growth of plants?

5. Why are plants necessary for the life of organisms living in the soil?

6. What is the source of the energy used by the plants, animals, and microorganisms in the soil?

Observations and Data

Number of plants	Number of animals	Plants identified	Animals identified

activity COMPARING ENVIRONMENTS

Study the environment of an aquarium. Make a list of the things it contains. What populations are present? How is the aquarium different from the room around it? How is it similar to the room? Repeat this activity with a terrarium.

MAKING SURE

2. Where would you be most likely to find cockroaches? Rats? Pigeons? How are their habitats similar? How are they different?

18:3   Population Change

How is a stable population different from an unstable one?

Over a year's time, the size of a population within a community may stay the same. The size of another population may change. A stable population remains about the same size from year to year. For example, the number of beech trees in a mature forest would be a stable population. This means that the total number of beech trees does not change much from year to year.

An unstable population changes in size from year to year. The dandelion population in a lawn can be unstable. When no one tends the lawn, the number of dandelions increases. When weed killer is sprayed on the lawn, the number of dandelions decreases.

FIGURE 18–6.   Spraying weed killer on this lawn (a) caused the dandelion population to decline (b).

a

b

Courtesy Chemlawn Corporation

Courtesy Chemlawn Corporation

Why does the number of individuals in a population change from year to year? This important question is not yet completely answered. It is known that the size of any animal population depends on the food supply. The birthrate for the species is also a factor. Those species that reproduce quickly can increase their number in a short time. Those that have enough food will be able to reproduce. Disease can also affect population size. The number of natural enemies of a species is also a factor.

Changes in the size of an unstable population may occur in cycles. These cycles are up-and-down trends in the population size over the years (Figure 18–7).

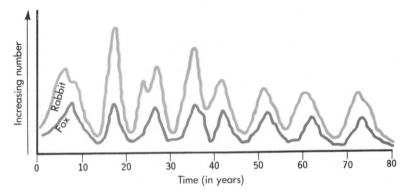

FIGURE 18–7. Some predator and prey populations rise and fall in regular cycles.

Individuals can be gained or lost in several ways by an animal population. Births and immigration (ihm uh GRAY shun) increase the size of the population. **Immigration** means movement into the community. Deaths and emigration (em uh GRAY shun) decrease the size of a population. **Emigration** means movement out of the community.

How are immigration and emigration different?

Consider the case of field mice living in a grain field. When the grain ripens, it is harvested in late summer. Some of it is left as waste on the ground. Mice eat grain as their major food source. Mice from nearby areas move into the grain field. This immigration causes an increase in the mice population. Research shows that the birthrate for mice increases when food is plentiful. This also causes an increase in the population. Eventually, the increased number of mice is checked by deaths, predators, and emigration.

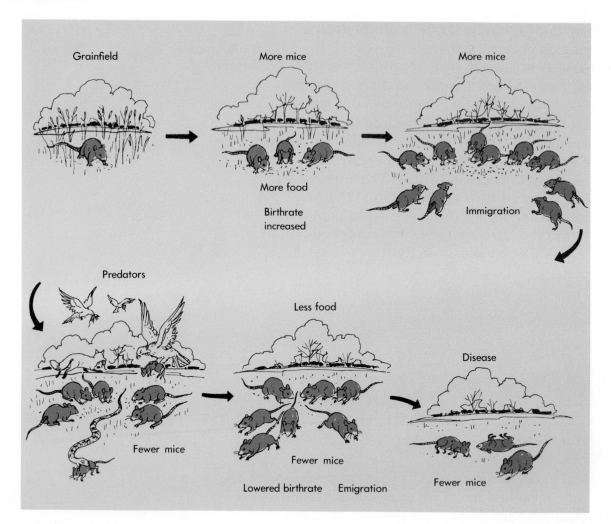

Grainfield

More mice

More mice

More food

Birthrate increased

Immigration

Predators

Less food

Disease

Fewer mice

Fewer mice

Lowered birthrate   Emigration

Fewer mice

FIGURE 18–8. Changes in the size of a field mouse population.

When a population becomes large, certain factors tend to limit its size. Predators and disease are the most important of these factors. As the number of mice increases, the natural enemies of the mice also increase. Hawks, snakes, and other mouse-eaters are attracted by their growing food supply—the mice. These predators eat the mice and reduce the mice population.

A large mouse population also leads to a smaller food supply. Some mice will not get enough to eat. Many will then move from the field and go elsewhere to find food. A lack of food also causes the birthrate to drop.

It is known that when the number of mice increases, epidemic diseases may start. Disease-causing bacteria may also be a kind of natural enemy. An increase in the number of individuals of a species increases the chance for contagious diseases to spread. There are more mice in the community. Thus, there is a greater chance for disease to be spread from sick to healthy mice.

The size of one population affects another. Both the number of bacteria and the number of mouse-eaters can increase when the number of mice increases. An increase in the number of one species affects the numbers of some other species.

MAKING SURE

3. What factors can affect the size of a rat population within a small city?
4. What factors affect the growth of the human population?
5. How does a change in a mice population affect the population of the mice's natural enemies?
6. How does a change in seasons affect changes in some animal populations?

18:4 Competition

The organisms within a community may compete for the things needed for survival. These include sunlight, food, water, and shelter. For example, trees in a forest compete for the available water. If a severe drought occurs, there may not be enough water for all. Some of the trees may die. Tall, mature trees limit the sunlight reaching the forest floor. Small, young trees compete for the available light. If a tree is in shade most of the time, it may grow very slowly or die.

Competition increases when many species have the same needs. Competition for the same food source has an effect on each species. One example of this has been observed in the laboratory. Two different

What may happen to plants and animals in competition for the things needed for survival?

FIGURE 18–9. Organisms in many communities compete for the same food source.

paramecia species were grown in separate dishes. Each was given the same food source. Both increased in number. Then, the two species were grown in the same dish. The same food source was used. Competition for the same food source became too great. One species did not survive.

A species may reduce or avoid competition with other species. One way is by living in different parts of a community. This fact has been observed in three related warbler species in a Pennsylvania forest. They each feed on the same food source—spruce trees. One species feeds mostly in the lower branches of spruce trees. Another feeds in the middle part. The third warbler species feeds on the outer tips of high branches.

Competition may be reduced by some birds and mammals in another way. Many of these animals set up territories. One or more animals defend a certain area or **territory.** If another animal comes near, it is usually chased out. As a result, there is little or no competition for the resources in the territory.

In what two ways may some birds and mammals reduce competition?

FIGURE 18–10. Bull elephant seals defend territories on their mating grounds.

Keith H. Murakami/Tom Stack & Assoc.

activity

POPULATION CHANGES

Objective: To study the effects of competition on the size of a population

Materials

beaker, 50-mL
dropper
dry yeast
microscope
1 slide and coverslip
spoon
sugar cube
water

FIGURE 18–11.

Procedure

1. Mix the yeast in 25 mL of water at room temperature.
2. Place a drop of the yeast-water mixture on the slide and add a coverslip.
3. Observe the yeast with the microscope. Count and record the number of yeast cells in your field of view.
4. Remove the slide and rinse it with water.
5. Add the sugar cube to the beaker and stir until it is dissolved.
6. Wait two minutes; then place a drop of the mixture on the slide and add a coverslip.
7. Observe the yeast under the microscope. Count and record the number of yeast cells in your field of view.
8. Repeat these observations every two minutes for 20 minutes. Remember to wash the slide and coverslip after each observation. Record all numbers.
9. Record any changes in appearance and odor of the solution in the beaker.

Observations and Data

No sugar, number of yeast cells:_____

Time (min)	Number of yeast cells
2	
4	
6	

Draw a line graph showing the relationship between the time and the number of yeast cells in the population.

Questions and Conclusions

1. What things were needed for the yeast to survive?
2. From your graph, describe the changes in the size of the yeast population.
3. When did the yeast population reach its highest number?
4. How might crowding, food, and waste products affect the size of a population?

FIGURE 18–12. In this field, succession is occuring as grasses are giving way to taller shrubs and trees.

Define succession.

Define climax community.

FIGURE 18–13. In the succession from lichens to maples and beeches, each stage has different dominant species.

MAKING SURE

7. Setting up territories tends to reduce the crowding of animals in a population. Why?
8. How does competition affect the number of living things in a community?

18:5 The Climax Community

Since populations change, communities undergo slow, gradual change. The process of slow, gradual change in a community is known as **succession** (suk SESH un). During succession, dominant species of plants and animals slowly give way to new dominant species. The end result of succession is called a **climax** (KLI maks) **community.** Each region follows a certain pattern of succession and climax. This depends on the climate and soil conditions. A climax community remains as long as the climate of the region does not change.

Succession can be seen in many regions. One example is in abandoned farm fields of northeastern United States. The land of the Northeast was once covered with forests. Trees were cut down by the settlers to make way for farms. However, it became unprofitable to farm some areas. As the fields were abandoned, "nature slowly took over." Grass, shrubs, and trees finally returned. Succession continued until the climax community was reached.

Lichens

Mosses, grasses, ferns, shrubs

Oak and Pines

Maple and Beeches

A freshwater pond community may be the first stage in a succession. Water, running into the pond, carries soil particles with it. With time, the pond may fill with soil and become a bog. A bog is an area of wet, spongy ground. Eventually, the bog may become a meadow. Finally, the meadow may become a forest. If the forest remains unchanged for a long time, it is the climax community.

FIGURE 18–14. Succession of a pond to a forest.

activity — COMMUNITY SUCCESSION

Prepare a hay infusion culture by boiling a handful of hay or dry grass in 1 L of water. Place the culture in a jar and add a few grains of boiled rice. Let the mixture stand for two days. Then add some pond water. Let the culture stand for 10 days. Each day, remove a drop of the culture liquid. Observe it under a microscope with low and high power. Record the changes in the species each day. What, if any, other species appear in the culture?

MAKING SURE

9. How does climate affect a climax community?
10. How does a succession of plants affect the succession of animals in a community?
11. Explain the succession that occurs when farmlands are abandoned.

18:6 Boundary Communities

What name is given to the area that separates two communities?

The boundary between two communities is a most interesting place because a great variety of species live here. A boundary is a region between two different communities. One boundary community is the seashore. The land that borders on a forest is another example.

A boundary region has the advantages of two communities. Usually more species live in this area than in either of the communities it separates. Boundaries provide the best environment for many plants and animals. Species common only to the boundary region live here. Also, species from both adjacent communities live here.

Frogs and snapping turtles live in boundaries between freshwater ponds and grassy meadows. They spend part of their life in water and part on land. Frogs lay their eggs in the water but come on land to catch insects for food. Snapping turtles do the opposite. They lay their eggs on land but get their food from the water.

Roger K. Burnard

FIGURE 18–15. The place where land and ocean meet has a unique boundary community.

18:7 Cooperation in Populations

Members of the same population use the same resources. If the resources are limited, individuals must compete with one another. Sometimes, members of the same species cooperate with each other. For example, wolves hunt together. A flock of birds may scare off an attacker. A crow may "stand guard" in a tall tree while the rest of the flock feeds in a cornfield. Ants live and work together in colonies. Cooperation helps the entire ant colony.

Cooperation is greatest among animals that live in societies (suh SI ut eez). A **society** is a group of individuals of the same species that live together in an organized way. Bees, ants, and wasps are organized into societies. Within a society, there is a division of labor. There is cooperation for the welfare of all.

Survival of an individual is based on the survival of the group. This fact is well illustrated by a honeybee colony. There are three kinds of honeybees—female queen, male drone, and female worker. The roles of the queen, drone, and worker are determined in large part by heredity. Under ordinary conditions there is only one queen in each colony. The queen is the only bee that lays fertilized and unfertilized eggs. The queen's contribution to the colony is to produce new male and female offspring. Drones produce sperm to fertilize the queen's eggs. This is their only role. Worker bees carry on work tasks necessary for the society's survival.

Worker bees perform many different jobs. In early life, they serve as nurse bees that feed the young bees. Later, they become housebees. Their jobs now include cleaning, storing honey, producing wax, and guarding the hive. Adult workers become field bees. Field bees collect nectar and pollen from plants.

FIGURE 18–16. Each wasp in the society has a certain job to do. Cooperation helps all members in a society live and survive.

Explain an example of cooperation in a population.

Why is cooperation usually greatest among animals living in societies?

MAKING SURE
12. How would the loss of a queen, drones, or workers threaten the survival of a hive?

18:8 Ecology

What is ecology? Why is it important?

The relationships between organisms and their environments is called **ecology** (ih KAHL uh jee). One of the most important relationships is the use of green plants by animals for food. Another is the decay of dead plant and animal matter. Decay returns the elements and compounds in dead matter to the soil. The decayed material is used as nutrients for growing plants. You have learned that disease, food supply, and many other factors can affect the size of a population. A change in the size of one population in an area can cause a change in the size of other populations. In other words, the life of any one species is related to the lives of other plants and animals in the environment. People who study the relationship between organisms and their environment are called ecologists.

Why is ecology important? Facts about living things can be used to save plants and animals that are in danger of becoming extinct. Extinct means all the members of a species die and the species is gone forever. For example, scientists study the life habits of the California condor, a species near extinction. They seek to learn how this bird raises its young, obtains food, and survives in the wild. If the scientists can find a way to increase the reproduction of the condor, they may save it from extinction.

Understanding ecology can also help preserve the environment. Scientists study the harmful effects of fertilizers, insecticides, and other chemicals. The knowledge gained may help us find ways to use these materials without causing harmful air and water pollution. Increasing the population of a species and preventing damage to forests by harmful insects are two problems attacked by ecologists.

Two important elements needed by living organisms are oxygen and carbon. In nature, these elements are part of the oxygen–carbon dioxide cycle. Here the word cycle means that each of these elements is used over and over again. Oxygen is a

Roger K. Burnard

FIGURE 18–17. Ecologists study relationships between living things and their environment.

Explain the oxygen–carbon dioxide cycle.

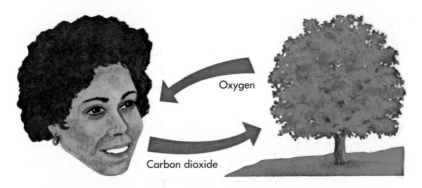

FIGURE 18–18. Oxygen and carbon dioxide are constantly being used and reused by animals and plants in the oxygen–carbon dioxide cycle.

gas present in air. Carbon is also present in air in the form of carbon dioxide gas. Animals remove oxygen from air and add carbon dioxide when they breathe. Plants take in carbon dioxide and give off oxygen during photosynthesis. The carbon in carbon dioxide is used along with water to make food. In the oxygen–carbon dioxide cycle, oxygen and carbon go from plants to animals and back to plants in a continuous cycle. Neither element is ever used up.

In the nitrogen cycle, nitrogen gas is removed from air to form compounds that are added to soil. Nitrogen-fixing bacteria take nitrogen gas and change it into nitrogen compounds. These bacteria live in colonies inside nodules, which are swellings on the roots of legumes. Legumes are a group of pod-bearing plants such as alfalfa, clover, and beans. Plants use nitrogen compounds from soil to make protein. Protein is needed for the growth and repair of tissues. Certain bacteria in soil break down organic matter and change the nitrogen in it into a compound called ammonia. Other bacteria change the ammonia to nitrate compounds. Another kind of soil bacteria converts nitrogen in compounds to nitrogen gas and returns it to the atmosphere.

USDA

FIGURE 18–19. Legume crops such as alfalfa return nitrogen to the soil.

MAKING SURE
13. How would the world change if there was no decay of dead plants and animals?
14. Describe the flow of carbon in the oxygen-carbon dioxide cycle.

Perspectives

Wolves in a Park?

Gene Frazier

Wolf Park appears to be an ordinary farm, but it is far from ordinary. Wolves, instead of corn and cows, are kept in large fenced enclosures. Here, behavioral research is done on wolves. The behavior of each wolf is studied and analyzed. All of the wolves born here are raised by both people and the wolves in the pack. In this way, scientists hope to learn more about the behavior of wolves.

Wolf Park's director is Dr. Erich Klinghammer. Dr. Klinghammer is an ethologist. An ethologist is a scientist who studies the inherited or typical behavior of a species. For Dr. Klinghammer, the purpose of Wolf Park is to educate the public about wolves. Wolf Park is open to the public on weekends from May to November. Also, groups of high school and college students may spend an entire day at the park learning about wolves.

Another way Dr. Klinghammer works to educate people is using the results of his research to solve problems. For example, in some places, wolves kill cattle. Using results from the park and other places, methods are being found to stop the killing of cattle. These methods do not include killing the wolves. One method is the use of dogs to chase the wolves. A current experiment is studying the hunting behavior of wolves. It involves bison (buffalo). Once a week, as many as six wolves are put with the bison. The wolves, as if they were hunting, fan out and test the bison to see if any are weak enough for an easy kill. The results of this experiment may provide further clues to solve the problem of wolves killing cattle.

Dr. Klinghammer also studies the mating behavior of wolves. He explains that wolves limit their numbers within a pack. In a small pack, about seven wolves, only the dominant male and female breed. When the pack is larger, more females may bear young. However, but if resources are limited, only one litter of wolf pups survives.

People seem to fear wolves less today than in the past. Dr. Klinghammer wants to continue to change people's attitudes towards wolves. For example, a wolf recently escaped from Wolf Park. The newspaper, radio, and television cooperated with the Park's staff. When they reported the escape, people did not panic. Two days later, the wolf walked back into the pen. No one was hurt.

If you were to ask Dr. Klinghammer about having a wolf as a pet, he would reply: "Wolves are not pets! They may look like dogs, but they are not dogs. When fullgrown, they challenge people for dominance [power]. Their needs are not met. They need other wolves and open spaces. Wolves belong to the wilderness." He would also add: "The only reason to keep captive animals is to remind us of their wild brethren . . . To me, the wolf is the best symbol of wilderness."

main ideas

1. A community consists of all of the living things in a given area.   18:1
2. Each species normally lives in a certain place called a habitat.   18:2
3. All living and nonliving things surrounding an organism make up its environment.   18:2
4. Populations are either stable or unstable. Changes in many unstable populations occur in cycles.   18:3
5. Through succession, dominant species slowly give way to new dominant species. This results in a climax community.   18:5
6. A society is an organized group of the same species which live together in cooperation.   18:7
7. Ecology is the science dealing with the study of relationships between organisms and their environment.   18:8
8. The oxygen, carbon, and nitrogen cycles are part of the environment.   18:8

vocabulary

Define each of the following words or terms.

climax community	emigration	population
community	environment	society
competition	habitat	succession
dominant species	immigration	territory
ecology		

study questions

DO NOT WRITE IN THIS BOOK.

A. True or False

Determine whether each of the following sentences is true or false. If the sentence is false, rewrite it to make it true.

1. Stable populations do not change much.
2. The environment of an organism includes only the nonliving things around it.
3. Ocean life is more abundant near coastlines.
4. Plants and animals are part of the oxygen–carbon dioxide cycle.

5. Food supply is the only factor that affects population size.
6. By defending their territories, animals reduce the amount of competition in a region.
7. The population of a species tends to decrease when there is a large food supply.
8. Succession usually occurs in a short time period.
9. Ecology is the study of the relationships among living organisms.
10. Most communities contain hundreds of populations.

B. Multiple Choice

Choose the word or phrase that completes correctly each of the following sentences.

1. All the oaks in a forest make up a (*community, habitat, population*).
2. Populations increase by (*death and immigration, birth and emigration, birth and immigration*).
3. A (*climax, succession, cycle*) is the slow and gradual change in a community.
4. When the grain in a field decreases, the mice population (*increases, decreases, remains the same*).
5. Plants and animals living together in a pond make up a (*habitat, community, population*).
6. An increase in predators causes (*an increase, a decrease, no change*) in the population of the species they eat.
7. The formation of a bog is a good illustration of (*competition, succession, emigration*).
8. Emigration causes the size of a population to (*increase, decrease, stay the same*).
9. Dominant plant species may make up (*less than 30%, 30% to 90%, 100%*) of all living things in a community.
10. The area between two communities is a (*climax, boundary, territorial*) community.

C. Completion

Complete each of the following sentences with a word or phrase that will make the sentence correct.

1. The total number of frogs in a pond is called a(n) _____.
2. The population of an ant colony is an organized _____.

3. The population of _____ in a community would eventually be reduced by a decrease in rabbits.
4. An abandoned field in northeastern United States may someday become a(n) _____.
5. A climax community is the end result of _____.
6. Photosynthesis is part of the oxygen–_____ cycle.
7. _____ and _____ tend to reduce the size of a population.
8. Slow changes in populations occur over many years during _____.
9. A(n) _____ community will remain as long as the climate stays the same.
10. Scientists who study the relationships among living things and their environment are _____.

D. How and Why

1. Explain why a change in the population size of one species may affect the size of another species.
2. Explain how a climax community is formed.
3. How does a population gain or lose individuals?
4. Give two examples of a community. Name the living things you might expect to find in these communities.
5. How does competition affect the size of populations? Give one example.

investigations

1. Obtain information from a library on an endangered species in your home state.
2. Obtain information on urban ecology, the relationship between people and their environment. Plan a study you can do to find out how the life of a city depends upon many different people doing many different kinds of jobs.

interesting reading

Harris, Susan, *Whales*. New York, NY: Watts, 1980.
Milne, Lorus and Margery, *Gadabouts and Stick-at-Homes: Wild Animals and Their Habitats.* San Francisco CA: Sierra Club, 1980.
Selsam, Millicent, *How Animals Live Together*. New York, NY: Morrow, 1979.

chapter

19

The grasshopper balanced on the edge of a sundew plant is the food which gives the sundew energy. All living things need energy to carry on life processes. Food supplies this necessary energy. What is a food chain and how is it related to a food web? How are predators different from parasites?

Alvin E. Staffan

410

Food and Energy

19:1 Food Chains

Every living organism needs energy for its life activities. Energy is needed for breathing, digesting food, circulating blood, and reproducing. Running, flying, and swimming are activities that increase an animal's need for energy. All the energy that plants and animals use comes directly or indirectly from the sun.

Green plants have one advantage over most other living things. They make their own food. Plants use the energy from sunlight to make sugar. This sugar is changed to starch and other substances which are stored food. Because animals cannot make their own food, they depend on plants or other animals for food. Many animals, such as deer and cows, eat only plants. Other animals, such as lions and wolves, eat only other animals. Some animals, such as humans, bears, and rats eat both plants and animals.

GOAL: You will continue the study of ecology. You will learn about food chains and webs and about the connection between food and energy.

FIGURE 19–1. A food chain shows a simple food relationship. A plant is always the first link in a food chain.

Explain what is meant by a food chain and give one example.

In a community there are food links between different plants and animals. A plant may be eaten by an animal. Another animal eats the animal that ate the plant. In turn, another animal eats this animal. A series of animals feeding on plants and/or other animals makes a **food chain.** The first link in a food chain is always a plant. One example of a food chain found in many forests is acorn–mouse–owl. Another example is wood–termite–anteater–lion. Food and the energy it contains are passed through a food chain. This transfer of energy begins at the source, which is plants. It then continues as one animal eats another animal.

FIGURE 19–2. In this food chain the eucalyptus tree is the producer and the koala bear is the consumer.

Miriam Austerman/Animals, Animals

Most animals eat more than one species as food. Thus, the term food chain does not always describe all food relationships. The term food web is more accurate. A **food web** is a complex feeding system containing more than one chain. In one food web, mice, rabbits, and deer eat plants. Owls eat both the mice and rabbits. Mountain lions eat both rabbits and deer. The food web formed in this way is shown in Figure 19–3.

What is a food web? Describe an example.

FIGURE 19–3. A food web shows a more accurate picture of the food relationships in a community. An animal may occupy different levels within a food web.

MAKING SURE

1. How is a food web different from a food chain?
2. Explain why all the energy animals use comes from the sun.
3. Why is the first link in the food chain always a plant?
4. Give an example of a food chain of which you are a part.

19:2 Producers and Consumers

Organisms in a food web that make their own food are called **producers.** All green plants are producers. All animals in a food web are consumers. **Consumers** cannot make food and must eat plants or other animals. There are many different kinds of consumers. Some are small plant-eaters, such as mice. Others are large flesh-eaters, such as lions. Mice and lions are usually the second and third links in the food chains of which they are a part.

Bacteria and fungi are both **decomposers.** They cause the decay or break down of dead plants and animals. Decomposers are always the last link in the food chain.

Scavengers (SKAV un jurz) are animals that feed on dead animals. Vultures and jackals are two examples of scavengers. These animals "clean up" the environment. Both decomposers and scavengers are consumers. They are important and necessary links in every food chain.

State the difference between a food producer, consumer, and decomposer. Name examples of each.

Why are scavengers and decomposers important consumers?

FIGURE 19–4. Decomposers (a) and scavengers (b) are vital links in food webs. Without them materials could not be recycled and used again.

a

Robert Fridenstine

b

Roger K. Burnard

activity

OBSERVING POND WATER

Objective: To study some producers and consumers in this community

Materials
dropper
4 jars, large (widemouth)/lids
microscope
4 samples of pond water (surface, under
  the surface, bottom, near shore)
slide and coverslip

FIGURE 19–5.

Procedure

1. Collect pond water in the jars from each location listed in the materials above. **CAUTION:** Be sure an adult accompanies you to obtain the pond water samples.

2. Place a drop of pond water from the surface sample on the slide.

3. Add a coverslip and examine the water using low power first and then using high power.

4. Make a sketch of several different organisms that you see. Record the color of each organism and the number of each organism present.

5. Remove the slide and wash it with water.

6. Repeat Steps 2 through 5 for each of your other samples of pond water. Be sure to sketch several organisms and record their colors. Also, record the number of each organism.

7. Determine if each organism you observed is a producer or a consumer. Producers usually are yellow, green, or blue-green. Consumers usually are colorless. Record your findings.

Observations and Data

Source of water sample	Sketches of organisms	Color and number	Producer or consumer

Questions and Conclusions

1. Did you find more producers or consumers in your samples? State a reason for your observations.

2. How are producers different from consumers?

3. In which sample did you find the most producers?

4. Where did most of the consumers live in the pond?

5. How did the producers obtain their food?

6. Where would you expect to find decomposers in the pond?

7. Draw a food web using your sketches of the organisms you observed in the pond water.

5. Classify the following as producer, consumer, or decomposer.

    (a) grass   (d) decay bacteria

    (b) rabbit   (e) bread mold

    (c) tree   (f) grasshopper

6. Why are decomposers and scavengers important in every food chain or web?

19:3 Energy Pyramids

Every organism needs energy. Green plants trap light and store this captured energy in the food they make. Some animals eat plants to obtain energy and others eat the animals that feed on plants. As food passes through a food chain, energy is obtained for use by each of the organisms in the chain. The energy captured by the green plants is used by all of the consumers in the food chain.

The acorn–mouse–owl food chain is a good example of the transfer of energy from one organism to another. An oak tree uses sunlight to make food and stores some of the food in its acorns. A mouse eats acorns. Most of the energy in the acorns is used by the mouse for its life activities. Only about 10 to 15 percent of the energy in the acorns is stored in the mouse. When an owl eats a mouse, most of the energy the owl obtains is used for the owl's life activities. Only 10 to 15 percent is stored in the owl's body.

What happens to energy as it moves through a food chain? Most of it is used for the life activities of the organisms in the food chain. These activities include cell division, circulation of blood, breathing, running, and flying. The loss of energy used for life activities can be pictured with an energy pyramid. A pyramid is wide at the bottom and pointed at the top. Each level in the pyramid is smaller in size than the level below it. Green plants, the producers in a

What does the shape of an energy pyramid show?

food chain, make up the first level of an energy pyramid. Animals that eat only plants make up the second level. Flesh-eating animals are in the third and higher levels.

In each successive level of an energy pyramid, there is less energy. The loss of energy is shown by the decreasing size of the pyramid from bottom to top. Most of the energy is in producers, such as oak trees or other green plants at the bottom. The least amount of energy is in the consumers at the top. Further, the shape of the pyramid shows there is a large number of producers supplying energy for a smaller number of consumers.

In the energy pyramid shown in Figure 19–6, producers make up the first level. Consumers make up all the remaining levels. This arrangement is true for all energy pyramids. Animals that eat only plants make up the second level. Flesh-eating animals make up the third and higher levels.

FIGURE 19–6. A general model of an energy pyramid (a) and a corn–mouse–owl energy pyramid (b).

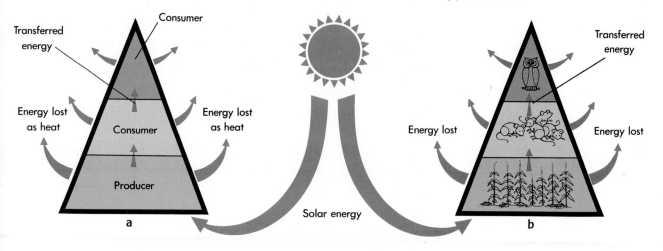

The pyramid's shape represents the energy lost in the food chain. With each successive level, there is less energy. For this reason, there is more energy available in a short food chain than in a long one. The decreasing size of the pyramid also represents the large number of producers needed to supply energy for a small number of consumers.

CONSTRUCTING AN ENERGY PYRAMID

(1) Cut four triangles, 30 cm on each side, out of a piece of cardboard. Tape the sides of the triangles together to form a pyramid. **(2)** Use a pen and ruler to divide the pyramid into three levels by marking two horizontal lines on each side of the pyramid (Figure 19–6). **(3)** Make a list of foods you ate yesterday. **(4)** Divide the foods listed into two groups, those that come from producers and those that come from consumers. **(5)** From old magazines, obtain small pictures of the producers and consumers in your food list. Also, obtain some pictures of people. **(6)** Paste the pictures of the producers on the pyramid in the lowest level. Paste the pictures of the consumers in the middle level. Paste the pictures of people in the top level. (Note: If you are unable to obtain pictures, make colored drawings of producers, consumers, and people for each level.) How many producers are in your energy pyramid? How many consumers? Why are the producers in the lowest level?

MAKING SURE

7. Why is the total food energy in each level of an energy pyramid less than in the level below it?
8. Which of these food chains will support more bass? Why?
   (a) plankton–bass   (b) plankton–minnows–bass
9. Why are green plants always in the bottom level of an energy pyramid?

19:4   Predators

Define predators. Why are they important in the food chain?

Predators are at the top of all food chains. A predator is an animal that feeds on other animals. Most predators, such as foxes, kill their prey. Prey is an animal that a predator uses for food. Some, such as mosquitoes, feed on only a part of their prey. Their prey usually does not die from an attack.

Predators help control the population of the prey species. This prevents the prey population from growing too large for the food supply. For example, the deer population in an area may become so large that there is not enough food for all the deer. Many of the deer die or become sick. The killing of deer by wolves and other predators helps keep the deer population from becoming too large.

In a community, the number of predators depends on the number of prey. For example, if the number of mice increases in a community, the number of predators, such as snakes and hawks, increases. As more mice are eaten by the predators, the mouse population decreases. As a result, the number of hawks and snakes decreases in the community.

Predators also have another effect on the prey species. They tend to attack older, ill, and injured members of a population. As a result, weak animals are removed. The remaining animals are healthy and strong. These animals are the ones most likely to survive and reproduce.

a

b

FIGURE 19–7. The timber wolf (a) kills its prey; a mosquito (b) does not. Both animals, however, are predators.

MAKING SURE

10. How might the population size of a predator species change if its prey began to increase in large numbers?

11. What would happen to a predator species if its prey species became diseased and began to die off?

19:5 Parasites

Another type of consumer lives and feeds in or on other living things. Tapeworms, fleas, and disease-causing bacteria are examples. These organisms are parasites. A parasite obtains its food and other needs from another organism called the host. Parasites spend most of their lives on or in the host. Most parasites harm their host organisms.

David Dennis

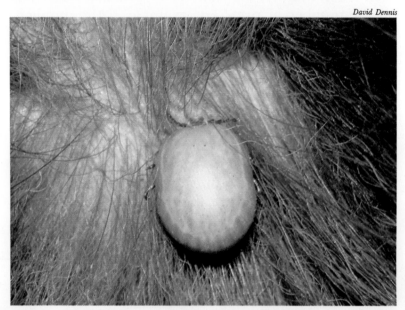

FIGURE 19–8. Ticks are parasites. They live on the blood sucked from the bodies of animals.

The life cycle of a parasite may include many stages. One or more stages may be spent on or in a host. Beef tapeworms have stages in both cattle and humans. A person becomes infected by eating raw or barely cooked beef that contains tapeworm larvae. These larvae become active in the person's intestine. Here, they grow into mature tapeworms. The heads of the tapeworms attach to the intestinal wall. The human intestine provides food, water, and a warm environment. Here the adult tapeworms produce eggs. The eggs are then shed through a person's feces. Tapeworms often weaken the human host because they take away food and cause bleeding in the intestine.

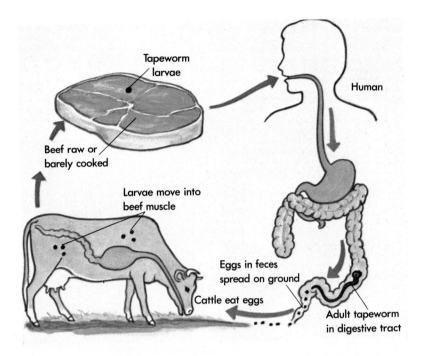

FIGURE 19–9. Life cycle of a tapeworm.

MAKING SURE

12. Parasites can make an animal ill. They can even cause death. Why does a parasite "lose" if it kills its host?

13. How can people protect themselves from becoming infected by beef tapeworms?

14. Why might a mosquito be considered a parasite as well as a predator?

19:6 Symbiosis

Symbiosis (sihm bee OH sus) refers to two organisms living together. In one form of symbiosis, one species benefits and the other species receives neither benefit nor harm. The benefit to one species may be shelter, food, or a surface on which to grow. For example, tropical orchids grow on the branches of larger trees. The orchids are attached to the trees but they do not take food from the tree or harm it in any way.

Define symbiosis.

List two examples of symbiosis.

Another example of symbiosis is the sea anemone that lives in harmony with only one fish species, the decoy fish. Sea anemones have tentacles which paralyze most fish that touch them. Yet, decoy fish swim freely among the tentacles. They do this without being harmed. What is the benefit? The sea anemones provide protection for decoy fish. Although anemones feed on other fish species, they do not harm decoy fish. It has been observed that decoy fish may "help" the sea anemone. When feeding, the fish drop bits of food. The food drifts down into the sea anemone's tentacles and becomes food for the sea anemone.

a

Allan Roberts

b
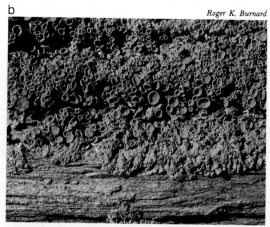
Roger K. Burnard

FIGURE 19–10. Symbiosis occurs between decoy fish and sea anemones (a) and in lichens (b).

In some cases of symbiosis, both species receive benefits from each other. A honeybee obtains nectar from a flower on a plant. At the same time, the honey bee aids in pollinating the plant by carrying pollen from one flower to another. A termite can eat wood because of certain protozoans that live in the termite's intestine. The protozoans help by digesting the cellulose in the wood. In turn, food for the protozoan is provided by the termite.

Another example of symbiosis where both species benefit is a **lichen** (LI kun). A lichen is an alga and a fungus living together. The alga makes food that is used by the fungus. The fungus supplies water and minerals for the alga. The partnership between alga and fungus allows lichens to grow almost anywhere, even on bare rock. Lichens may also grow on trees, decaying wood, and soil. A lichen may look like a leathery leaf, a scaly patch of paint, or a clump of moss. The color of a lichen may be gray-green, bright yellow, or orange. In the arctic, lichens provide food for animals. The best known of the arctic lichens is reindeer moss.

Steve Martin/Tom Stack & Assoc.

FIGURE 19–11. In a type of symbiosis, the small remoras receive a "free" ride by attaching to a shark. Remoras also obtain food scraps left by the shark.

activity THE STRUCTURE OF A LICHEN

Place a piece of lichen in a drop of water on a slide. Separate it with dissecting needles. Add a coverslip and observe the lichen with a microscope. Sketch and describe the appearance of the lichen. How are the algae different from the fungi?

MAKING SURE

15. How is symbiosis different from parasitism?
16. How do the alga and the fungus in a lichen benefit each other?
17. In a lichen, which is the producer and which is the consumer?

What Is IPM?

Roger K. Burnard

There are over a million insect species. Of these, only 10 000 species interfere with our activities. We call the interfering species pests. In the past, large amounts of pesticide were used against pests. At first, pesticides were successful. Insect-carried diseases were controlled. Crop production increased. Now, the problems of pesticide use are apparent. New generations of insects are resistant to pesticides. People are concerned about the effects of pesticides on the environment and human health. How can these problems be solved?

One suggestion is "integrated pest management" or IPM. IPM uses a combination of methods to control pests. One method is predation. In predation, insects that eat pests are used. For example, the praying mantis devours many garden pests such as grasshoppers. Perhaps some insects can become biological "fly swatters."

Viruses and bacteria are also useful in fighting pests. For example, a bacterium is used to control Japanese beetles. A virus is used to control cabbage loopers and tobacco budworms. Viruses and bacteria, which do not affect people, can be made into a powder. The powder is spread on plants that insects are damaging. Pests eat the bacteria or viruses while eating the plants. After eating the plants, the insects become sick and die.

Insects use a chemical "language" called pheromones. Through pheromones, insects communicate alarm, the presence of food, and readiness to mate. Pheromones can be used to control pests. For example, the pink bollworm was destroying many cotton fields. Scientists sprayed the air above the fields with a chemical which acted like the female bollworm's sex pheromone. The males reacted as if females were ready to mate. While searching for females, the males became exhausted and died. The bollworm population decreased by 75 percent.

Each year more disease-resistant and pest-resistant crops are developed. Plants such as marigolds and garlic produce chemicals that some pests dislike. Also, small amounts of pesticide seem to produce little harm to the environment. But, no single method works well alone. By carefully combining several methods, IPM can lead to successful crop production without harm to human health, wildlife, or the environment.

Tracy Borland

main ideas

1. A food chain is made up of a series of animals feeding on plants and/or other animals.   19:1
2. Food webs contain many food chains.   19:1
3. Producers, green plants and algae, make their own food. They are the first level of every food chain.   19:2
4. Consumers cannot make their own food.   19:2
5. Decomposers cause the decay of dead organisms.   19:2
6. Animals that feed on dead animals are scavengers.   19:2
7. Food energy is transferred from producer to each level of consumer in an energy pyramid.   19:3
8. Predators are consumers that are located at the top of food chains.   19:4
9. Parasites are consumers that live and feed on or in other living things.   19:5
10. Symbiosis is when two organisms live together. In some cases, the organisms benefit each other.   19:6

vocabulary

Define each of the following words or terms.

consumer	food web	producer
decomposer	lichen	scavenger
energy pyramid	prey	symbiosis
food chain		

study questions

DO NOT WRITE IN THIS BOOK.

A. True or False

Determine whether each of the following sentences is true or false. If the sentence is false, rewrite it to make it true.

1. Food energy is gained at each level of an energy pyramid.
2. Only producers can make their own food.
3. Decomposers are always the last link of a food chain.
4. Energy used by living organisms comes from the sun.

5. Both organisms always benefit from their relationship in symbiosis.
6. All parasites kill their hosts.
7. Predators help control the population of their prey.
8. A parasite is a predator.
9. More producers are needed to support a smaller number of consumers.
10. A food web contains many food chains.

B. Multiple Choice

Choose the word or phrase that completes correctly each of the following sentences.

1. Fungi are (*producers, consumers, decomposers*).
2. Energy loss in a food chain (*increases, stays the same, decreases*) as the number of links increases.
3. Algae are (*producers, consumers, decomposers*).
4. Transfer of food energy is shown best in a drawing of a(n) (*food chain, food web, energy pyramid*).
5. A mosquito is an example of a (*parasite, predator, scavenger*).
6. A tapeworm is an example of a (*parasite, predator, scavenger*).
7. (*Producers, Consumers, Decomposers*) are always the first link of any food chain.
8. An example of symbiosis is (*mold on bread, algae on fungi, ticks on dog*).
9. A person who eats only vegetables would be on the (*first, second, third*) level of an energy pyramid.
10. The adult beef tapeworm spends its life in (*cattle muscle, human intestine, soil*).

C. Completion

Complete each of the following sentences with a word or phrase that will make the sentence correct.

1. _____ cause the decay of dead plants and animals.
2. A lichen is an example of _____.
3. Most _____ is lost as it is transferred through a food chain.
4. Animals that eat other animals are _____ in a food web.

5. A(n) _____ cleans up the environment by eating dead animals.
6. The series of food links between plants and animals is called a(n) _____.
7. A(n) _____ is always at the base of an energy pyramid.
8. Fungi growing on a rotten log is an example of _____.
9. The _____ in a food chain traps solar energy.
10. Vultures and jackals are _____ in a food web.

D. How and Why
1. Why is more food energy available in a short food chain?
2. How are scavengers and decomposers alike? How are they different?
3. Describe a food chain that exists in a community near your school or home.
4. Describe two examples of symbiosis.
5. Why are decomposers always the last link in a food chain?

investigations

1. Prepare a bulletin board display or drawing of food webs. Show the many relationships between and among food chains.
2. Make a food chain mobile. Cut out pictures of different foods, plants, animals, and other organisms from old magazines. Paste the picture of each food or organism on an index card. Tie the cards together with string in a chain in the same order as the positions of the organisms in a food chain. Hang the mobile in your classroom.

interesting reading

Blaustein, Elliott H. and Rose, *Investigating Ecology*. New York, NY: Arco, 1978.
Pringle, Laurence, *Chains, Webs, and Pyramids: The Flow of Energy in Nature*. New York, NY: Crowell, 1975.
Scott, Jack Denton, *Window on the Wild*. New York, NY: Putnam's, 1980.

chapter 20

Pumpkins, gourds, and squash are members of the same family. Many of these different varieties have been produced through humans working with plant heredity. How can humans use the principles of heredity to produce desired characteristics in both plants and animals? What is mutation?

Dr. James Utzinger

Heredity

20:1 Inherited Traits

Every living organism is a product of its heredity and environment. **Heredity** is the passing of traits from parents to offspring. Through heredity, traits such as color, size, and shape are passed on from parents to offspring. The traits of an animal or plant often go back through many generations of ancestors. Why are some plants and animals very much like their parents while others are not? Scientists study heredity in search of answers to this important question.

A living organism has an inheritance (ihn HER ut unts) it receives from its parents. This inheritance consists of inborn traits or characteristics. Much has been learned about this subject by studying the heredity of plants, such as the pea, and animals, such as the fruit fly.

You may have seen fruit flies buzzing around some fruit or decaying plant tissue on a warm summer day. There are several reasons fruit flies are used for research on heredity. Hundreds of flies may be kept in a small container and fed on small amounts of food. Therefore, they are inexpensive to raise and require very little space. Another advantage of using fruit flies is that there are only about ten days between generations (jen uh RAY shunz). A

GOAL: You will learn how inherited traits are passed from parents to offspring.

Define heredity.

How do scientists study heredity?

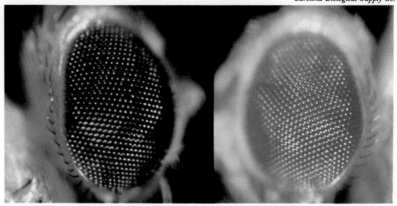

Carolina Biological Supply Co.

generation is the time it takes an offspring to mature and reproduce. Compare a generation of ten days for the fruit fly to six months for rabbits, four years for horses, and twelve years for elephants. The passage of traits can be followed much more quickly through many generations of fruit flies than any other animals. Fortunately, heredity works about the same for most plants and animals. Therefore, much of what has been learned about the fruit fly can be applied to other living things.

MAKING SURE
1. Why are elephants not used in heredity experiments?
2. What are the advantages of using fruit flies in heredity experiments?

20:2 Law of Dominance

Gregor Mendel (1822–1884), an Austrian monk, was one of the first persons to do research on heredity. Mendel studied heredity in pea plants. He observed that some pea plants were short and bushy, and others were tall and climbing. He saw that some pea plants produced yellow seeds and some produced green seeds. He also saw differences in the color of the flowers of the pea plants. Mendel experimented to find out how the traits of pea plants were passed from one generation to the next. He planted seeds from short pea plants and discovered they produced more short pea plants. Seeds from

Runk, Schoenberger/Grant Heilman Photography

FIGURE 20–2. Smooth pea seeds are dominant over wrinkled seeds.

these short plants also produced short plants. Every time Mendel planted the seeds from short pea plants, new short plants were produced.

Describe Mendel's experiments with pea plants.

When a trait such as shortness is inherited through several generations the trait is said to be pure. Thus, shortness is a pure trait in certain pea plants. The seeds from short pea plants produce more short pea plants. Other pure traits that Mendel discovered in pea plants were tallness, yellow seeds, and green seeds.

Mendel wondered what would happen if he crossed tall and short pea plants. Would the resulting plants be tall or short?

To cross pea plants, the stamens in the flowers of one plant are removed. The pistil is then pollinated with pollen taken from the other pea plant in the cross. Mendel crossed pure short and pure tall pea plants by transferring pollen from tall plants to short plants. Mendel observed that every pea plant from this cross was tall. Neither short nor medium plants were among the offspring. The offspring from a cross between plants that have different traits is called a **hybrid.**

Define: hybrid, dominant trait, recessive trait.

FIGURE 20–3. Developing a hybrid pea plant.

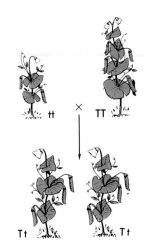

From his experimental results, Mendel theorized that a trait from one parent may cover or mask a trait from the other parent. This theory is now known as the **law of dominance.** In a hybrid, the trait that determines how the plant or animal will appear is said to be **dominant.** The trait which is present, but hidden or masked, is said to be **recessive.** In pea plants, tall is dominant and short is recessive. The pea plants are short only when tallness is not inherited.

activity
OBSERVING FRUIT FLIES

Objective: To observe various traits of fruit flies

Materials

2 baby food jars/lids
dark cloth
Drosophila fruit fly culture
hammer
hand lens
masking tape
nail
straight pin

Procedure

1. Label the jars *A* and *B*.
2. Punch three holes in each jar lid using the hammer and nail.
3. Cover the holes with masking tape.
4. Use a straight pin and make some small holes in the masking tape.
5. Transfer the fruit flies in the culture container to jar *A* using the following method. Tap the fruit flies to the bottom of the culture container. Remove the top of the container and immediately cover it with jar *A*. Cover the culture container with the dark cloth. The fruit flies should move into jar *A*. Remove jar *A* and cover the jar and the culture container immediately so the flies do not escape.
6. Observe the flies with the hand lens. Record the color of eyes, the shape and size of the wings, and the body color. Record the number of flies having each of the three traits in Table A.
7. After 24 hours, transfer the fruit flies to jar B. Use the transfer procedure you followed in Step 5. Return jar *B* to your teacher.
8. Store jar *A* at 20–25°C. Observe the jar daily and note the number of days it takes for new flies to appear.
9. Observe the new flies in jar *A* with a hand lens. Record in your data table the 3 traits you observe. Record the number of flies having each trait in Table B.

Observations and Data

A

	Traits	Number of Flies
Eye color		
Wing		
Body color		

B

	Traits	Number of Flies
Eye color		
Wing		
Body color		

Questions and Conclusions

1. What is the source of the flies that appeared in jar *A*.
2. Were the traits of these flies similar to or different from their parents? How?
3. Why are fruit flies used to study heredity?

20:3 Crossing Hybrids

Pea plants resulting from a cross between pure tall and pure short plants are true hybrids. Although they grow tall, the plants are not pure for this trait. Mendel also produced other hybrid pea plants, such as hybrid yellow seed plants. These plants resulted from a cross between pure yellow seed plants and pure green seed plants. The offspring plants produced yellow seeds, but they were not pure for this trait.

Mendel's next step in his study was to cross the hybrid pea plants he had produced. For example, he crossed hybrid tall pea plants with hybrid tall pea plants. What do you think resulted?

When the seeds from hybrid tall cross were planted, some of the resulting pea plants were tall and some were short. A careful counting showed that about three of every four plants were tall. Only about one out of four was short.

Mendel also crossed hybrid yellow seed plants with hybrid yellow seed plants. As a result, he obtained some plants that produced yellow seeds and some

Describe two examples of a hybrid cross.

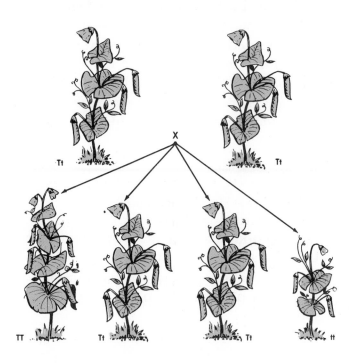

FIGURE 20–4. Cross of hybrid tall pea plants.

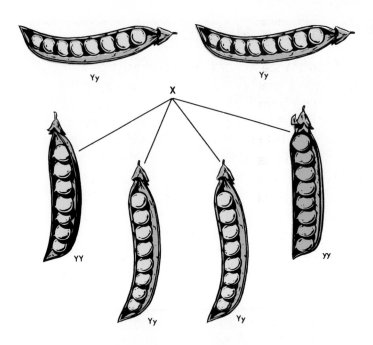

FIGURE 20–5. Cross of hybrid yellow seed pea plants.

Yy   Yy

X

YY

Yy   Yy

yy

What did Mendel learn when he crossed hybrids?

FIGURE 20–6. In this hybrid cross, the purple kernels in the corn are dominant.

Courtesy CCM: General Biological, Inc.

that produced green seeds. About three of every four plants had yellow seeds. Only about one out of four had green seeds.

The crossing of hybrid plants showed two things. First, hybrids do not produce only other hybrids. For example, hybrid tall plants can give rise to short plants. Second, inherited traits do not always appear in an individual. They may skip one or more generations. Mendel's conclusions can be summed up as follows:

(1) Some inherited traits are dominant. Others are recessive.

(2) When both dominant and recessive traits are present in an individual, only the dominant appear.

(3) Recessive traits may be passed from one generation to another without appearing. They may be found in a later generation.

Further experimentation has shown that the facts of inheritance in pea plants are also true in other plants and animals.

activity PROBABILITY AND COINS

Probability or chance affects the inheritance of traits. Some traits have a greater chance of appearing in the offspring resulting from a cross between two animals or plants. Toss a coin 50 times and keep track of the number of heads and tails. What is the chance of a head when the coin is tossed? What is the chance of a tail? Toss two coins together 50 times. Record the number of each combination: head–head, head–tail, and tail–tail. What is the chance of getting each combination? Combine your results with those of your classmates and determine the totals for the class. How does the chance of getting each combination change as the number of tosses increases? How is the tossing of two coins together similar to a hybrid cross?

MAKING SURE

3. Why is a recessive trait pure when it shows up in an organism?
4. Explain how a white kitten may be born even though both parents are black.

20:4 Blending

The law of dominance does not apply to all traits. Since Mendel's time, scientists have learned that some traits are inherited by blending. **Blending** is the inheritance of a trait that is a combination of the traits present in the parents. For example, white-flowered four o'clocks crossed with red-flowered four o'clocks produce all pink-flowered four o'clocks. Incomplete dominance is another term for blending.

Blending also occurs in shorthorn cattle. When red shorthorns are bred to white shorthorns, the offspring are roan. Roan is a blend of red and white hairs in the coat.

What is blending inheritance?

FIGURE 20–7. Roan cattle result from blending when red shorthorns are bred with white shorthorns.

Jean Wentworth

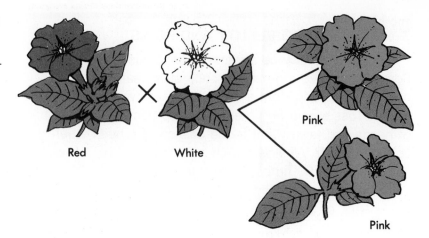

FIGURE 20–8. Flower color in four o'clocks is inherited through blending. Crossing red-flowered plants with white-flowered plants produced all pink-flowered offspring.

Red

White

Pink

Pink

activity

Obtain 20 hybrid soybean seeds. Soak the seeds in water for an hour. Then plant them in soil or sand. Keep the soil or sand moist. Plants should appear in 8 to 12 days. The leaves may be yellow, green, or yellow green. What is the number and percent of plants showing each color?

MAKING SURE

5. What experiments would you do to find out if a plant trait was dominant, recessive, or caused by blending? Describe the results you would expect in your experiments.

20:5 Chromosomes and Genes

Mendel described heredity in pea plants, but he did not explain how traits are passed on according to his results. It took scientists many years to discover how traits are passed from parents to offspring. Even now, all the answers are not known.

We do know that the nucleus of a cell is important in heredity. Under high magnification, tiny, dark grains are visible in a stained nucleus. This grainy material is called chromatin (KROH mut un). When a

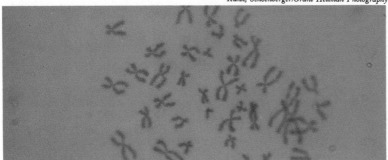

Runk, Schoenberger/Grant Heilman Photography

FIGURE 20–9. Chromosomes.

cell begins to divide, the chromatin forms thin, threadlike bodies. These threadlike bodies are called **chromosomes.** Chromosomes vary in size and shape, and almost always occur in pairs. Each chromosome in a cell nucleus has a mate in the same nucleus.

Define: chromosome, gene.

Each species has a certain number of chromosomes. The nucleus of every human body cell has 46 chromosomes that form 23 pairs. The number of chromosomes for various species is given in Table 20–1. Why are chromosomes important in studying heredity? Chromosomes contain **genes** that control the inheritance of different traits. Genes are arranged in a chromosome like beads on a string. Every inherited trait is controlled by at least one pair of genes. Like chromosomes, genes also occur in pairs. A gene in one chromosome has a mate in the other chromosome of the pair.

Where are chromosomes and genes located?

Table 20–1.
Species Number of Chromosomes

Species	Chromosomes
Fruit Fly	8
Housefly	12
Onion	16
Cabbage	18
Corn	20
Toad	22
Tobacco	24
Frog	26
McIntosh apple	34
Lizard	140

Height in pea plants is controlled by a single pair of genes. Seed color and flower color in pea plants are each controlled by a single pair of genes. Some traits, such as the size and shape of bones, eye color, and skin color are controlled by many pairs of genes. Also, a pair of genes may affect not one, but two or more traits.

It is not certain how a gene determines the traits of a plant or animal. It is known, however, that a gene is a part of a DNA molecule. Scientists believe that the DNA in a gene controls the chemical changes within a cell. By regulating chemical changes, the genes control traits such as height, seed color, eye color, and skin color.

Dominant and recessive traits can be explained by genes. One gene is dominant for a trait and the other is recessive. For example, in hybrid tall pea plants, the gene for tallness is on one chromosome. A gene for shortness is on the other member of the chromosome pair. The effect of the gene for tallness is dominant over the gene for shortness. The gene for tallness controls the chemical changes that make the plant grow tall.

Gerard Photography

FIGURE 20–10. Dominant and recessive traits within this population are determined by genes.

MAKING SURE

6. Why is a cell nucleus important in heredity?

20:6 Reduction Division and Fertilization

How does an organism get its genes? In the reproduction of plants and animals, sperm and eggs unite. Sperm and eggs are formed in a special type of cell division called **reduction division.** Reduction division is unlike the division of a body cell in which the chromosome number of the cells remains constant. In reduction division, the chromosome number of the dividing cells is reduced by half.

Reduction division actually consists of two divisions. The chromosome number for frogs is 26. In the first division stage of a male frog sex cell, 26 chromosomes pair up and duplicate. This duplication results in 52 chromosomes. They separate when the cell divides. Each of the two new cells has 13 double-stranded chromosomes. In the second division, the two cells with the double-stranded chromosomes divide to form four cells. Each of the four new cells has 13 chromosomes. Thus, reduction division in the frog starts with one cell having 26 chromosomes and ends with four sperm having 13 chromosomes each.

Explain how reduction division changes the chromosome number.

FIGURE 20–11. Body cell division (a) and reduction division (b). Note that the egg and sperm cells contain half the number of chromosomes contained in the original cell.

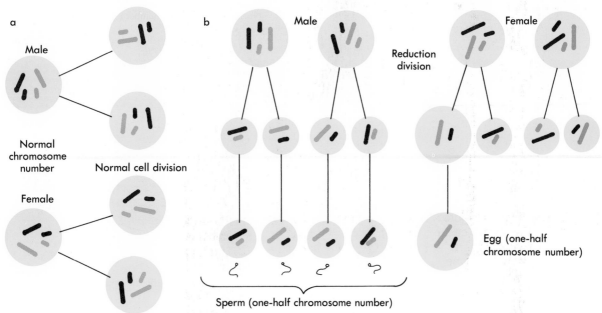

a

Male

Normal chromosome number

Normal cell division

Female

b

Male

Reduction division

Female

Sperm (one-half chromosome number)

Egg (one-half chromosome number)

In the female frog, the first stage is the same as in the male. However, one of the two cells with 13 double-stranded chromosomes dies. The remaining cell divides to produce two cells, each with 13 chromosomes. One of these cells dies. The remaining cell becomes the egg cell containing 13 chromosomes. Because a sperm and an egg cell each have half the species number of chromosomes, they have only half the number of genes.

Fertilization is the process by which a sperm cell and an egg cell unite to form a single cell. This process results in the chromosomes combining so that the species number of chromosomes is restored. Each frog egg and each frog sperm has 13 chromosomes. Thus, a fertilized egg has 26 chromosomes, the species number for frogs. Because half the chromosomes come from each parent, a new frog gets an equal number of genes from each parent. Through reduction division and fertilization, inherited traits are passed from parents to offspring.

How does fertilization restore the chromosome number of the species?

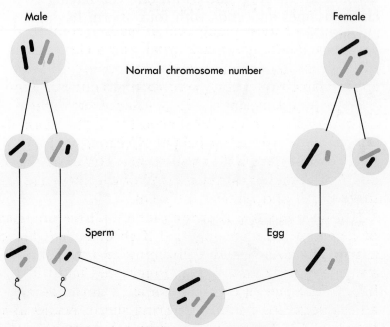

FIGURE 20–12. A zygote forms when a sperm cell fertilizes an egg cell. The zygote contains the same number of chromosomes found in each parent.

activity COMPARING BODY CELL DIVISION AND
REDUCTION DIVISION

Use a microscope to study prepared slides of onion root
tip, whitefish eggs, and animal testis. Observe the
differences between body cell division and reduction
division.

MAKING SURE
7. Corn plants have 20 chromosomes in each cell.
   Pollen and egg nuclei are produced by the corn
   in reproduction.
   (a) How many chromosomes are in a pollen
       nucleus and an egg?
   (b) How does fertilization restore the complete
       number of 20 chromosomes?

20:7 Sex Determination

The sex of most plants and animals is controlled
by genes. These genes are usually on a certain pair
of chromosomes called the sex chromosomes. Most
species have two types of sex chromosomes, X and
Y. The X chromosome is long and rodlike. The Y
chromosome is short and shaped like a "J." In many
animals, a female has a pair of X chromosomes
(XX). A male has XY chromosomes. Genes on the X
and Y chromosomes cause many of the features that
make males and females different.

A female has two X chromosomes. Therefore, each
of her eggs can have only one X chromosome. Since
a male has both X and Y chromosomes, half the
sperm will have an X chromosome, and half will
have a Y. Since all eggs contain an X chromosome,
an egg fertilized by an X-carrying sperm results in a
female (XX). An egg fertilized by a Y-carrying sperm
results in a male (XY).

How is sex in animals
produced by chromosomes?

FIGURE 20–13. X and Y
chromosomes determine the
sex of an organism.

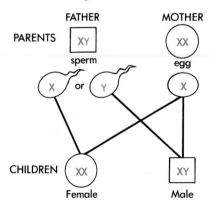

8. How are the sex chromosomes in males different from those in females?

9. What are the chances of an animal offspring being a female? Male?

10. What sex cell determines the sex of the offspring?

FIGURE 20–14. Development of an embryo from a fertilized egg.

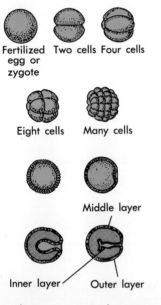

Fertilized egg or zygote   Two cells   Four cells

Eight cells   Many cells

Middle layer

Inner layer   Outer layer

How does a zygote become an embryo?

FIGURE 20–15. Development of a chick embryo at 56 hours (a) and 96 hours (b).

20:8 Reproduction

A fertilized egg is the beginning of a new member of a species. It is the first cell in a new animal or plant. The fertilized egg cell, called a **zygote** (ZI goht), divides to become four, eight, sixteen cells, and so on. The process continues until a new member of the species is formed. In these early stages of life, the organism is called an **embryo.** Figure 20–14 shows the early development of an embryo.

The early stages in the life of an embryo are basically the same in all backboned animals. First, many cell divisions occur. Then the cells form a hollow ball or sphere. One side of the sphere pushes inward to form a deep pocket. As a result, the embryo becomes shaped like a cup made of two layers of cells. More cells grow between these two layers to form a third layer of cells. These cell layers will form the various tissues, organs, and systems of the new animal (Figure 20–14).

a

b

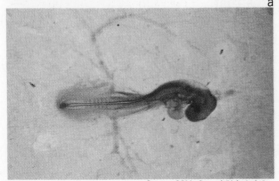

Courtesy CCM: General Biological, Inc.

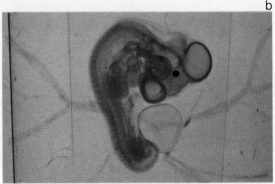

Courtesy CCM: General Biological, Inc.

In species such as the horse, cow, and sheep, one offspring is usually produced at a time. Once in a while, twins are produced. There are two kinds of twins—fraternal and identical. Fraternal twins result from two different fertilized eggs. They are no more alike than any two offspring from the same parents.

Identical twins come from one embryo that was formed from a single fertilized egg. In the very early stages of its development, the embryo divides in two. Each part then develops further as a separate embryo. Two offspring, called twins, are produced from the embryos. Because they come from the same egg and sperm, identical twins have the same genes. This fact explains why they are so much alike.

Explain how identical twins are different from fraternal twins.

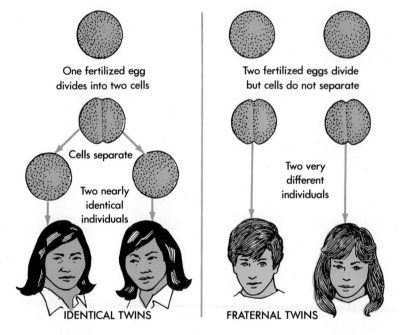

One fertilized egg divides into two cells

Cells separate

Two nearly identical individuals

IDENTICAL TWINS

Two fertilized eggs divide but cells do not separate

Two very different individuals

FRATERNAL TWINS

FIGURE 20–16. Identical twins come from a single fertilized egg. Fraternal twins come from two fertilized eggs.

MAKING SURE

11. Scientists often study twins to learn the effects of environment on development. What kinds of twins are used in this kind of research, identical or fraternal? Why are twins good subjects for these studies?

20:9 Mutations

What is a mutation?

A change in a gene or chromosome that causes a change in an inherited trait is called a **mutation** (myew TAY shun). A mutant is a living thing that has a mutation. Because a gene is made of DNA, a gene mutation is caused by a change in the DNA. DNA is a complex chemical that carries hereditary traits from one generation to the next. Hence, changes in the structure of DNA will result in changes in the traits passed to the offspring.

Many mutations occur from unknown causes. Other mutations result from exposure to X rays, nuclear radiation, and certain chemicals.

Although many mutations go unnoticed, some have been observed in animals and plants. Mutations may produce unexpected traits, such as short-legged dogs and seedless grapes. These mutants are produced by a change in one or more genes.

Many mutations are harmful to an organism. These mutations make the organism less likely to survive. For example, insects with a mutation that produces short wings do not fly well. Some harmful mutations can even cause death.

Albinism is a color mutation. In albinism, the genes for color are changed so that no color is produced. Thus, albino animals are usually white with pink eyes. Albinism occurs in many animals and plants, such as squirrels and corn.

FIGURE 20–17. Mutations produce yellow flowers (a) and an albino rattlesnake (b).

a

Brookhaven National Laboratory

b

Zig Leszczynski/Animals, Animals

activity ALBINISM IN TOBACCO

activity ALBINISM IN TOBACCO

Obtain tobacco seeds from a biological supply house. Place about 60 seeds on moist paper towels in the bottom of a glass baking dish. Keep the paper towels moist. After 6 or 8 days observe the seeds. What percent of the plants are albino? Can albino plants survive? Explain your answer.

MAKING SURE

12. Why might albinism be a harmful mutation?

20:10   Plant and Animal Breeding

Many domestic plants and animals are very different from their ancestors. These new varieties include seedless oranges, cattle without horns, and hens that lay eggs almost every day. Each new variety has special traits and often these traits can be passed on to the offspring. New varieties are produced by scientists and other people who breed plants and animals.

One process that scientists use to improve plant and animal breeds is called selection. **Selection** means to choose only certain individuals for reproduction. For example, a dairy farmer uses calves from high-producing milk cows to replace older cows in the herd. Selection is also used to

Define: selection, breed, purebred, crossbred.

FIGURE 20–18. The parents of these puppies were probably mixed breeds (a). This Braford resulted from a cross between a Hereford and Brahma (b).

a

Grant Heilman Photography

b

Allan Roberts

improve egg production. The fertilized eggs from high-producing hens are kept to raise more high-producing hens.

Through the process of selection, different breeds have been developed. A **breed** is a group of animals or plants that are alike in their traits and have a common ancestor. A member of a breed is called a **purebred** animal or plant. Purebreds breed true; that is, they pass their traits on to their offspring.

A cross between two different breeds results in a **crossbred,** or mixed breed. For example, a mongrel dog is a crossbred. A crossbred animal is often hardier and more disease-resistant than a purebred. This feature is called **hybrid vigor.** However, one disadvantage to crossing breeds of animals is that the traits of the offspring cannot be controlled. For example purebred pups resemble their parents, but there is a great variety among crossbred pups.

Disease-resistant plants have been produced by selection and crossing different varieties of breeds. In developing a disease-resistant variety, only the seeds from plants that are disease-resistant are planted. This selection is repeated generation after generation. Finally, after many selections and crosses, most of the plants will be disease-resistant.

In plants, artificial pollination is used to produce new varieties. Two breeds of plants with desirable characteristics are selected. Then pollen is transferred from the flower of one plant to the flower of the other plant. Many strains of hybrid corn have been produced this way. Hybrid corn has greatly increased corn production. The ears are larger, and the plants are more disease-resistant than the parents.

Many new plant breeds have come from mutations. These breeds include the California navel orange, pink grapefruit, and the nectarine. Mutations occur naturally in plants from time to time. X rays, nuclear radiation, and chemicals have been used to increase the mutation rate. Plant breeders select desirable mutants and use them to develop new varieties. New varieties of roses have come from mutations.

What is hybrid vigor?

How are new varieties of plants produced?

FIGURE 20–19. This woman is artificially pollinating a pine tree.

Weyerhauser

main ideas

1. Heredity is the passing of traits from parents to offspring. 20:1
2. The law of dominance states that a dominant trait will mask the recessive trait. 20:2
3. Blending occurs when none of the traits inherited is dominant. The offspring that results has a "blend" of the parents' traits. 20:4
4. Chromosomes contain the genes that control the inheritance of traits. 20:5
5. Reduction division results in sperm and eggs which have only half the number of chromosomes of a body cell. 20:6
6. Fertilization, the union of sperm and egg, restores the species number of chromosomes. 20:6
7. The sex of most living things is determined by the inheritance of X and Y sex chromosomes. 20:7
8. A mutation is a change in a gene or chromosome which results in a change in one or more traits. 20:9
9. Improved breeds of plants and animals are developed through selection and crossing. 20:10

vocabulary

Define each of the following words or terms.

blending	gene	purebred
breed	heredity	recessive trait
chromosome	hybrid	reduction division
crossbred	hybrid vigor	selection
dominant trait	law of dominance	zygote
embryo	mutation	

study questions

DO NOT WRITE IN THIS BOOK.

A. True or False

Determine whether each of the following sentences is true or false. If the sentence is false, rewrite it to make it true.

1. Blending is an example of dominance.
2. The law of dominance explains the inheritance of all traits.
3. Mendel experimented with pea plants.

4. Hybrids are the result of cross breeding.

5. A dominant trait may cover up a recessive trait.

6. The body cells and sex cells of a species have the same number of chromosomes.

7. A gene is made of DNA.

8. The union of a male sperm with a female egg restores the chromosome number for the species.

9. A fertilized egg develops into an embryo.

10. A purebred animal or plant has more hybrid vigor than a crossbred animal or plant.

B. Multiple Choice

Choose the word or phrase that completes correctly each of the following sentences.

1. A (*purebred, crossbred, mixed breed*) animal comes from a cross between two animals of the same breed.

2. (*Dominance, Blending, Mutation*) best explains how pink-flowered plants result from white-flowered and red-flowered parents.

3. (*Purebred animals, Crossbred animals, Mongrels, Hybrids*) are likely to breed true.

4. (*Hybrid corn, A purebred, A cocker spaniel, A beagle*) results from a cross between two varieties.

5. (*Fruit flies, Elephants, Horses*) have been used in many heredity experiments.

6. Seeds from pure tall pea plants produce (*short, tall and short, tall, medium*) pea plants.

7. A fertilized egg is called a (*zygote, crossbreed, chromosome*).

8. If two pea plants, hybrid for yellow seeds, are crossed, (*3 of 4, 1 of 4, 2 of 4*) offspring will produce green seeds.

9. When a body cell divides the chromosome number of a cell (*increases, decreases, remains the same*).

10. The number of chromosomes in an egg cell is (*half, two times, the same as, three times*) the number of chromosomes in a body cell.

C. Completion

Complete each of the following sentences with a word or phrase that will make the sentence correct.

1. A cross between tall and short pea plants illustrate the law of _____.

2. Roan color in cattle is produced from a type of inheritance called _____.
3. XX in humans are the sex chromosomes of a _____.
4. Inherited traits are controlled by pairs of _____ on chromosomes.
5. Twins formed from the same egg are called _____ twins.
6. Reduction division reduces the number of _____.
7. A sudden change in an inherited trait is called a(n) _____.
8. To choose only individuals with desirable traits for breeding is _____.
9. A trait that is masked by another trait is _____.
10. The _____ is an example of a mutant.

D. How and Why
1. How is it possible for a trait to skip a generation?
2. Why are identical twins different from fraternal twins?
3. How does hybrid vigor help an animal or plant?
4. Select a desirable quality of a fruit that you would like to develop and propose a method of development.
5. Why does the sperm of a male rabbit determine the sex of its offspring?

investigations

1. Obtain the latest information on recombinant DNA (gene transfer). Find out how this technique may be used to produce new varieties.
2. Do you have a favorite kind of dog? Do library research to find out how this variety of dog was developed through selective breeding.

interesting reading

Chedd, Graham, "Genetic Gibberish in the Code of Life," *Science 81*. Nov. 1981, pp 50-55.

Randall, Judith, "Breeding the Perfect Cow," *Science 81*. Nov. 1981, pp. 86-93.

Silverstein, Alvin and Virginia, *The Genetics Explosion*. New York, NY: Four Winds, 1980.

chapter

21

These butterflies are all related to one another. The genetic changes that produce differences in the butterflies have taken place over a long period of time. What changes in the environment could produce these kinds of changes? How can changes be caused by natural selection? What evidence shows that species are changing?

Descent and Change

21:1 Origin of Living Things

Scientists have proposed many theories to explain how life began. Most of these theories state that the first living things came from nonliving matter. How could nonliving matter form living organisms? Elements and compounds were the only matter present when the earth was formed. Perhaps some form of energy such as lightning caused simple molecules to combine. As a result, larger, more complex molecules formed. Some of the large molecules were the kinds present in living organisms.

In 1953, Stanley Miller, an American scientist, performed an important experiment. The experiment was based on the theory that the early atmosphere of the earth was much different than it is today. The early atmosphere probably was made of many gases, such as methane, ammonia, and hydrogen. Water was also present. In Miller's experiments, these gases combined to form amino (uh MEE noh) acids when an electric discharge passed through them. **Amino acids** are the building blocks of **protein** which is the basic material of living organisms. Amino acids contain carbon, hydrogen, nitrogen, and oxygen. According to scientific theory, a lightning bolt passed through a mixture of gases and caused the first amino acids to form.

GOAL: You will study the theories that scientists have proposed to explain the origin of life and changes in species.

Describe Stanley Miller's experiment.

FIGURE 21–1. Model of Miller's experiment.

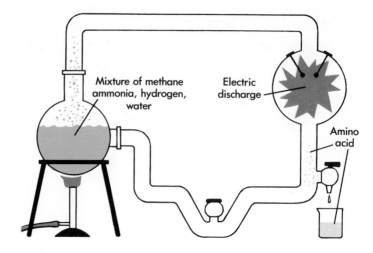

Mixture of methane ammonia, hydrogen, water

Electric discharge

Amino acid

How do scientists think the first forms of life developed?

FIGURE 21–2. Bacteria (a) and blue-green algae (b) were probably some of the earliest forms of life on Earth.

a

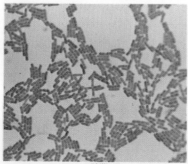

Phillip Harris Biological, Inc.

b

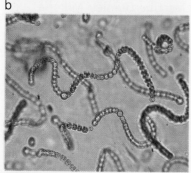

Robert Mitchell/Tom Stack & Assoc.

The theory does not stop here. It states that, in some way, the first amino acids combined to form proteins. These proteins then combined to form larger, more complex compounds. These compounds had the ability to reproduce themselves in some unexplained way. Exact copies of the proteins resulted. In other words, a protein molecule became a blueprint for making new protein molecules.

The theory states that the first simple forms of life began in the oceans. The land surfaces of Earth were not suited for life. They were covered with rough rock and no soil. The first living substances may have developed into simple one-celled organisms. These organisms may have been somewhat like the one-celled protists described in Chapter 14. From these simple organisms, more complex forms of life developed.

No one can be sure if the forming of the beginning of life from nonliving matter happened only once. It may have taken place many times and in many places. At this time, there is no evidence to answer this question. Perhaps no answer will ever be found.

MAKING SURE

1. According to theory, how did the first amino acids form on Earth?
2. Explain why the first simple forms of life probably lived in the ocean.

21:2 Darwin's Theory

Charles Darwin was a British scientist. He is given credit for developing a theory that explains why there is a great number and variety of plant and animal species. In 1831, the 22-year old Darwin sailed from England on a five year journey around the world aboard the British ship, the *Beagle*. Darwin was the ship's naturalist. Darwin's main job was to study the plants, animals, and rocks found along the coast of South America.

During his journey, Darwin collected and recorded as many species as he could find. After his return to England, he spent much time studying his samples, drawings and notes. Darwin was amazed at the number of different plants and animals he had observed. He wondered how so many different species came about.

How did Darwin obtain information for his theory?

G. Ziesler/Peter Arnold, Inc.

FIGURE 21–3. Some of the plant and animal species studied by Darwin were found on the Galapagos Islands.

For the next twenty years, Darwin collected evidence to support a new theory that he was developing. He visited farms throughout England and spoke with plant and animal breeders. He found that different plants and animals had been developed through the careful selection of breeding stock. For example, the race horse and the work horse had been developed through careful selection. Horses that could run swiftly were bred to produce very fast race horses. Stocky, strong horses were bred to produce better work horses. From such evidence,

Darwin began to think that selection might take place in nature. He developed a theory of **natural selection** that explained how new species were formed.

In 1858, Alfred Wallace, a British biologist, was working in Malaya. He sent Darwin a copy of a scientific article he was going to publish. Darwin was surprised to find his own ideas in Wallace's article. Wallace had come to the same conclusions as Darwin. This often takes place in science. Two scientists working alone make the same discovery or conclusions.

Both Darwin and Wallace concluded that different species of plants and animals were related. They also believed that new species were appearing. At the same time, other species were disappearing. Any new plant and animal species came from the old. However, the new species had different traits.

Darwin and Wallace agreed to present their findings to the world. Neither sought the major credit. Both men were interested in making their ideas known to people everywhere. Their theory is known as the **theory of evolution** by natural selection. It states that slow and gradual changes in living organisms occur over a period of many years. Changes result from a selection of those organisms that are best suited to the environment.

In 1859, Charles Darwin published his theory in a book called *The Origin of Species*. Darwin stated that among all living things there is a surplus of offspring. For example, a maple tree may release thousands of seeds each year. A female insect may lay thousands of eggs in one lifetime. All fish, birds, and reptiles produce many more offspring than are needed to maintain their number. However, only a small fraction of these live to become adults. In their natural environment, the food supply for animals is limited. There is not enough food for all. Thus, only those animals that get enough to eat will live. The plants and animals most likely to survive are those best suited to their surroundings. They are the fittest.

FIGURE 21–4. Charles Darwin (a) and Alfred Wallace (b).

a

b

Historical Pictures Service, Chicago

Historical Pictures Service, Chicago

a

b

FIGURE 21–5. The horned lizard (a) and the cactus (b) are adapted to survive desert conditions.

To survive, an organism must be able to avoid its enemies. It must remain healthy. It must also be suited to the environment. If the environment changes, many species may be destroyed. Suppose a humid area becomes a hot, dry desert. Many animal and plant species will die. Which ones will survive? The species that survive on the desert are those that need little water to live. They must also be capable of adjusting to very hot weather.

activity SEEDS AND SURVIVAL

Find a small tree that has pine cones on it. Count the number of seeds in one pine cone. Then, count the number of cones on the pine tree. Estimate the total number of seeds produced by the tree. Repeat this procedure for a milkweed pod and its plant. What is the advantage in producing many seeds?

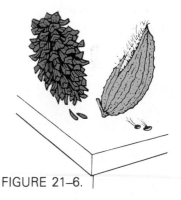

FIGURE 21–6.

MAKING SURE

3. When the climate of a region becomes very cold, a change in species may occur. Which kinds of animals will be more likely to survive, those with short hair or those with long hair? Explain.

4. How is the careful selection of plants for breeding related to Darwin's theory of natural selection?

21:2 Darwin's Theory   455

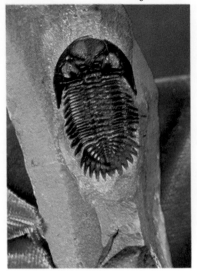

Roger K. Burnard

FIGURE 21–7. Trilobites became extinct millions of years ago.

What do fossils show about past life?

21:3 Fossil Evidence

Fossils provide evidence supporting the theory of evolution by natural selection. Fossils show that life in the past was very different from today. At one time there were huge forests of giant ferns, and dinosaurs roamed the earth. Fossils of one reptile species show it had wings and could fly. Woolly mammoths have been discovered preserved in ice in Siberia.

Fossil records show that species have changed during millions of years. In some cases these changes appear to be sudden and sharp. But most changes in plants and animals were slow and gradual. The changes in species over time caused most species to die off and new species to take their place. Scientists believe that the new species were descended from the old species. According to one theory, birds and reptiles are descended from the same ancestors.

Trilobites are an example of an animal for which there are many fossils. Trilobites lived about 500 million years ago. Trilobites no longer exist on the earth. They became **extinct** many years ago. However, species that resemble trilobites are alive today. Among these species are crabs and lobsters. It is possible that the trilobites that lived long ago are the distant ancestors of crabs and lobsters.

FIGURE 21–8. Fossil records show that tropical vegetation (a) once covered Greenland (b).

a

Rich Brommer

b

PHOTRI

The number of species alive today is much less than the number of species that have lived in the past and left fossils. Many species that lived in the past are now extinct. For example, dinosaurs and saber-toothed tigers no longer exist. Changes in the world that have taken place over millions of years may be responsible for the changes in species. Most noted of these changes are the changes in climate. The fossil record shows that at one time palm trees and tropical plants grew in Greenland. Now it is a cold arctic area. As changes in climate took place, only those living things with traits suited to the new environment survived. These species produced the new and different generations of plants and animals.

21:4 Natural Selection

In nature, selection occurs in many ways. In one experiment a field was seeded with grass seed. One section of grass was fenced off and allowed to grow to full height. The grass was allowed to grow so that it could be cut and dried to make hay. Another section was used as a pasture. This pattern was continued for three years—one half of the field was grown for hay and the other half was grazed. During the fourth year, seeds were taken from both sections of the field and planted. What do you think the grass grown from these seeds looked like?

Grass from the section used for pasture was short and rambling. Grass from the section used for hay was tall and straight. Form a scientific theory to explain the difference between plants from the pasture field and the hay field. For three years, the tall grass in the pasture was eaten by animals. This grass stood tall and erect and could be easily eaten. Most of the short rambling grass escaped being eaten because it grew close to the ground. Thus, the short grass in the pasture area lived to produce seeds for the next crop of grass. The next generation of grass in the pasture resembled its parents. It was short and rambling.

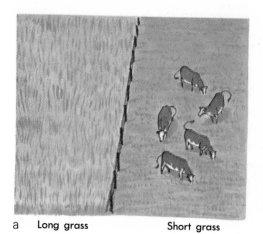

a   Long grass   Short grass

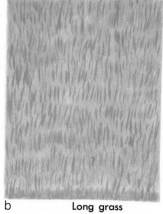

b   Long grass

c   Short grass

FIGURE 21–9. After four years, grass seed taken from the left side of the fence (a) will produce only long grasses (b). Seeds taken from the right side of the fence, however, will produce only short grasses (c).

How does the experiment with grass illustrate natural selection?

Explain how natural selection affects species.

Seeds from the hay field produced plants that were tall and straight. Tall plants received the sunlight needed to make food. They grew until they reached maturity. Short plants in the hay field were shaded by the tall plants. They did not get enough sunlight. The tall grass survived each year in the hay field. The short grass died.

There were two different environments in the field. In one, tall plants had the advantage, and they survived. In the other, short plants had the advantage, and they survived. The surviving plants determined the type of grass that grew in each area in the next generation.

The life and death struggle among plants and animals is the basis for natural selection. There are changes between generations in each plant and animal species. Some of the changes are advantages for the new generation. Others are disadvantages.

According to the theory of natural selection, the species that survive are those best suited to the environment. For instance, an animal may have a color that blends with the environment. It is less likely to be seen and killed by its enemies, therefore, it has a good chance to survive. An animal that does not need much food is able to stay alive when a food shortage occurs. Such an animal is better suited for survival than an animal that needs a large food supply.

Roger K. Burnard

FIGURE 21–10. Can you find the golden plover chick among the plants in the photo? Because of its protective coloration, predators also have a difficult time finding it.

MAKING SURE

5. Rats have lived in cities for centuries. Why is a rat most fit to survive in a large city?
6. Why is it unlikely the housefly will become extinct as long as there are people on Earth?

21:5 Changes in Species

Theories of evolution propose that living things can change from generation to generation. Over time, these changes may be great enough to produce new species. Some species alive today will someday become extinct. New species will take their place. Descent and change in living things goes on now just as it has in the past.

Descent and change means that living things may change from one generation to the next. As shown in Figure 21–11, the horse is a clear example of descent and change. Fossils of the first known horse show that it was about the size of a fox. Through many generations, the horse has increased in size. It developed a larger head and lost all but one toe on each foot. The modern horse is very different from the early horse, its ancestor.

What does descent and change mean?

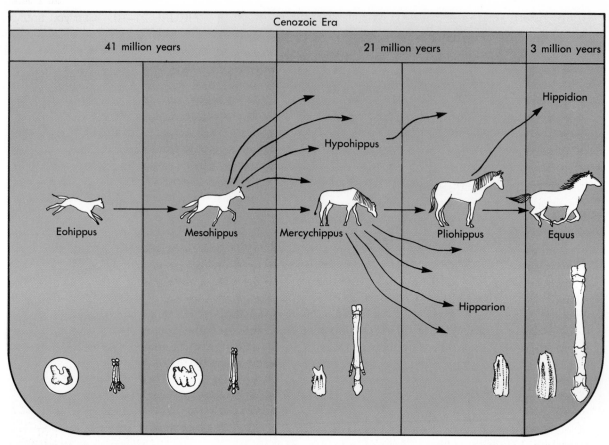

FIGURE 21–11. In the evolution of the horse, the number of toes decreased from four to only one. Teeth have also changed.

Much evidence shows that living things are still changing. About 1850, dark-colored peppered moths were observed near Manchester, England. Earlier these moths had been very light in color. Where did the dark moth come from? In the early 1800s in England, many factories were built. Their chimneys gave off large amounts of soot. The soot settled all across the country. In many areas, the soot collected on the trunks and limbs of trees.

Before the factories were built, the light-colored moths blended with the color of the tree trunks. But, when the light-colored moths landed on the dark soot-covered trees they could be seen by birds. They were soon eaten. The dark moths could not easily be seen against the dark tree trunks and were not eaten by birds. Dark moths survived to reproduce more dark-colored moths.

Evidence was needed to explain the change in moth color. A scientist set up several high speed cameras near some soot-covered trees. Many moths were released. Half of the moths were dark. Half of the moths were light. The cameras recorded the birds eating moths. The photos showed that the birds ate more light-colored moths than dark-colored moths.

Only those plants and animals that survive and reproduce pass their traits to a new generation. Who is most likely in each generation to survive and reproduce? It is those individuals that are best suited or adapted to their environment. For example, some bacteria are resistant to antibiotics. (an ti bi AHT ihks). They are more likely to survive and reproduce than bacteria that are not resistant.

How do scientists determine whether or not a scientific theory is acceptable? They look for evidence to support, change, or reject the theory. Scientists have been testing Darwin's theory since he first presented it in 1858. Many of the questions that they have raised still remain unanswered. The main points of Darwin's theory are listed below.

(1) Every organism comes from another organism.
(2) In all species of plants and animals more offspring are produced than are needed to replace the parents.
(3) There is a variety of traits among individuals in a species.
(4) Conditions for life on earth have changed in the past and will continue to change in the future.
(5) In each generation, the organisms best suited to their environment survive and produce the new generation. This process is called natural selection.
(6) Natural selection causes some species to become extinct.
(7) Natural selection causes some species to develop into new and different species.

FIGURE 21–12. The ability of a species to survive may depend on the environment. Which moth in each photo is most likely to escape being eaten?

Describe the peppered moth experiment.

State the main points in Darwin's theory.

7. Air pollution control devices are used to reduce the amount of soot in the air. How might this change affect the color of moths in the future?
8. How is the horse an example of descent and change?
9. How might natural selection cause a species to become extinct?
10. How do scientists determine whether a theory is acceptable?

21:6 Mutations and Change

It is known that organisms best suited to the environment are most likely to survive. Suited means that an organism has the traits needed for survival in the place where the organism lives. A fish survives in water because it has gills, but it cannot live on land. The fish is not suited to life on land. A green plant survives because it uses sunlight to make food. However, the green plant will not live long in total darkness. It is not suited to an environment without light.

How do organisms acquire the traits that increase their chance of survival? One way is through mutations. A change in color, a loss of toes, and a resistance to an insecticide may result from mutations. Suppose a change in color causes a reptile to blend better with the surface on which it lives. The color change would provide protection and increase the reptile's chance of survival. The loss of one or more toes may enable an animal to run faster. If so, there is a greater chance of the animal surviving by escaping its predators. If a fly becomes resistant to a poisonous insecticide, the fly increases its chance of survival in an environment where people spray insecticides.

When a harmful mutation occurs, the ability of an organism to survive will decrease. A mutation that prevents a plant from making chlorophyll would result in the death of the plant. If death occurs at an

How can mutations be helpful and harmful?

FIGURE 21–13. These short legs on a basset hound are caused by a mutation. The legs of most dogs are usually longer.

Grant Heilman Photography

early enough age, the organism has not lived long enough to reproduce. In this case the mutant trait is not inherited.

Mutations are inherited. Therefore, mutations that help organisms survive are passed on to the offspring of the organisms. As a result, over millions of years, mutations may have caused many changes in species. Some mutations may have caused some species to become extinct. However, many mutations may have caused new species to appear. The new species survive because they are better suited to the environment.

How might mutations change a species?

What causes mutations? Nuclear radiation, certain chemicals, and high temperature's can cause mutations. Radiation levels on earth may have been very high in the past. If so, many mutations may have occurred in plants and animals that lived long ago. These changes may have taken place at a high rate. As the landscape and climate of earth changed, natural selection may have taken place. Organisms with mutations suited to the new environment would have survived. Eventually, new species would have developed that would be much different from their ancestors.

Kodansha

FIGURE 21–14. Mutations caused by variations in morning glory seedlings.

MAKING SURE

11. How is mutation related to the processes of natural selection?

Perspectives

Reading for Meaning

Your textbook has many study aids to help you understand and remember what you read. One of these aids helps you understand the vocabulary; especially, the new scientific words.

New words or terms are highlighted in boldface type when each is first used. At this time, the definition will be given. The definition may be given in the same sentence in which the word appears or in the same paragraph. You can note the definition by the verbs which link the word with its meaning. Look for verbs such as are, is, mean, and means. There may be verbs such as explained and states. The important thing to remember is that whenever you see a word in boldface print, the definition is close by.

Let us look at some examples from Chapter 21.

A sentence in Section 21:5 states

New term   Verb   Definition

Descent and change <u>means</u> that living things may change from one generation to the next.

A sentence from Section 21:1 is interesting since there are two definitions in the same sentence.

New term

Amino acids <u>are</u> the building blocks of **protein** — Definition
which <u>is</u> the basic material of living organisms.

Verb

Section 21:2 contains the following information:

Verb   New term

Their theory is known as the **theory of evolution** by natural selection. It <u>states</u> that slow and gradual — Definition
changes in living organisms occur over a period of many years. Changes result from a selection of those organisms that are best suited to the environment.

For each of the new terms listed below (1) determine the definition, (2) note the verb, and (3) state where the definition is found.

    natural selection   extinct   mutations

You may wish to check each of your textbook definitions with either the glossary in your textbook or a dictionary. The dictionary meanings may contain more information about the words or more than one meaning may be given for some words. The meanings that you will find in your glossary or in your textbook will apply to those which have been discussed.

main ideas

1. The atmosphere of early earth may have been much different from what it is today. 21:1

2. Changes in the environment may result in the appearance of new species and disappearance of old species. 21:2

3. Darwin's theory of evolution by natural selection states that a slow, gradual change in living things occurred over a long period of time. 21:2

4. According to Darwin's theory, those species suited to the environment survive and produce offspring. 21:2, 21:4, 21:5

5. Fossils provide evidence of changes in living things. 21:3

6. Many species that lived in the past do not exist today. Many species living today were not always present. 21:3

7. Evidence indicates that living things are still changing. 21:5

8. Mutations may have caused the changes in species. 21:6

vocabulary

Define each of the following words or terms.

amino acid	extinct	protein
descent and change	natural selection	theory of evolution

study questions

DO NOT WRITE IN THIS BOOK.

A. True or False

Determine whether each of the following sentences is true or false. If the sentence is false, rewrite it to make it true.

1. Charles Darwin developed his theory of evolution while sailing on a ship.

2. Darwin's theory of natural selection was never published.

3. New varieties of plants and animals are developed through the process of selection.

4. Darwin and Wallace developed the same theory.

5. Some scientists believe the first life was formed in the oceans.

6. Some scientists believe that life came from nonliving substances.

7. Changes in living things over the years have generally been fast and dramatic.
8. The early atmosphere of earth is believed to have been the same as it is today.
9. Scientists have yet to find any evidence of natural selection.
10. Through the years, certain chemical insecticides have become less effective in controlling flies.

B. Multiple Choice

Choose the word or phrase that completes correctly each of the following sentences.

1. An animal that is suited to its surroundings is likely to (*survive, move away, not survive*).
2. Natural selection results in a species (*remaining the same, changing, becoming less suited to the environment*).
3. Amino acids are the building blocks of (*viruses, proteins, protists*).
4. Dinosaurs and (*lobsters, birds, trilobites*) may have the same ancestors.
5. A mutation (*always, sometimes, never*) increases an animal's chance for survival.
6. The early atmosphere of the earth may not have contained (*hydrogen, methane, oxygen*).
7. The number of species that have lived in the past is (*greater than, less than, the same as*) the number of species alive today.
8. Fossils show that today's horse is (*larger, smaller, the same*) size as its ancestors.
9. Evolution by natural selection is a (*fact, theory, scientific law, myth*).
10. Mutations are caused by (*changes in genes, evolution, natural selection*).

C. Completion

Complete each of the following sentences with a word or phrase that will make the sentence correct.

1. The first life on Earth may have begun in the _____.
2. Evolution means that over a period of many years living things _____.
3. One evidence of natural selection can be seen in the remains of living things called _____.

4. _____ records show that species have changed during millions of years.

5. Many changes in living things may have come about through changes in the earth's _____.

6. The first living material most likely came from _____ substances.

7. Flies that are resistant to certain insecticides are more plentiful today than in 1945. The survival of these flies is an example of _____.

8. The short grass in a hay field has less chance to survive than the _____ grass.

9. In all species of living things there is a(n) _____ of offspring.

10. A(n) _____ species is one that is no longer present.

D. How and Why

1. How did Darwin's voyage lead to the development of his theory of evolution?

2. What are the main parts of Darwin's theory of evolution by natural selection?

3. Why are more bacteria resistant to antibiotics today than in 1960?

4. What natural protection do a polar bear and a rabbit have?

5. The dodo is an extinct bird. It had a large, heavy body and small wings. Using these two facts, why do you think the dodo became extinct?

investigations

1. Compare the theory of evolution to other theories that explain the origin and development of life on Earth. Do these theories conflict with one another? Write a report discussing the ways the theories agree and disagree.

interesting reading

Freedman, Russell, *They Lived With the Dinosaurs*. New York, NY: Holiday House, 1980.

Ricciuti, Edward R., *Older Than the Dinosaurs: The Origin and Rise of the Mammals*. New York, NY: Crowell, 1980.

Taylor, Ron, *The Story of Evolution*. New York, NY: Warwick Press, 1981.

side roads

BIOMES

A biome is an area characterized by certain plants and animals. Climate determines the plants and animals, or life forms, found in each biome. A biome can also be called a life zone. There are at least seven major land biomes on Earth.

In the tundra biome, winters are long and cold with temperatures as low as −40°C. Summers are also cold with temperatures between 0°C and 15°C. The tundra receives little precipitation, only 10 to 15 cm per year. The growing season lasts only two months. Although the surface thaws in the summer, a layer of frozen soil, permafrost, remains below. Permafrost prevents large plants, such as trees, from rooting. Therefore only small plants grow in the tundra. A few birds, mostly migratory, and rodents along with animals such as caribou and the arctic fox live there.

The tiaga is the largest land biome. The growing season is a little longer than the tundra. The ground thaws in the warmer seasons. The temperature ranges between −24°C in the winter and 22°C in the summer. The average precipitation for the year is 35 to 40 cm. Evergreens thrive in this cool, moist climate. Conifer and aspen forests provide food and shelter for animals such as elk, moose, lynx, beaver, ducks, and geese.

The temperate deciduous forest biome has four distinct seasons. Rainfall averages 65 to 150 cm each year. The temperature ranges from −24°C to 38°C. Here deciduous forests of oak, maple, or hickory offer food and shelter to many woodland animals such as red fox, rabbit, and weasel. Many of these animals hibernate during the winter when the trees produce no food. The deciduous forests once covered the

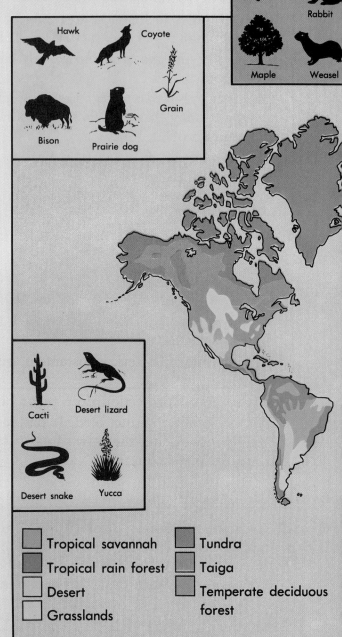

Hawk Coyote Grain Bison Prairie dog

Red fox Rabbit Maple Weasel

Cacti Desert lizard Desert snake Yucca

Tropical savannah Tundra
Tropical rain forest Taiga
Desert Temperate deciduous forest
Grasslands

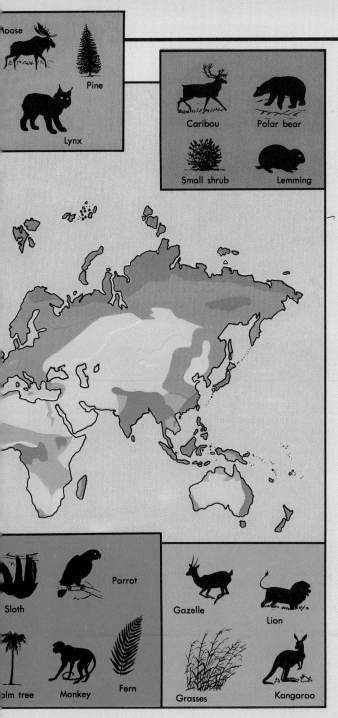

Temperatures range from 0°C to 25°C. Plant life in the grassland biome consists of grasses and rarely a tree. This is the area where large crops of grains are grown. Grazing animals such as cattle and sheep and burrowing animals such as prairie dogs are found there. Predators such as coyotes and hawks live in this biome.

In the tropical savannahs, there is a yearly rainfall of 100 to 150 cm, but it occurs during a short rainy season. The rest of the year is dry with frequent grass fires. Temperatures are warm, between 20°C and 30°C. Again, grasses and a few trees are found here. Many of the animals such as the gazelle obtain their food by grazing. Kangaroos are found in this biome. Predators such as the lion are present also.

Rain falls nearly every day in the tropical rain forest biome, 200 to 225 cm a year. Temperatures are near 25°C all of the time. Plants grow rapidly in this moist, warm climate. There are no seasons. Plants such as vines and palm trees and animal life such as parrots, monkeys, and sloths abound. Life forms are too abundant to count. Trees are so dense that the forest floor is in darkness. Many of the animals are tree dwelling.

The desert biome has high temperatures during the day followed by cool nights. The temperature range is 10°C to 38°C. The rainfall is less than 25 cm per year. A few plants such as cacti and yucca have adapted to this hot, dry climate. Snakes and lizards are common in this biome. Most desert animals have adapted to the climate by sleeping during the heat of the day. They are active during the cooler nights.

northern part of the United States, much of Europe, and the Far East.

In the grassland biome, rainfall varies between 25 and 75 cm per year.

unit
6
Conservation

Disneyworld is more than an amusement park. It has lakes, forests, and swamps for preserving wildlife. The buildings are designed to conserve energy. Resources are recycled. How can Disneyworld be a model for planning other communities? How can you help preserve the environment in your community?

471

chapter

22

This land was formerly unfit for farming. The land is now productive. Wise conservation practices with one resource, such as water, can result in other resources being managed wisely also. How can conservation of soil, water, and air be best achieved? What steps can be taken to better manage these resources in the future?

Steve Lissau

Soil, Water, and Air Conservation

22:1 Conservation of Natural Resources

Natural resources are those things in the environment that are useful to people. Soil, water, and air are three valuable natural resources. Natural resources such as lakes, forests, and seashores are enjoyed by many. We use these resources for recreation to promote good physical and mental health. Natural resources such as forests, coal, iron, natural gas, and minerals have economic value. They are needed for construction, heating, and transportation. Solar energy is one of the most important of all natural resources.

Natural resources can be classified as either renewable or nonrenewable. Renewable resources are those which can be used and replaced. Forests and other living things are examples. A nonrenewable resource is one which cannot be replaced. Examples are coal, air, and natural gas.

More and more people are taking an interest in conservation (kahn sur VAY shun). **Conservation** is the wise and careful use of natural resources. A person who practices conservation uses natural resources with as little waste as possible. The aim is to leave an adequate supply of resources for the future.

GOAL: You will learn the methods used in the conservation of natural resources such as soil, water, and air.

Define natural resources.

What is conservation of natural resources?

Table 22–1.	
Some Careers in Conservation	
Forest Ranger	Protection and care of state and federal forests
Air Quality Engineer	Design and installation of air pollution control equipment
Ecologist	Scientific study of the relationship between living things and the environment
Soil Conservationist	Planning and use of soil conservation methods
Water Quality Technician	Tests water for pollution

a

Ohio Department of Natural Resources

b

U.S. Department of Energy

FIGURE 22–1. Trees are a renewable resource (a). Fossil fuels cannot be replaced in a person's lifetime (b).

22:2 Soil

How is soil made?

Soil did not exist when the earth was first formed. Instead, soil was made from solid rock that was broken into particles by weathering. Formation of soil is a slow, continuous process. It takes between 200 and 400 years to form 1 cm of soil.

Soil is made of two layers. The upper layer is **topsoil,** and the lower layer is **subsoil.** Topsoil is the part in which most plants grow. Topsoil contains rock particles, humus, and many kinds of living organisms. **Humus** is the material formed from the decay of dead plants and animals. Humus makes soil more crumbly and increases its water-holding

Explain the difference between topsoil and subsoil.

capacity. The fertility of topsoil depends on the amount of minerals, humus, and living things present. Bacteria, molds, yeasts, earthworms, and insects are some of the living things found in topsoil. Subsoil consists only of rock particles of various sizes. Subsoil is lighter in color than topsoil because it does not contain humus.

FIGURE 22–2. The color of soil depends on the rocks from which the soil formed.

Soils in different areas vary in color, composition, and depth. The properties of soil affect the kinds of plants that will grow. Soils rich in humus are dark in color. They are usually the most fertile for raising crops. Some farm soils are naturally acidic. Lime is spread on the soil to decrease the acidity. Adding fertilizer to soil increases its fertility. **Fertilizer** is used to increase the organic matter and mineral nutrients in the soil.

activity GROWING PLANTS IN DIFFERENT SOILS

(1) Soak 12 bean seeds in water overnight. (2) Label three flowerpots A, B, and C. (3) Fill pot A two-thirds full of topsoil, pot B two-thirds full of subsoil, and pot C two-thirds full of sand. (4) Plant 4 bean seeds in each pot. (5) Place the pots in a warm, sunny location and water them regularly. Be sure to water the three pots equally. (6) When the beans sprout, measure and record the height of each bean plant once a day for two weeks. (7) Record the appearance of each plant. (8) Determine an average growth per day for each pot. In which pots did the plants grow the most? The least? Explain your answers.

22:3 Soil Erosion and Mineral Loss

What causes soil erosion?

Nearly 3 000 000 metric tons of topsoil are lost by erosion each year in the United States. Rainwater loosens and washes away topsoil. Winds dry out topsoil and blow it away. In many places, soil erosion exceeds the rate of soil formation.

Rainwater may either run off the surface or soak into the ground. Runoff water has enough force to carry soil particles. Even a slow flow of water will easily wash away loose soil. The steeper the slope, the faster the runoff water travels and the greater the erosion.

Plants are the best protection against soil erosion. Grass stems and leaves cover soil surface. Runoff moves over the protective carpet of grass and causes little soil erosion. Also, plant roots hold the soil particles together. In a forest, the trunks of trees and exposed roots slow the speed of runoff. When water travels slowly, it has less carrying force.

a   *Ohio Department of Transportation*   b   *Grant Heilman Photography*

FIGURE 22–3. Ground covers such as grasses are planted on the slopes near highways to prevent erosion (a). Erosion can be a problem between rows of crops (b).

Erosion is heaviest where row crops, such as corn, tomatoes, and beans, are planted on steep slopes. Row crops are grown in rows with exposed soil between the rows. The exposed soil makes pathways for runoff. If the field is steep, the runoff travels swiftly and the rate of soil erosion is high.

Topsoil is ruined in ways other than erosion. Growing the same crops year after year removes soil minerals. Minerals in the soil are mainly those minerals present in the rock from which the soil came. The removal of minerals decreases soil fertility. To keep the soil fertile, these minerals must be returned to the soil.

Rainfall also reduces the mineral content of topsoil. Water soaking into the soil dissolves minerals and carries them deep into the subsoil. Here they are of little benefit to growing plants. This removal of minerals from topsoil by water is called **leaching.** Organic matter in the soil helps to prevent leaching by absorbing water and holding the topsoil.

What is leaching and why is it harmful?

activity SOIL DRAINAGE

(1) Obtain three funnels of equal size and label them *A, B,* and *C.* Support each one over a beaker. **(2)** Place a small wad of cotton in the bottom of each funnel. **(3)** Fill funnel *A* half-full with dry sand. Fill funnel *B* half-full with dry clay. Fill funnel *C* half-full with dry loam. Loam is a kind of topsoil that is rich in humus. **(4)** Pour 250 mL of water into each funnel. **(5)** Record the amount of water that runs into each of the beakers in 10 minutes. Which soil allows the most water to pass through? Which soil would allow the most leaching?

22:4 Soil Conservation

Soil conservation is important to both city and rural dwellers. We all depend on soil for food. By conserving topsoil, a farmer may obtain high crop yields. At the same time, the condition of the soil is maintained for future use. Soil conservation has helped many farmers improve soil fertility. As a result, even better crop yields are obtained.

What are good soil conservation methods? Recall that soil erosion is greatest on steep, uncovered land, and humus is important to the fertility and water-holding capacity of topsoil. Therefore, anything done to keep soil covered, reduce rapid runoff, and increase the amount of humus aids soil conservation.

Plowing back and forth across a sloped field is called **contour plowing.** Contour plowing produces horizontal ridges in the soil which reduces runoff.

Describe four methods used to conserve topsoil.

a

b

FIGURE 22–5. Contour plowing is a good conservation practice (a). Terraces keep the soil from eroding away and allow farmers to grow crops on very steep slopes (b).

FIGURE 22–6. Root nodes on this alfalfa plant remove nitrogen from the air and return it to the soil.

Contour plowing can reduce soil erosion by nearly 50 percent. Very steep slopes are sometimes **terraced.** A terraced slope looks like a flight of very wide steps. Carving the land in this way is expensive. It is profitable only if the soil is very fertile and a valuable crop is grown. Citrus orchards and grapes are often grown on terraced hillsides.

Crop rotation is another soil conservation method. In crop rotation, one crop is grown one year and a different crop is grown the next year. Different crops vary in the kinds and amounts of minerals taken from the soil. By changing the crops that are grown, the nutrient loss can be reduced. Minerals are replaced by the decay of organic matter and by adding mineral fertilizer.

Grasses and legumes (LEG yewmz), such as alfalfa and clover, help guard against erosion. They have many uses in soil conservation programs. For example, some farmers plant strips of these plants between strips of row crops. This practice is called **strip-cropping.** Runoff is decreased by the covered strips of soil. This method allows a sloping field to be planted in row crops, yet prevents erosion.

Many farmers plant oats or other grains after the main crop is harvested in the fall. The grain grows a few centimeters high before the first frost. It serves as a ground-cover crop during rainy winter months. In the spring, the grain plants are plowed under. They increase the humus content and supply the nitrogen to the soil. A crop that is grown as a cover and plowed under before maturity is called a green manure crop.

Wind erosion is also a problem in soil conservation. **Shelter belts** are very effective against wind erosion. Shelter belts are thick rows of trees that break the wind. They reduce wind erosion by breaking the wind's speed.

activity   MODEL OF A CONTOUR PLOWED FIELD

(1) Put a 2 cm thick layer of plaster of paris in a small baking dish or pie pan. Spread the plaster until it evenly covers the pan. Smooth the surface to make it flat. **(2)** With the wide end of a pencil, make a series of parallel grooves across the plaster. The grooves should be about 0.5 cm deep and 1 cm apart. Allow the plaster to harden for one day. **(3)** Hold the pan over an empty pan or sink and tilt it slightly so the grooves point down. Use a sprinkling can to sprinkle water on the surface of the plaster. Does it run off or stay on the plaster? **(4)** Repeat this procedure with the grooves horizontal. What happens to the water? Compare your observation with rainfall on a contour plowed field.

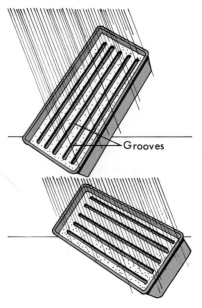

Grooves

FIGURE 22–7.

22:5 Water Resources

Water is needed by all plant and animal life. People require vast amounts of water. The average American uses about 250 L of water every day. Also, many industries need large quantities of water to make their products. For example, it takes about 250 000 L of water to produce one metric ton of steel.

People obtain water in many ways. The water supplies of many cities come from rivers or lakes. Chicago gets its water from Lake Michigan, one of the Great Lakes. Los Angeles obtains water from the Colorado River. Other cities get water from underground springs or from wells.

How is water obtained for use by people?

Water is also obtained from reservoirs (REZ urv worz). Reservoirs serve as basins to collect rainwater. Much of New York City's water supply travels through pipes from reservoirs in rural areas more than 160 km away.

22:6 Water Conservation

List the goals of water conservation.

Water conservation has three basic goals. The first is to increase the amount of water that soaks into the ground and the quality of water collected and stored. The second is to clean polluted water and to keep unpolluted water clean and usable. The third is to stop the wasteful use of water.

Planting grass and trees, terracing, and contour plowing can increase groundwater. More groundwater may be obtained by building check dams and storage reservoirs, which reduce flooding. By damming the water in streams that lead to rivers, the runoff can be trapped.

Water pollution is a problem in many streams and rivers. In some places, industrial wastes are dumped into nearby water. Some large cities release untreated sewage into rivers and oceans. This sewage may contain nitrogen and phosphorus compounds. These compounds act as fertilizers for algae. Decay of algae that die at the end of the summer growing season uses oxygen. If there is a large increase in the amount of algae in a lake or pond, fish will die from a lack of oxygen. Dumping large amounts of wastes in lakes and streams kills animal and plant life. It can spread disease-causing organisms. It also makes the water unfit for recreation.

FIGURE 22–8. Pollution can result when topsoil, sewage, and other debris are washed into the water supply during a flood (a). Pine Flat Dam on King's River, CA, prevents flooding and provides a reservoir for recreation (b).

a

Bureau of Reclamation

b

U.S. Army

Sewage treatment plants help to keep water clean. In a sewage treatment plant, the sewage is stored in large tanks. Here it is stirred constantly as air passes through it. Harmful compounds are changed by the air into harmless substances. When the process is completed, the sewage may be put into river and ocean waters without harmful effects. Also, purified water separated from the sewage can be used for irrigation.

Much of our water supply is wasted every day. In flushing a toilet or taking a shower, more water is used than is really needed. Decreasing the waste of water aids water conservation.

How can pure water supplies be increased?

22:7 Water Sources for the Future

Water conservation practices will not solve all water problems. Many parts of the world simply do not have enough water for drinking and for growing crops. In some areas, thousands of people die from lack of water and food. New sources of fresh water are desperately needed now and in the future.

Changing ocean water to fresh water is a possible solution to the water problem of some arid regions. Ocean water cannot be used directly for drinking or for irrigating land. The ocean's salts kill plants and ruin the soil for crops. However, with the salts removed, this water could supply all of our needs for irrigating land and drinking. One way that seawater can be changed to fresh water is by heating the water so that it evaporates. The salt is left behind, and the evaporated water is collected.

Explain how evaporation produces pure water.

U.S. Department of the Interior

FIGURE 22–9. Seawater is changed to fresh water at this desalination plant.

FIGURE 22–10. Polluted air contains acids and other substances which can damage property as well as affect a person's health.

Name four substances that pollute air.

What is photochemical smog?

FIGURE 22–11. Sometimes polluted air is trapped near the surface by a temperature inversion. A layer of warm air prevents the air near the surface from rising.

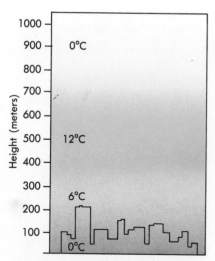

22:8 Air Pollution

If you live in or near a large city, you may have noticed that the air is sometimes hazy and unpleasant to breathe. Air that contains material from smokestacks, industrial waste, and motor vehicles is polluted air. Polluted air contains chemicals that can harm your health. These chemicals can also kill plants, reduce crop yields, and harm animals.

The two major air pollutants in the United States are carbon monoxide and sulfur dioxide. **Carbon monoxide** is a colorless, odorless gas. Ninety-five percent of all carbon monoxide in cities comes from the engines of motor vehicles. An excess of carbon monoxide in the air can cause suffocation and death.

Sulfur dioxide is a colorless gas that has an unpleasant odor. Most sulfur dioxide pollution results from the burning of oil and coal that contain sulfur. Sulfur burns to form the compound sulfur dioxide. Sulfur dioxide dissolves in the rain forming acid rain. Acid rain increases the acidity of soil and of water in lakes, streams, and rivers. The soil may become too acidic, killing plants. Fish living in the water will die if the stream becomes too acidic. Acid rain destroys metal, concrete, stone, and paint on buildings and cars.

Nitrogen oxides, hydrocarbons (hi druh KAR bunz), and small particles are other substances that pollute the air. They are products of burning fuels. A mixture of smoke and waste gases is called **smog.** Photochemical smog is the product of the reaction between sunlight and nitrogen oxides and hydrocarbons. "Photochemical" refers to a chemical change that occurs in the presence of light. Photochemical smog irritates the linings of the nose and throat. It also causes the eyes to water and sting.

How can air pollution be reduced? One way is to remove solid, unburned particles formed when fuels are burned. Filters placed in smokestacks can remove these particles. Another way is to burn fuels more completely. The production of waste gases is reduced in complete combustion. Many industries burn natural gas instead of coal and oil. Natural gas burns more completely. It releases fewer wastes into the air and causes less pollution.

Electric generating plants use large amounts of coal and oil. They release much sulfur dioxide into our air. Air pollution could be reduced if a different fuel were used to produce electricity.

Hydrocarbons, carbon monoxide, and nitrogen oxides are the main pollutants in automobile exhausts. Some devices have been developed which reduce auto exhaust pollutants. One device increases the amount of air in the gasoline-air mixture used by the engine. Gasoline burning is more complete and fewer pollutants are produced. Another device, called a catalytic converter is attached to an exhaust pipe. This converter changes carbon monoxide to nonpoisonous carbon dioxide.

Many scientists are studying alternatives to the gasoline engine. Engines that burn hydrogen gas do not produce pollutants. Turbine engines burn fuel more completely than a gasoline or diesel engine. Electric automobiles operating on rechargeable batteries do not produce waste gases and other pollutants.

FIGURE 22–12. Electric cars are being used in some cities to help control pollution.

How can air pollution be reduced?

activity DETECTING AIR POLLUTION

Pollution particles may be detected with a glass jar (screw cap), block of wood, and cellophane or masking tape. (1) Unscrew the cap and nail it, inside up, to the wood. (2) Wrap some tape around the glass jar with the sticky side exposed to the air. (3) Screw the jar back into the cap. (4) Select a site where the jar will be exposed to breezes from all directions. Try to place it a few meters above the ground or on a rooftop. (5) Label the four sides of the tape N, S, E, and W to correspond to the compass points. (6) At the end of one week, remove the jar and observe the tape. Darkening of the tape shows many particles have been trapped. From which direction did most of the pollution particles arrive?

FIGURE 22–13.

Perspectives

skills

Using Graphs

Graphs are used often to show and explain scientific information. The study of science involves your understanding many facts and seeing how they are related. The ability to interpret graphs makes it possible for you to acquire much information quickly. The *bar* graph below shows how land is used in a typical community.

1. What part of the community uses more land than any other. How many hectares are used?

2. What part of the community uses the least amount of land?

3. Determine the total number of hectares used for all activities.

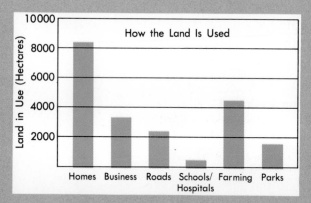

Line graphs show change such as growth, development over a time period, or a process. The following graph shows changes in air pollution levels for a time period of a typical day in a city.

1. How would you account for the highest amount of pollution to occur around 5:00 P.M.?

2. What do you think causes the first peak of pollution around 9:00 A.M.?

3. When does the lowest level of pollution occur? Why?

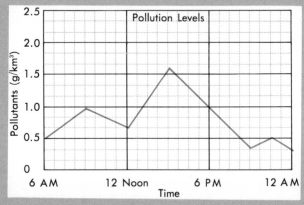

Circle graphs show the parts of a whole in the form of percentages. Even without percentages given, you can see the relative areas given to each part of the circle graph. The circle graph below shows water usage for a typical household.

1. In a household, what two uses of water amount to about two thirds of the total?

2. If a typical household uses 1020 L of water per day, how many liters would be used for bathing?

3. Suppose you had to conserve water and you were requested to cut the amount you used by 40 L. Using the graph, list all the ways by which you might be able to decrease the amount of water you use.

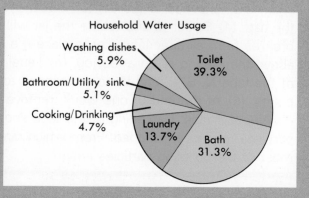

main ideas

1. Soil, water, and air are three important natural resources. 22:1
2. Topsoil is made by the weathering of rock and the decay of organic materials. 22:2
3. Erosion is a natural process. The rate of erosion is high where soil is exposed to rain and wind. 22:3
4. Soil conservation practices reduce the erosion and leaching of topsoil. 22:4
5. Water conservation practices can help provide an adequate supply of pure, fresh water. 22:6
6. Heat energy is needed to convert seawater to fresh water. 22:7
7. The air of some large cities is polluted through the addition of dust, vapor, and fumes by industries and motor vehicles. 22:8
8. Air pollution can be reduced through the use of devices that remove pollutants from smokestacks and engine exhausts. 22:8
9. New types of engines use fuel more efficiently and thereby reduce air pollution. 22:8

vocabulary

Define each of the following words or terms.

carbon monoxide
conservation
contour plowing
crop rotation
fertilizer
green manure crop

groundwater
humus
leaching
natural resources
pollution
shelter belt

smog
strip-cropping
subsoil
sulfur dioxide
terracing
topsoil

study questions

DO NOT WRITE IN THIS BOOK.

A. True or False

Determine whether each of the following sentences is true or false. If the sentence is false, rewrite it to make it true.

1. Natural resources such as minerals and forests have no economic value.
2. Weathering changes rock to soil.

3. It takes about ten years to form 1 cm of topsoil.
4. Subsoil and topsoil are both rich in humus.
5. Humus increases the ability of soil to hold water.
6. Topsoil is removed by erosion.
7. Water conservation is closely related to soil conservation.
8. Water erosion is greater on slopes than on flat land.
9. Most carbon monoxide is produced during the burning of oil and coal.
10. Increasing the runoff of rainwater on farm fields is good for water conservation.

B. Multiple Choice
Choose the word or phrase that completes correctly each of the following sentences.
1. (*Strip-cropping, Fertilizing, Contour plowing*) increases the mineral content of soil.
2. Soil erosion is likely to be greatest in a field planted in (*corn, clover, grass*).
3. (*A tree, Coal, Air*) is a renewable resource.
4. (*Subsoil, Humus, Topsoil*), consists only of rock particles.
5. The best protection against soil erosion is (*grass, corn, trees*).
6. Groundwater is increased through (*contour plowing, leaching, fertilizing*).
7. Soil nutrients are returned to the soil by (*strip-cropping, leaching, fertilizing*).
8. Erosion is heaviest in (*cover crops, row crops, strip-cropping*).
9. A mixture of smoke and waste gas is called (*sulfur dioxide, smog, carbon monoxide gas*).
10. Industrial air pollution can be reduced by burning (*natural gas, coal, oil*).

C. Completion
Complete each of the following sentences with a word or phrase that will make the sentence correct.
1. Dumping untreated sewage into a river causes the water to become _____.
2. Water may be obtained from _____ which serve as basins to collect rainwater.

3. The wise and careful use of natural resources is _____.
4. _____ is spread on soil to decrease its acidity.
5. Alfalfa and clover are examples of _____.
6. Plowing that follows the natural slope of the land is _____ plowing.
7. Acid rain increases the _____ of soil and water.
8. _____, _____, and _____ are three ways of preventing floods.
9. _____ is one method of purifying ocean water.
10. Most of the air pollution in our cities comes from _____ and _____ in the air.

D. How and Why

1. Why is soil conservation important to people who live in cities?
2. What causes soil erosion?
3. How do contour plowing and strip-cropping prevent erosion?
4. How does crop rotation increase fertility?
5. What can be done in homes to decrease the waste of water?

investigations

1. Obtain a soil testing kit and test the acidity of a variety of soil samples.
2. Visit your local water treatment plant to learn how your community obtains its water.
3. Obtain information about organic gardening. Learn how this method increases soil fertility.
4. Obtain a career pamphlet that describes jobs in conservation.

interesting reading

Hahn, James and Lynn. *Environmental Careers*. New York, NY: Franklin Watts, 1976.

Millard, Reed, *Clean Air – Clean Water for Tomorrow's World*. New York, NY: Messner, 1977.

National Geographic Society, "An Atlas of Energy Resources," *National Geographic*. February 1981, pp. 58-69.

side roads

REBIRTH OF A MOUNTAIN

Few trees stood on the once majestic slope. It was as if a giant scythe had swept over the mountain. The ground was covered with a thick layer of gray ash. The same ash extended many kilometers into the air. Lakes and streams were filled with mud, trees, and dead animals. That was the scene near Mount St. Helens after the eruptions in May and June of 1980. The mountain was a lifeless wasteland.

The volcanic eruptions affected the lives of many people. Roads and towns were threatened with destruction. Water levels rose as the lakes and rivers filled with mud and ash. Rivers such as the Toutle overflowed and cut new channels into the landscape. Trees and mud carried along the swiftly moving river piled up against bridges and almost destroyed them.

To save the bridges, the United States Army Corps of Engineers launched the largest emergency project ever undertaken. More than 100 million cubic meters of material were moved. The Corps of Engineers redug the mud-clogged channel

John Marshall

of the Columbia River and built dams and levies to allow the water to flow freely.

While the Army Corps of Engineers struggled to save the rivers and lakes, the United States Forest Service worked to restore the land. Fallen trees were removed and seedlings planted. The new trees had to root in the fertile soil below the ash since the ash was low in nitrogen. Tractors were needed in some areas to clear away the ash that was too deep for the seedlings to grow. New trees growing on the slopes helped to control erosion, and with less erosion, the streams began to clear.

Many people continue to work hard to restore the forests and streams. However, they have had only a small effect on the mountain. Much of the restoration must be done by nature alone.

Natural processes start when wind and rain clear the ash from the air. Once the air is clean, animals can return to the land in search of food and water. Animals help to disperse seeds onto the barren soil. The seeds, however, can only grow where

John Marshall

488

there are cracks in the ash through which the roots can grow. The cracks are made as animals walk across the ash. With this process, plants begin to grow at the edges of the damaged area and work toward the center.

Another form of plant recovery is taking place in the middle of the damaged land. The roots of some plants such as fireweed and thistle are explosed as the surface erodes. New plants that grow from these roots provide food for animals. As the food supply increases, more animals return. Animals create more places for plants to grow and insects help pollinate the plants. Through this interaction, life slowly returns to the mountain.

Most of the plants now growing in the damaged area near Mount St. Helens are not the trees that once covered the land.

The tightly packed mud and ash do not allow tree roots to get enough air. Nature, however, has a solution—the pocket gopher. This small rodent digs holes and tunnels and lives underground. The gophers survived the eruption and are found all over the mountain. Normally, forest specialists consider the gophers pests because they eat seeds. In this case, however, their tunnels allow air and water to reach the tree roots. With the help of the gophers, trees such as Douglas firs, noble firs, and hemlocks are growing once again on the slopes.

As scientists watch the mountain recover, they study the patterns of new life. They learn about plant succession in each area and how animals help the recovery processes. This knowledge shows scientists how to help nature recover other damaged lands.

chapter

23

Deer and forests are natural resources. Human changes in natural resources can be either helpful or harmful. Because of some past changes, some resources may cease to exist. What can be done to ensure adequate supplies of natural resources in the future? What are some good forest and wildlife conservation practices?

Roger K. Burnard

Forest and Wildlife Conservation

23:1   Forest Resources

Forests cover about 2.5 million km² of the United States—about one third of the total land area of the country. Federal, state, and local governments own about 0.8 million km² of forest. Private industry owns about 0.9 million km². Farm woods make the rest.

Forests fill many needs. Besides having a natural beauty, they are the habitat for a wide variety of wildlife. Forests offer recreation and a supply of raw materials for many products. Lumber, plywood, timber, and paper are the major wood products.

Forest fires destroy the trees, topsoil, and animals that live in the forest. Losing a forest destroys the habitat in which the wild animals live. Fires also cause air and water pollution. After a fire in Paradise Canyon, California, one class took a field trip to see its effects. They talked with the forest rangers who managed the forest where the blaze occurred.

GOAL: You will learn the methods used in the conservation of forest and wildlife resources.

List three reasons why forests are an important resource.

FIGURE 23–1. After the trees are gone, the soil can be quickly eroded by rain.

How do forest fires harm a watershed?

The students learned that many trees had been destroyed. Wild animals had been killed or driven from the burned area. Also, much of the humus in the topsoil had been destroyed. Brush and trees on a watershed had been destroyed. A **watershed** is a region from which all runoff water drains into the same main body of water. For example, all the land that sheds its water into a certain pond is the watershed for the pond. The large drainage basin of the Mississippi River is another example of a watershed.

Loss of grasses, brush, and trees exposed the forest soil to erosion. Without the soil's protective cover, topsoil was being washed into the water supply. When the autumn rains came, the soil was lost as muddy runoff water. Bodies of water within the watershed became polluted with mud. Many plants and animals living in the polluted water died. Some flooding occurred because of the increased runoff water. Floodwaters carried soil into small reservoirs and even into streets in a nearby town.

Steps were taken by foresters to solve the problems created by the forest fire. A forester is a person whose job is to care for a forest. Foresters planted mustard and rye grass seed. These grasses grow very quickly and prevent further wind and water erosion. Tree seedlings were also planted. However, at least 20 years is needed to fully restore a forest. Meanwhile, the wildlife and the beauty of a forest are lost.

FIGURE 23–2. Lumber mills cut timber into boards for houses and other building uses.

activity

A WATERSHED

Objectives: To model and observe a watershed

Materials

aquarium
metric ruler
pieces of flat rock about 5 cm in length
plants, small
putty
sand
sod or moss
sprinkling can

Procedure

1. Cover the bottom of the aquarium with pieces of flat rock.
2. Place a second layer of rocks over two thirds of the first layer as shown in Figure 23–3. Place a third layer of rocks over two thirds of the second layer.
3. Seal the spaces between the rocks on the top and sides next to the glass with the putty.
4. Add sand to the end of the aquarium with the three complete rock layers. Fill the end three-fourths full of sand.
5. Shape a hill from the sand so that the foot of the hill is 2.5 cm tall. Form a small lake on top of the hill.
6. Uncover the bedrock at the foot of the hill to expose part of the ledge.
7. Cover the sand with the sod or moss and plant the small plants in it.
8. Sprinkle water into the lake on the hill until it is full.
9. Observe and record what happens to the water.

10. Fill the lake again and sprinkle water on the hillside. Observe and record what happens to the water and the landscape.

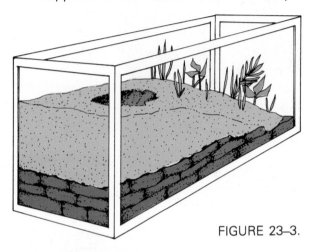

FIGURE 23–3.

Observations and Data

Record observations from Steps 9 and 10.

Questions and Conclusions

1. What happened to the water that you added to the lake in Step 8?
2. What happened to the water that you added in Step 10?
3. From your observations how do you think streams are formed?
4. From your observations how do you think lakes are formed?
5. What will happen to the lake on top of the hill during very dry weather?
6. What area of your model is the watershed?
7. Into what area of your model does the watershed drain?

Roger K. Burnard

FIGURE 23–4. Clear cutting leaves an area open to wind and rain erosion. Many years are necessary for a clear-cut area to reseed itself.

How has the amount of forest land been reduced?

23:2 Forest Conservation

At one time, nearly half of our country was covered with forests. Most of the forests were cleared for farmland during the days of early settlement. The original timber stands of the Northeast and Midwest are now gone. They were cut, burned, grazed, and plowed until few trees remained. If these practices had continued, forests would now be scarce. Today, most of our lumber comes from the Far West. Forest resources must be conserved to fill the demand for wood. Forest conservation includes the careful regulation of tree growth in a forest and the wise use of wood as a natural resource.

How were the forestry practices of the past unwise? Lumbering methods were much different years ago than they are today. What is known as clear cutting was practiced. Clear cutting removes all trees from a very large area. No young trees are left to grow and no older trees remain to reseed the area. Only bare stumps remain when the loggers finish.

Forest conservation practices in the United States began in 1905. President Theodore Roosevelt signed a bill that created the United States Forest Service. The Forest Service is part of the United States Department of Agriculture. It operates national forests and offers guidance to those who manage public and private forests. The agency also employs scientists and technicians to search for and test new and improved conservation practices.

FIGURE 23–5. Much wood is used for the making of paper products.

Gerard Photography

activity WOOD PRODUCTS

Your class should be divided into small groups (4 to 5 students per group). Each group should then make a list of as many wood products as they can. After 15 minutes, find out which group(s) listed the most products. Combine the lists from the groups and tally the total number of wood products listed by the class. How long was your group's list? What were some of the most unusual products named by the class?

23:3 Forest Conservation Practices

Forest conservation is the use of different methods for preserving and increasing the number and size of trees in forests. Many forests are grown as crops which are harvested from time to time. Periodically the mature trees are harvested, and young trees are planted on the cut over land. The young trees grow to replace those that were removed. Successful forest conservation involves several practices. These practices are described below.

Preventing forest fires is one practice. Forest fires can be caused by lightning bolts or volcanic eruptions. However, about 90 percent of all forest fires are caused in some way by people. Most fires are the result of carelessness.

What is forest conservation?

What causes forest fires?

FIGURE 23–6. A forest fire warden watches for any signs of smoke or fire (a). Each year, insect pests destroy valuable forests (b).

a

Grant Heilman Photography

b

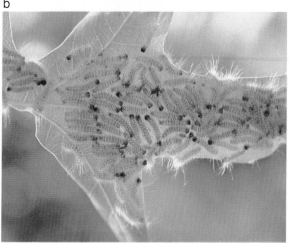

Rich Brommer

National and state forests are supervised by forest rangers. From their high towers and airplanes, the rangers watch for smoke. As soon as smoke or fire is spotted, they determine its exact location. Then, fire fighters and their equipment are brought to the scene. If the fire is very large or far from main roads, airborne equipment may be used.

Define: improvement cutting, selective cutting, block cutting, reforestation.

Unwanted trees in a forest are removed through **improvement cutting.** Crooked, aged, and diseased trees, as well as trees of less desirable species are cut. This practice makes room for the growth of healthy, more valuable trees. Improvement cutting increases the lumber yield and improve its quality.

In **selective cutting,** only mature trees are cut. They are carefully selected and marked before the lumbering begins. Younger trees are left for future cutting. When selective cutting is practiced, a good crop of trees is obtained every few years.

In **block cutting,** a section of trees is cut from the forest. Trees that remain around the block will reseed the cut area. In time, the cut area will be restored. Sometimes the cut block is planted with seedlings to speed the regrowth.

Reforestation is the renewing of the forest by seeding or by planting young trees. Some lumbering companies grow their own young trees. This is done for the reforestation of lands from which they have cut trees. Many state governments grow young trees in nurseries for reforestation.

How may insects and disease harm forests?

Fighting harmful insects and disease is another practice. Harmful insects and diseases cause widespread destruction of forests. The American chestnut tree was once a valuable timber tree from the Northeast. Most of these trees have been destroyed by a disease accidentally introduced from Asia in 1892.

Dutch elm disease is another problem. It has been spreading through the Midwest for years. A bark beetle helps to spread the disease. One known treatment is to cut and destroy an infected elm tree as soon as the disease is found. This method can slow the spread of the disease.

23:4 Vanishing Wildlife

Forests are homes for some wildlife. Wildlife is also found in deserts, grasslands, rivers, lakes, and farm fields. Wildlife includes all untamed animals and plants. Destruction of habitats and overhunting can reduce wildlife numbers. In some cases, a species may be completely killed off. A species that no longer exists is said to be extinct. We may be able to find substitutes for wood, coal, and oil, but we can never replace an extinct species.

One example of an extinct species is the passenger pigeon. The last one died in the Cincinnati Zoo in 1914. At one time, there were more than 2 billion passenger pigeons in the United States. John Audubon, the famous naturalist, reported seeing flying flocks of these birds so thick that they blocked the sun. Thousands of these birds roosted together in trees at night. Could their extinction have been prevented?

Passenger pigeons were the victims of hunters. The birds were easy prey because of their roosting habits. Hunters came at night and killed hundreds of passenger pigeons at a time. Sacks full of them were taken away to be sold the next day. Farmers also killed hundreds of the birds and left them on the ground as animal food.

Finally, there were only a few passenger pigeons left. Perhaps a disease caused the death of those that managed to survive hunters. Whatever the cause, the passenger pigeon is now extinct.

Some other species, such as the bald eagle and the whooping crane, are near extinction. These are endangered species. An **endangered species** is one whose numbers are so small it could easily become extinct. If its members are not protected, the endangered species is likely to disappear. It is estimated that there are only a few dozen whooping cranes in the United States. How long will they remain? These birds could become extinct although they are protected by law. They could be wiped out by disease, harmful effects of pesticides, or illegal hunting.

What is an endangered species?

FIGURE 23–7. Three endangered animal species are the Florida manatee (a), the Santa Cruz salamander (b), and the black-tailed prairie dog (c).

a

b

David Dennis

c

Tim Cullinan

Every plant and animal is affected by its surroundings. If the environment changes, a species may decrease in number or completely disappear from a region. Yet, some other species may increase in number due to the change. For instance, years ago the snowshoe rabbit thrived in the Northeastern forests. When the forests were cleared for farming, the snowshoe rabbit disappeared from the region. Surprisingly, the number of cottontail rabbits increased. They were better able to survive in farm fields than in the forest. Clearing the land for farming caused a decrease in snowshoe rabbits and an increase in cottontail rabbits.

23:5   Wildlife Resources

Explain why wildlife is a valuable resource.

Various types of wildlife resources benefit people. For example, fish provide us with food. Game fish in lakes, rivers, and streams also provide the enjoyment of fishing. Waterfowl, big game, and upland game (rabbits, quail, grouse, and pheasants) provide sport for hunters. Money spent for hunting and fishing helps support many small communities. Wildlife adds to the beauty of the field and forest. Many people think wildlife is worth preserving just for its natural beauty. What do you think?

How can wildlife help control pests?

Wildlife can help control pests. Hawks, owl, crows, and snakes eat mice and rats. They also reduce the number of insects. One scientist found more than 200 caterpillars in a crow's stomach. This gives you some idea of the usefulness of wildlife insect-eaters.

Grant Heilman Photography

Ohio Department of Natural Resources

a

b

FIGURE 23–8. Clearing land for development destroys wildlife habitat (a). Keeping our waters clear and clean has many values (b).

23:6 Wildlife Conservation

Destruction of wildlife has come about largely because of changes in natural habitats and unwise hunting practices. The changes in natural habitats have mostly been caused by humans. People have cleared forests, plowed grasslands, burned underbrush, and drained swamps. Each of these practices has reduced the number of wild plants and animals. Water pollution has made many of our lakes, rivers, and streams unfit for life. The hunting of wolves, eagles, foxes, and other species has also reduced wildlife resources.

Wildlife conservation helps ensure that all wildlife species will continue to exist in future years. Wildlife resources may be conserved in many ways. Both city and country dwellers can help. Bird feeders are one kind of conservation practice. Seeds are put in the feeders for birds to eat. This is very helpful to them in winter when food is scarce.

One of the best things that can be done for wildlife is the planting of shrubs and trees. These provide natural cover for animals. Many trees and bushes produce nuts and fruits that provide food for wildlife. Unfortunately, most American farmers like to keep their fences free of bushes and young trees. Some farmers poison or clip them each year to prevent further growth. Cleared fence rows are free from wildlife as well as brush.

How are wildlife habitats harmed or destroyed?

Describe three wildlife conservation practices.

FIGURE 23–9. Woodlots and brushy fence rows between fields of crops provide good habitats for wildlife.

Kansas Department of Economic Development

All states have game laws to protect wild animals. These laws restrict the months in which certain animals may be hunted. They also limit the number of animals that may be killed by each hunter. In some areas, fishing is allowed only during certain seasons. Also, the size, weight, and number of fish that may be kept are regulated. To be effective, game laws must be enforced.

State conservation departments raise game birds and fish for stocking fields and streams. Trout, bass, and other fish species are raised in fish hatcheries. They are then shipped in special trucks to lakes and streams where they are released. In some states, young pheasants are raised and sold to sport clubs for stocking the land on which members hunt.

activity   CONSERVATION WITH A BIRD FEEDER

Construct a wooden bird feeder. Set it outside your classroom window or near your school building. Place one type of seed in the feeder. Keep a record of the number and kinds of birds that visit it.

If possible, put another bird feeder near the first one. Place a different type of food in it. Record the number and kinds of birds that visit this feeder. How do the two feeders compare in the kinds and numbers of birds?

MAKING SURE
1. What are the methods used by people to help conserve wildlife?

23:7 Wildlife Refuges

What is a wildlife refuge?

Wildlife refuges are areas in which wild animals and their habitats are protected. Special efforts are made to provide water, protective cover, and winter feeding within a refuge. In some refuges, no hunting or trapping is allowed. In others, hunting may be limited. Wildlife refuges are often owned and managed by national or state governments. However, some refuges are owned and controlled by private groups.

Yellowstone National Park in Wyoming became the first federal wildlife refuge in 1894. The killing of wildlife there is forbidden. The park, along with its protected resources, is a credit to the efforts of the early conservationists. The federal government now operates 356 wildlife refuges under the National Wildlife Refuge System. These refuges are maintained by the United States Fish and Wildlife Service. They cover about 30 million acres of land.

The Migratory Bird Treaty between the United States and Canada aids conservation of migratory birds. Migratory birds are those that travel north in summer and south in winter. Migratory bird refuges have been created to maintain and increase these bird populations. Under a law called the Duck Stamp Act, every duck and goose hunter over 16 years of age must buy a special "duck-stamp" each year. Funds collected from the purchase of the stamps are used to maintain waterfowl refuge areas.

Permanent wilderness areas are regions untouched by civilization. Many of these areas have been set up in the West. The aim is to preserve them in the wild state so that people can enjoy them now and in the future. They are "forever wild." Although people can camp and hike in these areas, no roads, motor vehicles, or power lines are allowed. People enter only on foot or horseback.

Explain the purpose of permanent wilderness areas.

FIGURE 23–10. The Everglades in Florida is protected by federal law. No hunting or trapping is allowed (a). Bird sanctuaries provide food and cover for migratory flocks (b).

a

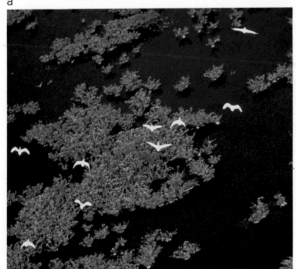

Richard Frear/National Park Service

b

U.S. Fish and Wildlife Service

Perspectives

frontiers

The Peregrines Return

Ron Wilcocks/Animals, Animals

The Peregrines are back! Peregrine falcons are hunting birds that were once common from the tundras in Alaska and Canada to Mexico. These birds have suffered from the widespread use of pesticides. Peregrines absorbed high concentrations of pesticide from their food. As a result, females could not keep enough calcium in their bodies to produce strong egg shells. Very few young birds hatched. Older birds died. In 1969, Peregrines were recognized as an endangered species.

The Peregrine Fund was established in 1970 to fund research at Cornell University. The director of the research is Professor Tom Cade. His first goal was to encourage Peregrines to reproduce in captivity. If enough offspring could be produced, Peregrines could be returned to the wild. At that time, there were no Peregrines east of the Rocky Mountains. In 1975, young Peregrines were released in the eastern United States.

One Peregrine took up residence in a 35-floor building in downtown Baltimore, Maryland. Her name was Scarlett. For two years Scarlett was alone. Then, a potential mate named Rhett was placed in a special cage on the 33rd floor of Scarlett's building. A dead quail was placed outside the cage. In Peregrine courting behavior, a male presents a female with a food offering. Scarlett flew to Rhett's cage making courting calls. She picked up the quail and began eating. After that, she began staying next to Rhett's cage during the day and roosting on top of it at night. Scarlett began scraping her nest, preparing for the next generation she and Rhett would produce.

When Peregrines mate, it is for life. Instead of building a nest, they scrape a depression in the dirt. There the female lays three to five eggs which are tan with brown spots. The female incubates the eggs while the male hunts their food. After about 30 days, the chicks hatch. They are covered with a fluffy white coat of down. The chicks grow quickly. After five or six weeks, the young Peregrines take to the air. By autumn, when Peregrines migrate south, the young birds are on their own.

By 1980, Peregrines had been released in several cities. There the high buildings were similar to the high, rocky cliffs of the Peregrines' natural habitat. Welcome back Peregrines!

The *Peregrine Fund Newsletter*, vol. 8, 1980.

U.S. Fish and Wildlife Service

main ideas

1. Forests and wildlife are two important natural resources. 23:1, 23:4
2. Forests may be destroyed by fires, insects, disease, and unwise lumbering practices. 23:1, 23:2
3. Forests are valuable because of their beauty, their role in preventing erosion, and as a source of raw materials. 23:1, 23:2
4. Good forest conservation ensures an adequate future supply of forest products. 23:3
5. Some wildlife species are extinct. Others are endangered species and are near extinction. 23:4
6. Civilization tends to drive away many wildlife species. 23:6
7. Wildlife conservation protects game animals, game fish, birds, and other wildlife species. 23:6
8. Wildlife requires protective cover, food, and clean water for survival. 23:7
9. Wildlife refuges provide protected areas for wild animals. 23:7

vocabulary

Define each of the following words or terms.

block cutting
clear cutting
endangered
  species
game laws

improvement
  cutting
migratory bird
  refuge
permanent
  wilderness area

reforestation
selective cutting
watershed
wildlife refuge

study questions

DO NOT WRITE IN THIS BOOK.

A. True or False

Determine whether each of the following sentences is true or false. If the sentence is false, rewrite it to make it true.

1. Forest fires are harmful to soil, water, and wildlife.
2. Loss of ground cover during a forest fire prevents erosion.
3. Forests aid soil and water conservation.
4. Reforestation destroys forests.
5. Lightning can cause a forest fire.
6. Forest land may be easily eroded after a forest fire.

7. Clear cutting is a good forest conservation practice.
8. Shrubs and trees are important for wildlife conservation.
9. Improvement cuttings are made to remove dead and diseased trees.
10. Block cutting is harmful to forest conservation.

B. Multiple Choice

Choose the word or phrase that completes correctly each of the following sentences.

1. About (*90, 20, 10*) percent of forest fires in the United States are caused in some way by people.
2. The (*elm, American chestnut, white pine*) is a tree species that has been almost totally destroyed by disease.
3. The (*bald eagle, bison, passenger pigeon*) is a species that has become extinct in the last 100 years.
4. The (*snowshoe rabbit, cottontail rabbit, whooping crane*) is near extinction.
5. It takes at least (*20, 100, 200*) years before a forest is fully restored after a forest fire.
6. The United States Forest Service was created in (*1892, 1894, 1905*).
7. A species that no longer exists is said to be (*protected, endangered, extinct*).
8. A region from which all runoff water drains into a certain body of water is a(n) (*refuge, reservoir, watershed*).
9. (*Block cutting, Improvement cutting, Selective cutting*) involves the careful choosing and marking of mature trees before cutting.
10. Clearing the land in the Northeastern forests causes an increase in (*snowshoe rabbits, deer, cottontail rabbits*).

C. Completion

Complete each of the following sentences with a word or phrase that will make the sentence correct.

1. Today, most of our lumber comes from the _____ part of the United States.
2. State _____ laws protect wildlife from too much hunting.
3. The large drainage basin of the Mississippi River is an example of a _____.

4. _____ and _____ are two conservation practices that help wildlife.
5. The _____ operates national forests and employs forest conservationists.
6. The process of removing unwanted trees from a forest is called _____.
7. Areas in which wild animals and their habitats are protected are wildlife _____.
8. Two endangered species include _____ and _____.
9. _____ birds are those that travel north in summer and south in winter.
10. The passenger pigeon was an animal that decreased in numbers until it became _____.

D. How and Why
1. What important products are obtained from forests?
2. How may forests be preserved for future use?
3. How may wildlife be preserved for future generations?
4. How do wildlife refuges help to preserve wild animals?
5. Some states pay hunters to kill crows and hawks. Is this wise? Explain your answer.

investigations

1. Obtain information on the food preferences of wild birds. List the food habits of birds that make them valuable to agriculture. Explain why birds need greater energy than most other animals.
2. Obtain a book on trees from a library. Learn to identify 10 trees in your area. You can locate trees planted on street and in parks. List the uses of these trees.

interesting reading

Burt, Olive W., *Rescued: America's Endangered Wildlife on the Comeback Trail*. New York, NY: Messner, 1980.

Jackson, James P., *Pulse of the Forest: A Guide to the Variety of Life in Our Broadleaf Woodlands*. Washington, D.C.: American Forestry Association, 1980.

Ruggiero, Michael A., *Spotter's Guide to Wildflowers of North America*. New York, NY: Mayflower, 1979.

Appendix

Appendix A

Scientific Notation

Scientific notation greatly simplifies the handling of large and small numbers. They are shortened by expressing decimal places as powers of ten. A power of ten is the number of times a number is multiplied by ten. The number 6 000 is written as 6×10^3 or $6 \times 10 \times 10 \times 10$.

A number is written in scientific notation by moving the decimal point until a single digit is to the left of the decimal point. The number of places the decimal point moved is the exponent of the power of ten. For a number larger than one, the decimal point is moved left, and the exponent is positive. For a number smaller than one, the decimal point is moved right, and the exponent is negative. The number 0.002 is written 2×10^{-3} or 2 multiplied by 1/10 three times—$2 \times 1/10 \times 1/10 \times 1/10$.

Example:
The estimated volume of water in the Pacific Ocean is 700 000 000 000 m³. What is the volume written in scientific notation?

Solution

Step 1: Write the number and the unit.

$$700\ 000\ 000\ 000\ m^3$$

Step 2: Move the decimal point until a single digit is to the left of it.

$$7.00\ 000\ 000\ 000\ m^3$$

Step 3: Count the number of places you moved the decimal point. Use that number as the exponent.

$$700\ 000\ 000\ 000\ m^3 = 7.0 \times 10^{11}\ m^3$$

$$\text{The volume of water} = 7 \times 10^{11}\ m^3$$

Example:
One second is 0.000 011 5 day. How is it written in scientific notation?

Solution

Step 1: Write the number and unit.

$$0.000\ 011\ 5\ day$$

Step 2: Move the decimal point until a single digit is to the left of it.

$$0\ 000\ 01.1\ 5\ day$$

Step 3: Count the number of places you moved the decimal point and use that number as the exponent.

$$0.000\ 011\ 5\ day = 1.15 \times 10^{-5}\ day$$

$$1\ s = 1.15 \times 10^{-5}\ day$$

Appendix B

Science Classroom Safety

The science classroom is a safe place in which to perform activities if you are careful. You must assume responsibility for the safety of yourself and your classmates. Here are some safety rules to help guide you in protecting yourself and others from injury.

1. Do not perform activities that are unauthorized. Always obtain your teacher's permission.
2. Study your assignment. If you are in doubt about a procedure, ask your teacher for help.
3. Use the safety equipment provided for you. Know the location of the fire extinguisher, safety shower, fire blanket, and first aid kit.
4. Safety glasses and safety apron should be worn when any activity calls for heating, pouring, or mixing of chemicals.
5. Report any accident, injury, or incorrect procedure to your teacher at once.
6. Smother fires with a towel. If clothing should catch fire, smother it with a blanket or coat or quench it under a safety shower. **NEVER RUN.**
7. Handle chemicals and bend glassware only under the direction of your teacher. If you spill acid or another corrosive chemical, wash it off immediately with water. Never taste any chemical substance or draw poisonous materials into a glass tube with your mouth. Never inhale chemicals. Keep combustible materials away from open flames.
8. Place broken glass and solid substances in designated containers. Keep insoluble waste material out of the sink.
9. When your activity is completed, be sure to turn off the water and gas and disconnect electrical connections. Clean your work area. Return all materials and apparatus to their proper places.

First Aid

1. Report all accidents or injuries to your teacher at once.
2. Know where and how to report an accident or injury. Know the location of the phone and fire alarm, and where to locate the nurse.
3. All cuts and bruises should be treated as directed by the instructions included in your first aid kit and should then be reported to a nurse or physician.
4. In case of severe bleeding, apply pressure or a compress directly to the wound. **GET MEDICAL ATTENTION IMMEDIATELY.**
5. If any substance is spilled or gets into your eyes, wash them with plenty of water and notify your teacher for additional aid.
6. Minor burns should be immersed in cold water immediately. In cases of severe burns, **NOTIFY YOUR TEACHER AT ONCE.**
7. In case of fainting or collapse, give the person fresh air and recline him/her so that the head is lower than the body. **NOTIFY YOUR TEACHER AT ONCE.** Mouth-to-mouth resuscitation may be necessary. Call a nurse or physician.
8. In case of poisoning, **NOTIFY YOUR TEACHER WHO WILL CALL A PHYSICIAN AT ONCE.** Note the suspected poisoning agent.
9. If any solution, acid, or base is spilled on you or your desk, wash the area with plenty of water at once. Baking soda (sodium bicarbonate) may be used on acid burns and boric acid on base burns. **NOTIFY YOUR TEACHER AT ONCE.**

Appendix C   Weather Tables

Table C-1.   Relative Humidity (%).

Dry Bulb °C	Difference between wet and dry bulb readings in Celsius degrees									
	1	2	3	4	5	6	7	8	9	10
10	88	77	66	55	44	34	24	15	6	
11	89	78	67	56	46	36	27	18	9	
12	89	78	68	58	48	39	29	21	12	
13	89	79	69	59	50	41	32	22	15	7
14	90	79	70	60	51	42	34	26	18	10
15	90	80	71	61	53	44	36	27	20	13
16	90	81	71	63	54	46	38	30	23	15
17	90	81	72	64	55	47	40	32	25	18
18	91	82	73	65	57	49	41	34	27	20
19	91	82	74	65	58	50	43	36	29	22
20	91	83	74	67	59	53	46	39	32	26
21	91	83	75	67	60	53	46	39	32	26
22	92	83	76	68	61	54	47	40	34	28
23	92	84	76	69	62	55	48	42	36	30
24	92	84	77	69	62	56	49	43	37	31
25	92	84	77	70	63	57	50	44	39	33

Table C-2.   Wind Force

Terms used by U. S. National Weather Service	km per hour	Specifications for use on land	Beaufort number
Calm	<1	Calm, smoke rises vertically	0
Light air	2–5	Direction of wind shown by smoke draft	1
Light breeze	6–12	Wind felt on face; leaves rustle	2
Gentle breeze	13–20	Leaves and small twigs in constant motion	3
Moderate breeze	21–29	Raises dust and loose paper	4
Fresh breeze	30–39	Small trees in leaf begin to sway	5
Strong breeze	40–50	Large branches in motion	6
Moderate gale	51–61	Whole trees in motion	7
Fresh gale	62–74	Breaks twigs off trees	8
Strong gale	75–87	Slight structural damage occurs	9
Whole gale	88–101	Trees uprooted; much structural damage	10
Violent storm	102–120	Rarely experienced; widespread damage	11
Hurricane	>120	Devastation occurs	12

Appendix D

The Microscope and Its Use

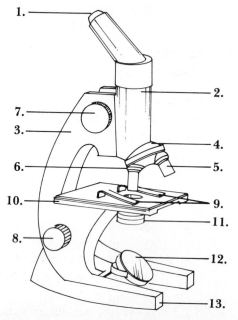

1. Eyepiece
2. Body tube
3. Arm
4. Revolving nosepiece
5. Low power objective lens
6. High power objective lens
7. Coarse adjustment lens
8. Fine adjustment knob
9. Stage clips
10. Stage
11. Diaphragm
12. Mirror
13. Base

These procedures should always be followed when using the microscope.

1. Always carry the microscope with both hands. Hold the arm with one hand. Place the other hand beneath the base.

2. Place the microscope on the table gently with the arm toward you and the stage facing a light source. The top of the table should be cleared of other objects.

3. Look through the eyepiece and adjust the diaphragm so that the greatest amount of light comes through the opening in the stage. The circle of light is called the field of view.

4. Turn the nosepiece so that the low power objective lens (10×) clicks into place.

5. Always focus first with the coarse adjustment and the low power objective lens. Raise the body tube by turning the coarse adjustment knob.

6. Turn the nosepiece until the high power objective lens clicks into place. Use only the fine adjustment with this lens. There will be less light coming through the opening in the stage.

7. Be sure to keep your fingers from touching the lenses.

8. Use only special lens paper to clean the lenses.

9. Before putting the microscope away, always turn the low power objective into place over the stage.

10. Raise the body tube until the low power objective is about two or three centimeters from the stage.

Appendix E

Classification of Living Organisms

	Phylum	Examples
Monera Kingdom	Schizomycophyta	Bacteria
	Cyanophyta	Blue–green algae
Protista Kingdom	Euglenophyta	Euglenas
	Chrysophyta	Golden algae, diatoms
	Pyrrophyta	Dinoflagellates
	Sarcodina	Amoebas, foraminifera
	Ciliophora	Ciliates, paramecia
	Mastigophora	Flagellates
	Sporozoa	Sporozoans
	Myxomycota	Slime molds
Fungi Kingdom	Zygomycota	Sporangium fungi—bread mold
	Basidiomycota	Club fungi—mushrooms, shelf fungi, rusts, smuts
	Ascomycota	Sac fungi—yeasts, pencillium mold
Plant Kingdom	Phaeophyta	Brown algae
	Chlorophyta	Green algae
	Rhodophyta	Red algae
	Bryophyta	Bryophytes—liverworts, mosses
	Tracheophyta	Vascular plants
	Lycopsida	Club mosses
	Psilopsida	Psilopods
	Sphenopsida	Horsetails
	Pteropsida	Ferns, conifers, flowering plants
Animal Kingdom	Porifera	Sponges
	Coelenterata	Coelenterates—jellyfish, coral
	Platyhelminthes	Flatworms—tapeworms, planaria
	Nematoda	Roundworms—hook worms
	Annelida	Segmented worms—earthworms, leeches
	Mollusca	Mollusks—snails, clams
	Arthropoda	Arthropods—insects, spiders, crustaceans
	Echinodermata	Echinoderms—starfish, sea urchins
	Chordata	Chordates—fish, amphibians, reptiles, birds, mammals

Appendix F

Measuring with the International System (SI)

The International System (SI) of measurement is accepted as the standard for measurement throughout most of the world. Four base units of the International System are listed in Table F–1.

Table F–1. SI Base Units

Measurement	Unit	Symbol
Length	Meter	m
Mass	Kilogram	kg
Time	Second	s
Temperature	Kelvin	K

Other measurement units are combinations of the base units or are considered supplementary units. Celsius temperature is a supplementary unit. The Celsius scale (°C) has 100 equal graduations between the freezing temperature (0°C) and the boiling temperature of water (100°C). The following relationship exists between the Celsius and kelvin temperature scales:

$$K = °C + 273$$

Larger and smaller units of measurement in SI are obtained by multiplying or dividing the base unit by some multiple of ten. The new unit is named by adding a prefix to the name of the base unit. Examples are given in Table F–2.

Table F–2. Common SI Prefixes

Prefix	Symbol	Multiplier	Prefix	Symbol	Multiplier
	Greater than 1			Less than 1	
Mega-	M	1 000 000	Deci-	d	.1
Kilo-	k	1 000	Centi-	c	.01
Hecto-	h	100	Milli-	m	.001
Deka-	da	10	Micro-	μ	.000 001

Several units derived from the base units of SI are listed below.

Table F–3. Units Derived from SI Units

Measurement	Unit	Symbol	Expressed in base units
Energy	Joule	J	$kg \cdot m^2/s^2$
Force	Newton	N	$kg \cdot m/s^2$
Power	Watt	W	$kg \cdot m^2/s^3$ (J/s)
Pressure	Pascal	Pa	$kg/m \cdot s^2$ (N/m²)

Glossary

Glossary

The glossary contains all of the major science terms of the text and their definitions. Below is a pronunciation key to help you use these terms. The word or term will be given in boldface type. If necessary, the pronunciation will follow the term in parenthesis.

PRONUNCIATION GUIDE

a . . . back (BAK)
er . . . care, fair (KER, FER)
ay . . . day (DAY)
ah . . . father (FAHTH ur)
ar . . . car (KAR)
ow . . . flower, loud (FLOW ur, LOWD)
e . . . less (LES)
ee . . . leaf (LEEF)
ih . . . trip (TRIHP)
i(i+con+e) . . . idea, life (i DEE uh, LIFE)
oh . . . go (GOH)
aw . . . soft (SAWFT)
or . . . orbit (OR but)
oy . . . coin (KOYN)

oo . . . foot (FOOT)
yoo . . . pure (PYOOR)
ew . . . food (FEWD)
yew . . . few (FYEW)
uh(u+con) . . . comma, mother (KAHM uh, MUTH ur)
sh . . . shelf (SHELF)
ch . . . nature (NAY chur)
g . . . gift (GIHFT)
j . . . gem, edge (JEM, EJ)
ing . . . sing (SING)
zh . . . vision (VIHZH un)
k . . . cake (KAYK)
s . . . seed, cent (SEED, SENT)
z . . . zone, raise (ZOHN, RAYZ)

A

acceleration (ak sel uh RAY shun): rate at which speed changes

acceleration of gravity: rate of acceleration of a falling body; 9.8 m/s² near the earth

action force: a force producing movement in one direction

actual mechanical advantage (A.M.A.): the number of times a machine multiplies the effort force

air: mixture of gases, fine dust particles, and water vapor

air mass: huge body of air covering a land or ocean area

algae: one-celled plants which contain chlorophyll

alloy: mixture of two or more metals

amino (uh MEE noh) **acid:** building block of protein; contains carbon, hydrogen, nitrogen, and oxygen

amoeba: one-celled organism that moves by changing its shape

amphibian: back-boned animal that lives part of its life in water and part on land

anemometer: instrument used to measure wind speed

aneroid (AN uh royd) **barometer:** instrument used to measure air pressure by contraction and expansion of bellows inside the instrument

angiosperms (AN jee uh spurmz): seed plants which have flowers and produce seeds inside a fruit

annual: plant that grows, reproduces, and dies during one growing season

anticline (ANT ih kline): upward fold of a rock structure

anticyclone: huge area of air in which the pressure is higher than the air around it.

Archimedes' principle: when the mass of the displaced liquid is equal to the mass of the object, the object floats

area: number of square units required to cover a surface

arthropod: phylum of animals that have jointed legs; insects, spiders, crayfish, shrimp

atmosphere: air that surrounds the earth, extends 900 km above the earth's surface

atom: smallest part of an element that still has the properties of that element

atrium: part of the heart; receives blood returning from the lungs; pushes blood into ventricle

B

bacteria: one-celled organisms with cell walls; classified by shape: sphere, rod, or spiral

barometer (buh RAHM ut ur): instrument used to measure air pressure

bedrock: solid rock crust near the surface of the earth

Bernoulli's principle: the pressure in a moving stream of fluid is less than in the fluid around it

bile: substance produced in the liver; aids the breakdown of fat

bird: warm-blooded vertebrate covered with feathers; lays eggs

blending: inheritance of a trait that is a combination of the traits present in the parents

block cutting: forest conservation method in which a section of trees is cut from a forest

Boyle's law: the pressure of a gas increases as its volume decreases

breed: group of animals or plants which have a common ancestor

buoyancy (BOY uhn see): upward push of a fluid on an object placed in the fluid; equal to the mass of the fluid displaced by the object.

burning: chemical change in which atoms of a substance combine with atoms of oxygen in air releasing heat and light

C

carbon monoxide: colorless and odorless gas that is poisonous

Carboniferous Period: fifth time section of the Paleozoic Era

cartilage: dense, strong, rubbery tissue

cell: basic unit of structure and function in all living things

cell membrane: thin layer surrounding the cell

cell wall: outer layer surrounding the cell membrane of a plant cell

cellulose: complex compound in plant fibers and cell walls

Cenozoic (sen uh ZOH ihk) **Era:** one of the four major divisions of the history of the earth following the Mesozoic Era and extending into the present time; known as the "Age of Mammals"

centimeter (cm): unit of length; 1/100 of a meter

centripetal (sen TRIHP ut ul) **force:** force that keeps an object moving in a circular path

chain reaction: provides a steady supply of energy; neutrons released during nuclear fission cause other atoms to split

Charles' law: pressure of a gas increases when it is heated, provided the volume of the container does not change

chemical change: change in the chemical properties of a substance so that one or more new substances with different compositions and chemical properties are produced

chemical equation: shorthand information of a chemical reaction containing symbols and formulas

chemical formula: group of letters and numbers used to stand for the elements and ratio of elements in a compound

chemical symbol: one or two letters, the first of which is always a capital, used to stand for an element

chlorophyll: green substance in plant cells that is used to make food

chromatin (KROH mut un): grainy material that forms chromosomes when a cell begins to divide

chromosome: threadlike bodies formed from chromatin; contain genes that control the inheritance of different traits

circular motion: the motion of an object along a curved path

cirrus cloud: feathery appearing cloud at high altitudes, composed of ice crystals

clear cutting: forestry practice in which all trees are removed from a very large area

climate: average weather for a region over a period of years

climax community: end result of succession in a community

cloud: collection of water droplets or ice particles in the air

cloud ceiling: altitude at which the cloud cover becomes broken or overcast

cloud cover: cloudiness measured by the portion of sky covered by clouds

cold front: region where a cold air mass moves against a warm air mass

community: all living things within in a certain area

competition: organisms compete for the things needed for survival

compound: contains two or more elements joined by a chemical bond

conservation (kahn sur VAY shun): wise and careful use of natural resources

consumer: an animal that cannot make its own food and must eat plants and animals

continental margin: portion of the seafloor lying next to the continents

continental shelf: smooth, gently sloping portion of the ocean floor that borders the coastlines of a continent

contour line: a line drawn on a map joining points of the earth's surface having the same elevation

contour plowing: plowing back and forth across a sloped field

control: the part of an experiment that is held constant; a standard of comparison for results

convection currents: movements of warm and cold air due to different air pressures; water movements due to differences in water density

core: center section of the earth; inner region is solid iron and nickel; outer region is liquid

covalent (koh VAY lunt) **bond:** formed when atoms share electrons

Cretaceous (krih TAY shuhs) **period:** third and last time section of the Mesozoic Era

crop rotation: soil conservation method in which one crop is grown one year and a different crop is grown the next year

crossbred: mixed breed

crust: thin, rocky outer layer of the earth; consists of all continents and ocean floors that surround the earth

cubic meter (m³): unit for measuring volume

cumulus cloud: puffy, flat-based cloud and composed of water droplets

cyclone: region of low air pressure

cytoplasm: jellylike material between the cell membrane and the nucleus

D

deceleration (dee sel uh RAY shun): negative acceleration

declination (dek luh NAY shun): the angle formed with the geographic north pole when the compass needle points to the magnetic north pole

decomposer: microbe that causes the decay or breakdown of dead plants and animals

density (DEN suht ee): mass per unit of volume; expressed in g/mL or g/cm³

descent and change: living things may change as they pass from one generation to another

Devonian Period: fourth time section of the Paleozoic Era; known as the "Age of Fishes"

dew point: temperature at which water vapor first begins to condense

diffusion: movement of molecules from a region where they are more concentrated to regions where they are less concentrated

DNA: complex molecule in the nucleus controlling the cell's activities

dominant (DAHM uh nunt) **species:** a species that exists in the greatest number within a community

dominant trait: trait that determines how a plant or animal will appear

drag: force of air against an object that moves through it

E

earthquake: shock wave caused by a sudden slippage of a rock along a fault

ecology (ih KAHL uh jee): study of relationships between organisms and their environment

efficiency (ih FISH uhn see): comparison of work output and work input of a machine

effort arm: distance from the effort force to the fulcrum of a lever

effort force: force applied to a lever

egg: sex cell produced by a female organism

electron (ih LEK trahn): basic part of an atom with a very small mass and a negative electric charge

element: substance that cannot be broken down into simpler substances

embryo (EM bree oh): organism in the first stages of development

emigration (ehm ih GRAY shun): movement out of a community

endangered species: one whose numbers are so small that it could easily become extinct

energy: the ability to do work

energy pyramid: a pyramid structure to show how energy is used in a food chain; each successive level of the pyramid has less energy

entomologist (ent uh MAHL uh just): scientist who studies insects

environment (in VY ruhn ment): surroundings of an organism

epicenter: the point on the earth's surface directly above the focus of the earthquake's center

era: major division of earth's history

erosion (ih ROH zhuhn): carrying away of rocks and soil by wind, moving water, or moving ice

excretion: process by which wastes are removed from an organisms body

exoskeleton: skeleton on the outside of an animal's body

exosphere (EK so sfihr): layer of atmosphere farthest from the earth and extending from about 600 km outward into space

experiment: a method used to seek an answer to a question or test a hypothesis

extinct: no longer existing

F

fault: break in the earth's crust along which movement occurs

fern: plant having no flowers or seeds and life cycle with two stages; larger than mosses and liverworts

fertilization: joining of pollen and egg nuclei in plants; union of egg and sperm cells in animals

fertilizer: substance used to make soil more fertile

fission: process by which bacteria and other organisms reproduce by dividing into two parts

flatworm: type of worm; flat in shape

flower: modified stem that contains organs for reproduction

fluid: substance can move and change shape without separating

food chain: series of animals feeding on plants and/or other animals

food web: complex feeding system containing many food chains

force: any push or pull on an object

fossil: evidence of past life such as the preserved remains or traces of plants and animals

fossil fuels: formed when plants and animals that died many years ago; coal, oil, gasoline, natural gas

friction (FRIK shun): a force that slows down or prevents motion

front: region where two air masses come together

fulcrum: point at which the lever rotates

fungí: organisms like yeast, mold, and mushrooms which contain no chlorophyll and live on dead organic matter or living organisms

G

game laws: laws protecting wild animals by restricting the months in which certain animals may be hunted

gas: state of matter that has mass and occupies space

gene: body in a chromosome; controls the inheritance of different traits

genus: a group of closely related species

geologist (jee AHL uh just): scientist who studies the structure, formation, and history of the earth

geology: science that studies the earth and its structure, formation, and history

geothermal: heat energy within the earth

germination: early growth of an embryo plant

graduated cylinder: a cylinder with unit markings that is used in measuring volume.

gram (g): SI unit of mass; 1/1000 of a kilogram

green manure crop: crop that is grown as a cover and plowed under before maturity

groundwater: water in the ground

gymnosperms (JIHM nuh spurmz): seed plants that produce seeds that are not enclosed in a fruit

H

habitat: place where a species of plant or animal normally lives

heredity: passing of traits from parent to offspring

host: organism on which a parasite lives and feeds

humidity: the amount of water vapor in the air

humus: organic matter added to soil in the decay process

hurricane: stormy tropical cyclone where huge amounts of warm, moist air are rising

hybrid: offspring from a cross between organisms which have different traits

hybrid vigor: hardier and more disease resistant; usually found in a crossbreed or hybrid

hydroelectric: electric power produced by moving water

hygrometer (hi GRAHM uht ur): instrument used to measure relative humidity

hypothesis (hi PAHTH uh sus): a possible solution to a problem

I

ideal mechanical advantage (I.M.A.): greater than the machine's actual mechanical advantage; friction and weight are not considered

igneous (IHG nee us) **rock:** rock formed by the cooling of hot liquid matter forced up from deep within the earth

immigration: movement into a community

improvement cutting: forest conservation practice in which unwanted trees are removed

inclined plane: a slanted surface which may be used for raising objects to higher places; a simple machine

index fossil: fossil used to identify specific rock layers; also called a guide fossil

inertia (ihn UR shuh): tendency of matter to stay at rest, or in motion, unless acted upon by a force

International Date Line: on the opposite side of the earth from the prime meridian; imaginary line of longitude that is 180°

International System of Units or SI: modern form of the metric system

invertebrate: animals that do not have an internal skeleton

ion: atom with an electric charge

ionosphere: region of the atmosphere containing all of the thermosphere and parts of the mesosphere and exosphere that absorbs large amounts of radiation

isobar: line on a weather map that connects points having the same air pressure

isotope: form of an element that is different in mass because it has a different number of neutrons in its nucleus

J

jet stream: swift, forceful winds in the upper troposphere

joule (J): the unit of work; equivalent to one newton-meter (N · m)

Jurassic Period: middle time section of the Mesozoic Era

K

kilogram (kg): SI unit of mass; 1000 grams

kilometer (km): SI unit of length; 1000 meters

kinetic energy: energy of motion

kingdom: one of five main groups in the classification of all living things

L

large intestine: intestine through which waste products move to be excreted from the body

latitude (LAT uh tewd): imaginary lines on the earth's surface, shown on a map or globe, that run east and west parallel to the equator

lava: molten rock that flows from a volcano; turns into solid rock upon cooling

law of conservation of energy: energy can change forms but cannot be created or destroyed

law of conservation of momentum: momentum cannot be created or destroyed

law of dominance: theory that a trait from one parent may cover up or mask a trait from the other parent

law of uniform change: past changes in the earth were caused by forces, such as weathering and erosion, that still exist today

leaching: removal of minerals from topsoil by water; reduces fertility

lever: a bar that is free to move about a fulcrum; simple machine

lichen (LY kuhn): an alga and a fungus which exist together and benefit each other

lift: an upward force on wings of a plane that enables it to fly

liquid: state of matter that has a definite volume but does not have a definitie shape.

liter (L): base unit of volume in SI

liver: organ that produces the digestive juice, bile

liverwort: small, many-celled plant similar to mosses that contains chlorophyll

longitude (LAHN juh tewd): imaginary lines on the earth's surface, shown on a map or globe, that run north and south through the poles

longshore current: flow of water along the shore

M

machine: device that can change the speed, direction, or amount of a force

magma: molten rock material within the earth and from which igneous rocks are formed

magnetic field: the field of magnetism that surrounds the earth; the earth is a giant magnet

magnetic north pole: located about 1670 kilometers from the geographic north pole near Bathurst Island in northern Canada

magnetic south pole: located near the coast of Antarctica about 2670 kilometers from the geographic south pole

mammal: warm-blooded vertebrate, that has hair, and feeds its young with milk

mantle: slowly "flowing" solid rock surrounding the outer liquid core of the earth; consists mostly of solid silicon, oxygen, aluminum, iron, and magnesium

mass: amount of matter present in a body

matter: anything that has mass and takes up space

meridian (muh RIHD ee unz): another name for a line of longitude

mesosphere (MEZ uh sfir): layer of atmosphere lying above the stratosphere and extending from about 50 km to 80 km above the earth's surface

Mesozoic (mez uh ZOH ihk) **Era:** one of the four major divisions of the history of the earth following the Paleozoic Era; known as the "Age of Reptiles"

metabolism: sum of all the chemical processes in living things that keep them alive

metamorphic (met uh MOR fihk) **rock:** rock created by a change in igneous or sedimentary rock

metamorphosis: series of changes that animals such as frogs and insects through during their life

meter (m): base unit of length in SI

meteorology (meet ee uh RAHL uh gee): scientific study of weather

metric system: decimal system of measurement; units are based on tens or multiples of tens

microclimate: climate in a small area

microorganism: organism so small, we use a microscope to view them

Mid-Atlantic Ridge: mountains extending north and south along the center of the Atlantic Ocean floor

migratory bird refuge: area created to maintain and increase these bird populations

milligram (mg): SI unit of mass; 1/1000 of a liter

milliliter (mL): SI unit of volume; 1/1000 of a liter

millimeter (mm): SI unit of length; 1/1000 of a meter

mineral: inorganic substance which has a definite chemical composition and a crystal form

mixture: two or more elements or compounds mixed together but not chemically joined

mollusk: soft-bodied animals which may or may not have hard shells or shell-like coverings

momentum (moh MENT uhm): quantity of motion; mass of a body multiplied by its speed

monera: one of five kingdoms

moss: small, many-celled plant that contains chlorophyll

mutation (myew TAY shun): change in a gene or chromosome producing a change in an organism

N

natural resources: things in the environment that are useful to people

natural selection: process by which organisms best adapted to their environments survive to produce fertile offspring

neutron: basic part of an atom with a mass slightly larger than that of a proton and no electric charge

newton (N): unit of force; amount of force needed to accelerate 1 kilogram at a rate of 1 meter/second^2

newton-meter (N·m): unit of work; also a joule

nimbus cloud: cloud associated with precipitation

nuclear fission: a single large nucleus splits into small nuclei

nuclear fusion: two or more nuclei join to form one larger nucleus

nucleus: 1. central core of an atom which contains protons and neutrons 2. structure near the center of a cell which controls its life activities

O

observation: observed results of a test or experiment using senses or machines

occluded front: region where a cold front and a warm front contact each other

ocean-basin floor: flat portions of the ocean floor

ocean currents: huge streams of water which flow within certain well-defined boundaries

oceanography (oh shun AHG ruh fee): scientific study of oceans

Ordovician Period: second time section of the Paleozoic Era

organ: a group of tissues working together to perform a function

organism: a whole and complete living thing

osmosis (ahs MOH sus): diffusion of water through a membrane

ozone: changed from oxygen by the sun's radiation in the stratosphere; it absorbs ultraviolet rays

P

paleontology (pay lee ahn TAHL uh gee): study of prehistoric living things through fossils

Paleozoic (pay lee uh ZOH ihk) **Era:** one of the four major divisions of the history of the earth following the Precambrian Era

pancreas: organ that produces many digestive enzymes

paramecium: protist, one-celled and shaped like a slipper; covered with short hairlike structures called cilia

parasite: type of consumer that lives and feeds in or on other living things

perennial: plant that lives for several growing periods

period: 1. time section of an era; 2. time between the passage of two successive crests of a wave

permanent wilderness area: region untouched by civilization

Permian Period: sixth and last time section of the Paleozoic Era

photosynthesis: process by which a plant uses sunlight to make food

physical change: occurs when a substance changes from one form to another without a change in its composition

plankton: tiny animal and plant life that drift about in the sea

plasma: 1. state of matter that is extremely hot and composed of electrical properties; 2. liquid part of blood

plate: huge segments of the earth's crust that are slowly drifting in a certain direction

plate tectonics: theory explaining earth's surface structures formed by movement of large crustal plates

polar easterlies: winds coming from the poles and deflected to the east

pollen: tiny grains produced by the stamen of a flower; contain nuclei for reproduction

pollination: transfer of pollen from stamen to pistil

pollution: waste products in the air, water, on land

population (pahp yuh LAY shun): total number of any one species living in a community

potential energy: energy of position or stored energy

power: rate at which work is done

Precambrian (pree KAM bree un) **Era:** from the time the earth was first formed over 4.5 billion years ago; lasted 4 billion years

precipitation: moisture that falls from the atmosphere

predator: an animal that feeds on other animals; usually kill their prey

pressure: force per unit of area

prey: an animal that is killed and eaten by another animal

prime meridian: passes through Greenwich, England and is 0° longitude

process of science: methods scientists use to search for knowledge and answers to problems

producer: an organism which makes its own food

product of science: scientific facts and ideas that have been discovered throughout the years

protein: complex compound basic to the structure and function of a cell and many of its products

protists: one of the main groups of living things include bacteria and other microscopic organisms

proton: basic part of an atom with a mass about 1800 times that of an electron; has a positive charge

protoplasm: "living material" of the cell

pulley: wheel that turns on an axle; a simple machine

purebred: member of a breed

Q

Quarternary Period: last time section of the Cenozoic Era including the present time

R

radial symmetry: similar body parts extending out from the center

radioactive dating: method for finding the age of a rock based on the rate of decay of certain radioactive elements

reaction force: force always equal in size and opposite in direction to an action force

recessive trait: a hidden or masked trait that is present

reduction division: special type of cell division in which the chromosome number is reduced in half

reforestation: forest conservation method in which the forest is renewed by seeding or planting young trees.

relative humidity: percent of water vapor in the air based on the amount the air can hold at a certain temperature

reptile: cold-blooded animal that is usually covered with scales

resistance force: the force that is overcome when work is done

respiration: release of energy from the breakdown of food within the cell

revolution: movement of the earth in a curved path or orbit around the sun; any heavenly body in orbit around another heavenly body

rhizome: underground stem

rip current: occurs when longshore currents go back to sea

RNA: complex molecule in the nucleus controlling the cell's activities

rotation: turning of the earth about its axis

roundworm: worms with rounded, tubelike bodies

S

salinity (say LIHN ut tee): a measure of dissolved salts in a given mass of water

scavenger (SKAV un jur): animal that feeds on dead animals; a consumer

science: a process for solving problems by using facts and ideas already discovered in the search for new knowledge and answers to problems

scientific method: a problem-solving process which includes making a clear statement of the problem, collecting information, forming a hypothesis, testing the hypothesis, accepting or rejecting the hypothesis, and reporting the results

scientist: person who uses the methods and skills of science

screw: a circular inclined plane; a simple machine

sedimentary (sed uh MENT uh ree) **rock:** rock formed by the cementing of tiny particles such as clay, sand, gravel, or limestone shells

seismic sea wave: wave produced by an earthquake

seismogram (SIZE muh gram): recording made by a seismograph needle

seismograph (SIZE muh graf): machine used to record the shock waves in the earth

selection: process in which certain individuals are chosen for breeding

selective cutting: forest conservation method in which only mature trees are cut

shelter belt: thick rows of trees that break the wind

Silurian Period: third time section of the Paleozoic Era

small intestine: part of intestine where most of food digestion and absorption takes place

smog: mixture of smoke, fog, and waste gases

society: group of individuals of the same species which live together in an organized way

solid: state of matter that has a definite volume and shape

specialized cell: a cell in an organism that has a specific job to do

species: a single, distinct group of living things

speed: how fast an object is moving; distance an object travels per unit of time

sperm: sex cell produced by a male organism

spinal cord: a long bundle of nerves that connects the brain to other parts of the body

spiracle: tiny opening in the exoskeleton of an insect; allows air to enter the body

spore: cell formed by many protists for reproduction

sporozoan (spor uh ZOH unz): one-celled protist not able to move around to obtain food; obtains food from the organism in which it lives

standard time zone: one of the four time zones by which the United States is divided; pacific, mountain, central, and eastern

stimulus: anything in the environment that causes a change in behavior

stratosphere (STRAT uh sfihr): layer of atmosphere lying above the troposphere and extending from about 11 km to 50 km above the earth

stratus cloud: gray flat cloud composed of water droplets and covering a large portion of the sky

strip-cropping: soil conservation method in which farmers plant strips of grass, clover or alfalfa between strips of row crops

subatomic: particle within an atom

sublimation (sub luh MAY shun): physical change in which a gas changes directly to a solid or a solid directly to a gas

subscript: small number in a formula used to show how many atoms are in a molecule

subsoil: lower layer of soil

succession: process of slow, gradual change in a community

sulfur dioxide: colorless gas that has an unpleasant odor; results from burning coal and oil

surface tension: force that holds particles on a liquid's surface together

surge: a mass of water that produces an abnormal rise in sea level along a seacoast

symbiosis (sihm bee OH sus): two organisms live together in common effort so both will benefit

symbol: shorthand way of writing the names of elements

syncline (SIHN kline): downward fold of a rock structure

system: groups of organs within an organism working together to perform certain functions

T

terminal speed: point at which a falling body stops accelerating; reached when air resistance against a body equals the pull of gravity

terracing: soil conservation method in which very wide steps are formed on very steep slopes

territory: a certain area defended by animals

Tertiary Period: first time section of the Cenozoic Era

theory of evolution: changes in living organisms that occur over a period of many years

thermosphere (THUR muh sfir): layer of atmosphere lying above the mesosphere and extending from about 80 km to 600 km above the earth

tide: periodic rise and fall of the ocean along a seacoast

tissue: a group of cells performing the same function

topographic (tahp uh GRAF ihk) **map:** map which shows landscape heights of mountains and depths of valleys

topsoil: upper layer of soil

tornado: special kind of cyclone in which winds rotate rapidly around a low pressure center about 60 m in diameter

trade winds: winds that blow east to west between the equator and 30° latitude

transpiration: loss of water through the leaves of a plant

trilobite (TRY luh bite): most plentiful marine animal in the Cambrian Period

troposphere (TROHP uh sfihr): layer of atmosphere extending from the ground to an average height of 11 km above the earth where most weather occurs

tuber: tip of a rhizome that is enlarged because of the storage of food in its cells.

U

uncomformity: a time period for which no rock is left

undertow: water flowing back into the ocean underneath the incoming waves

unit: fixed amount used as a standard in measurement

V

ventricle: part of the heart; receives blood from the atrium; pushes blood through vessels to the lungs and other body parts

vertebrate: an animal that has an internal skeleton

virus: smallest living thing known; made of DNA or RNA and protein; capable of causing disease

volcano: opening in the earth's crust from which molten rock and gases escape, sometimes violently

volume: 1. space occupied or filled by an object; 2. loudness of a sound

W

warm front: region where a warm air mass moves forward as a cold air mass moves away

watershed: region from which all runoff water drains into the same main body of water

watt: the unit of power; one watt is equivalent to 1 joule per second

wave period: time between the passage of two seccessive wave crests

weather: condition of the atmosphere at a certain time and place

weathering: breaking down of bedrock by the action of water, ice, plants, animals, and chemical changes

wedge: two inclined planes together; a simple machine

weight: amount of force (pull) which the earth exerts on an object

westerlies: winds traveling from west to east in the middle latitudes

wheel and axle: wheel attached to an axle; a simple machine

wildlife refuge: area in which wild animals and their habitats are protected

wind: air movement caused by differences in temperature and air pressure

work: a force acting through a distance

Z

zygote: fertilized egg cell

Index

Index

M

Machine, 83–100; compound, 98–100; efficiency of, 94–97; ideal, 96; simple, 83–97; *act.,* 85; 90; 92; *illus.,* 84; 86; 87; 89; 94; See also Engine

Magma, 172, 189, 190

Magnet, 161–163; *illus.,* 161; 162; 163

Magnetic field, 162, 163; *illus.,* 163

Magnetic north pole, 161; *illus.,* 161

Magnetic south pole, 161; *illus.,* 161

Magnetometer, 162

Malaria, 309

Mammal, 212; *illus.,* 364; 378; 379

Mammary gland, 379

Mammoth, 212

Manganese, 281

Mantle, 170, 172

Map, 156–158; *act.,* 156; 157; 158; 164; *illus.,* 155; 156; 157; 158; 159; 160; 161

Marble, 183, 205

Marchantia, 319; *illus.,* 319

Mass, 17, 26, 108, 112, 113, 120, 135; of earth, 150; measurement of, 69; *act.,* 156; 157; 158

Mass spectrometer, 216

Mastodon, 212

Matter, 23–26; chemical change in, 52, 53; inertia of, 107, 108; nuclear change in, 56, 57; physical change in, 50–53; states of, 25, 26; *act.,* 24; *table,* 26

Measurement, 12–19; of area, 14, 15; of density, 26, 27; of force, 67–71; of length, 12–14; of liquid pressure, 132; of mass, 17, 69; of speed, 116, 117; of temperature, 48; of volume, 15; of weight, 68, 69; *act.,* 15; 16; 68; 70; 117; 132; *table,* 12

Mechanical advantage, 86–89; actual, 86, 89; ideal, 87, 88, 89, 91, 93; of levers, 86–89; of pulley, 89; of wedge, 93; of wheel and axle, 91

Melting, 50

Mendel, Gregor, 430–438

Meniscus, *illus.,* 15

Mercury barometer, 224; *illus.,* 225

Meridian, 155

Mesosphere, 223; *illus.,* 223

Mesozoic Era, 204, 210, 211; *table,* 204

Metabolism, 292, 369

Metamorphic rock, 174, 183; *illus.,* 183

Metamorphosis, 354; *act.,* 373

Meteorite, 216

Meteorology, 251

Meter, 12

Metric system, 12–19; *act.,* 15; 16; *table,* 12

Microclimate, 255

Microorganism, 300

Mid-Atlantic Ridge, 173, 266

Migration, 376, 377

Migratory Bird Treaty, 501

Milk, 379

Miller, Stanley, 451

Millipede, 353

Mineral, 175, 206, 281; *act.,* 176; *illus.,* 175; *table,* 175; 176

Mixture, 35–37; *act.,* 36; 37; 52

Mold, 303, 304; *illus.,* 303; *table,* classification, 298

Molecule, *act.,* 34

Mollusk, 351–353; *illus.,* 352

Molt, 358

Momentum, 120, 121

Monera, 298, 300–302; *act.,* 302; *illus.,* 300; 301; *table,* classification, 298

Monument Valley, *illus.,* 168

Moon, 215, 216

Mosquito, *illus.,* 419

Moss, 318, 319; *illus.,* 319

Motion, 107–123; circular, 117–119; linear, 107–117; *act.,* 108; 114; 116; 117; 119

Mt. St. Helens, 190; *illus.,* 146; 147; 488; 489

Mountain, 173, 229

Mountain breeze, 229

Mountain goat, 386, 387

Mountain lion, *illus.,* 299

Mouth, *illus.,* 346

Mushroom, 303, 304; *table,* classification, 298

Mutation, 444, 445, 446; and evolution, 462, 463; *act.,* 445; *illus.,* 445; 462; 463

N

National Weather Service, 251; *illus.,* 251

National Wildlife Refuge System, 501

Natural resource, 473

Natural selection, 454, 457–459

Neutron, 30

Nerve, 363, 371; *illus.,* 357

Nerve center, *illus.,* 357

Nerve cord, *illus.,* 357

Nervous system, 347, 350, 357

Newton, 67

Nitrogen, 221

Nitrogen cycle, 405

Nitrogen-fixing bacteria, 405

Nodule, 281, 282, 405

Nonrenewable resource, 473

North America, 172, 173

North American plate, 184, 185

North Pole, 155, 161, 162

Nuclear change, 56

Nuclear fission, 56, 58, 59

Nuclear fusion, 56, 59

Nuclear membrane, *illus.,* 294

Nuclear power plant, 58

Nuclear reactor, 58, 128

Nucleus, 30, 293, 295, 307; *illus.,* 294

Nymph, 358

O

Oak, 391

Obsidian, 190

Occluded front, 246; *illus.,* 246

Q

Quartz, 175; *table,* 176
Quartzite, 183
Quaternary Period, 212, 213; *table,* 204
Queen bee, 403

R

Radiation, 226
Radial symmetry, 350
Radio wave, 223
Radioactive dating, 199, 216
Radioactive decay, 199
Radioactive element, 199
Rain, 236; acid, 482
Rance River, 278
Reactant, 54
Reaction force, 114
Recessive trait, 431, 438
Red blood cell, 371
Reduction division, 439, 440; *illus.,* 439
Reforestation, 496
Reindeer moss, 423
Relative humidity, 232, 233
Remoras, *illus.,* 423
Renewable resource, 473
Reproduction, 292, 301, 374, 377, 442, 443
Reptile, 210, 373–375; *illus.,* 373; 374
Resistance force, 84
Respiration, 296, 302, 305; *illus.,* 296
Respiratory system, 357
Response, 292
Revolution, 152
Rhizoid, 319
Rhizome, 325; *illus.,* 326
Right atrium, 371
Rip current, 276; *illus.,* 276
RNA, 295, 311
Rock, 174–185; age of, 198, 199, 203, 216; erosion of, 178; igneous, 174, 179 180, 199; meta-

morphic, 174, 183; sedimentary, 174, 180–183, 196, 197, 203, 206; weathering of, 177, 178, 196, 197; *act.,* 176; 178; 180; 182; 183; 185; *illus.,* 175; 177; 179; 196; 198; 199; 206; 213; cycle, 174
Rock formation, 184–185
Root, 322, 323; *act.,* 323; *illus.,* 322; 323
Root hair, 322; *illus.,* 322
Rotation, 151, 227; *illus.,* 151
Roundworm, 345; *illus.,* 345
Rudder, 140
Rust, 55

S

Salamander, *illus.,* 369; 388
Salinity, 263, 265
Salt, 32, 262, 263
San Andreas Fault, 185
Sandstone, 182, 183
Scavenger, 414; *illus.,* 414
Science, 5, 6; career in, 6–8; method of, 8–11; using skills, 8, 9; *act.,* 6; *table,* 7
Scoria, 190
Scorpion, 354; *illus.,* 354
Screw, 93, 94
Sea anemone, 422
Sea breeze, 229
Sea floor, 266–268; *illus.,* 267; 268
Sea life, 269, 270; *illus.,* 269; 270
Sea urchin, *illus.,* 350
Seasons, 152–154; *act.,* 154; *illus.,* 153
Seawater, 261–266, 481; density of, 264, 265, 272; temperature of, 264, 265; *act.,* 264; 266; *table,* composition, 262
Seaweed, 280; *illus.,* 281
Secondary wave, 187
Sediment, 181
Sedimentary rock, 174, 180–182, 197, 198, 203, 206; *act.,* 180; 182; 183; *illus.,* 180; 181
Seed, 321, 333–336; *act.,* 334; 335; 455; *illus.,* 333; 334

Seed coat, 333
Seed dispersal, 335; *illus.,* 335
Seed leaf, 333
Seed plant, 321, 333–336
Seismic sea wave, 279, 280
Seismograph, 186, 187; *illus.,* 187
Selection, 445, 446
Selective cutting, 496
Sepal, 331; *illus.,* 331
Sewage treatment plant, 481
Sex cell, 320, 439
Sex chromosome, 439
Sex determination, 441; *illus.,* 441
Sex organ, 348
Sexual reproduction, 320, 348
Shale, 182, 183
Shark, *illus.,* 365; 423
Shell, 352
Shelter belt, 479
Shoot, *illus.,* 326
SI unit, 12–17; *table,* 12
Sierra Nevada Mountains, 211
Silurian Period, 208; *table,* 204
Simple eye, 357; *illus.,* 356
Skeletal system, *illus.,* 364
Skeleton, 363, 364, 366, 374, 375
Slate, 183
Sleet, 236
Slime band, 348
Sling psychrometer, 233; *act.,* 233; *illus.,* 232
Small intestine, 371
Smog, 482
Snail, 350; *illus.,* 207; 352
Snake, 374; *illus.,* 342
Snow, 236
Society, 403
Sodium, 262
Sodium chloride, 32, 34
Soil, conservation of, 474–479; *act.,* 475; 477; 479
Soil erosion, 476, 477; *act.,* 477
Solar energy, 57; *act.,* 59
Solar radiation, 226
Solid, 25; *table,* 26
Solution, 36, 37; *act.,* 37
Sound, speed of, 122
South Pole, 155, 161